FOUNDATIONS OF CONTINUUM THERMODYNAMICS

FOUNDATIONS OF CONTINUUM THERMODYNAMICS

Edited by

J. J. DELGADO DOMINGOS, M. N. R. NINA AND
J. H. WHITELAW

A HALSTED PRESS BOOK

JOHN WILEY & SONS
NEW YORK—TORONTO

Published in the U.S.A. and Canada by
HALSTED PRESS
a Division of John Wiley & Sons, Inc., New York

Printed in Great Britain

Library of Congress Cataloging in Publication Data

International Symposium on the Foundations of Continuum Thermodynamics, Bussaco, Portugal, 1973.
Foundations of continuum thermodynamics.

"A Halsted Press book."
Includes index.
1. Thermodynamics—Congresses. 2. Statistical thermodynamics—Congresses. I. Domingos, J. J. Delgado, ed. II. Nina, M. N. R., ed. III. Whitelaw, James H., ed. IV. Title.

QC310.15.I57 1973 536'.7 74-23460

ISBN 0-470-21777-4

Proceedings
of an
International Symposium
held at
BUSSACO, PORTUGAL

Sponsored by the Portuguese
Ministry of Education

Honorary President:	J. VEIGA SIMÃO, LISBON
Scientific Committee:	J. J. DELGADO DOMINGOS, LISBON
	P. GERMAIN, PARIS
	J. KESTIN, PROVIDENCE, R.I.
	J. MEIXNER, AACHEN
	R. S. RIVLIN, BETHLEHEM, Pa.
Executive Secretary:	M. N. R. NINA, LISBON
Scientific Editors:	J. J. DELGADO DOMINGOS, LISBON
	M. N. R. NINA, LISBON
	J. H. WHITELAW, LONDON

Preface

The contributions contained in this volume were presented at an International Symposium on the Foundations of Continuum Thermodynamics held at Bussaco, Portugal, from 22 to 26 July 1973. The symposium had its origin in informal discussions between Professors Domingos and Kestin early in 1971; these discussions led to the formation of the Organisation Committee which formulated the following purposes for the symposium:

> to arrange a thorough exchange of views on the Foundations of Continuum Thermodynamics between a small number of the most active contributors to this field, and so to make it possible for representatives of different approaches to understand the other's point of view.
>
> to attempt to work out a commonly agreed point of view on the physical foundations of the subject.
>
> to make the results of these deliberations available to the scientific community at large.

This volume of proceedings is intended to fulfill the last of these purposes.

The symposium programme is closely reflected in these proceedings. Sixteen papers were presented and, of these, five were designed specifically to comment and expand upon a topic discussed in a previous paper. A seventeenth lecture was presented by P. Germain and had the purpose of reviewing the achievements of the symposium. This lecture was subsequently written as a paper and is included here; it represents an up-to-date review of the state of the art. The programme included eleven open forum sessions which allowed lively and extensive discussions: a selection of the more important comments is included in these proceedings in the form of dialogue presented in discussion sections which follow the relevant lectures.

We hope that these proceedings will assist teachers and researchers in thermodynamics and related subjects to appreciate the current views of the leading workers in continuum thermodynamics and to learn from their efforts. This volume cannot completely communicate the stimulating atmosphere of the symposium but we hope that the discussion sections, particularly, will provide an indication.

JJDD
MNRN
JHW

Participants

BORGES, A. J.	Universidade de Coimbra, Portugal
BROTAS, A.	Instituto Superior Técnico, Lisboa, Portugal
CALLEN, Herbert B.	University of Pennsylvania, USA
CHAVES, M. R.	Universidade do Porto, Portugal
COSTA, J. A. M. P.	Instituto Superior Técnico, Lisboa, Portugal
COSTA, J. Providência e	Universidade de Coimbra, Portugal
DOMINGOS, J. J. D.	Instituto Superior Técnico, Lisboa, Portugal
FALCÃO, A. F. O.	Instituto Superior Técnico, Lisboa, Portugal
FILIPE, M. A.	Faculdade de Ciências de Lisboa, Portugal
GERMAIN, Paul	Université de Paris, France
GLANSDORFF, Paul	Université Libre de Bruxelles, Belgium
DE GROOT, S. R.	Instituut voor Theoretische Fysica, Amsterdam, Netherlands
KESTIN, Joseph	Brown University, USA
LARANJEIRA, M. F.	Universidade de Luanda, Angola
LEAL, A. B.	Universidade de Luanda, Angola
LEE, Erastus H.	Stanford University, USA
LEMOS, A. M. F. T.	Instituto Superior Técnico, Lisboa, Portugal
MANDEL, J.	Ecole Polytechnique de Paris, France
MASON, E. A.	Brown University, USA
MEIXNER, Joseph	Institut für Theoretische Physik, Aachen, West Germany
MILLER, Donald G.	University of California, USA
MÜLLER, Ingo	The Johns Hopkins University, USA
NASSER, S. Nemat-	Northwestern University, USA
NINA, M. N. R.	Instituto Superior Técnico, Lisboa, Portugal
PINA, H. L. G.	Instituto Superior Técnico, Lisboa, Portugal
PINHEIRO, M. F.	Universidade do Porto, Portugal
PORTELA, A. G.	Instituto Superior Técnico, Lisboa, Portugal
PRIGOGINE, I.	Université Libre de Bruxelles, Belgium
REIS, M.	Université Libre de Bruxelles, Belgium
RIVLIN, Ronald S.	Lehigh University, USA
SCHLÖGL, F.	Institut für Theoretische Physik, Aachen, West Germany
SIDOROFF, F.	Université de Paris, France
SILVA, J. Machado da	Universidade do Porto, Portugal
SILVA, J. Ferreira da	Universidade do Porto, Portugal
SILVA, J. F. Azevedo e	Faculdade de Ciências de Lisboa, Portugal
SOUSA, A. C. Mendes de	Universidade de Lourenço Marques, Mozambique

SOUSA, J. A. B. Menezes	Universidade do Porto, Portugal
TELLES, A. Silva	Universidade Federal do Rio de Janeiro, Brazil
TISZA, Laszlo	Massachusetts Institute of Technology, USA
VENTURA, M. T.	Laboratório Nacional de Engenharia Civil, Lisboa, Portugal
WHITELAW, J. H.	Imperial College, United Kingdom

Contents

1. From Thermostatics to Thermodynamics

J. J. Delgado Domingos†

Abstract

Regarding thermodynamics as the last branch of classical physics, its structure results as a consequence of energy conservation and the trivial facts concerning dissipation and heat flow. Entropy emerges as a logical inference for systems in equilibrium which are described by only one internal coordinate. In nonequilibrium, more than one internal variable can exist, allowing the possibility of several partial entropies.

The concept of a fundamental thermodynamic equation is introduced and a set of postulates suggested to build a new structure. All results of classical thermostatics are recovered if no internal constraints exist. Compatibility with the results of stability in classical thermodynamics and continuum mechanics is shown.

1.1 Introduction

The aura of universality which thermodynamics enjoys has always induced a tendency to seek from thermodynamics directions which could not be found in other branches of physics. More recently, thermodynamics has been asked to give specific answers when applied to such common systems as solid continua. These applications have originated approaches and motivated theories which have shaken the foundations to a degree which could have been unthinkable a few years ago. Many professionals, who believed that they had mastered the theory are the first to recognise now that unsuspected problems exist and that many previously accepted concepts and conclusions had their generality based on the vagueness of its formulations. Discussions and controversy arise in thermodynamics, not in thermostatics, because, for those concerned with continua, thermostatics is too trivial to deserve attention. It is certainly true that in many practical situations thermostatics becomes useful when the system ceases to be thermostatic. However, it is also true that classical thermodynamics is mainly thermostatics, and that almost all concepts and definitions of thermostatics have been transposed without much discussion to continuum thermodynamics. The transpositions appear, either in the form of a principle of local state or as primitive ideas in axioms. Naturally, difficulty in understanding is to be expected between

† Instituto Superior Técnico, Lisbon.

one approach and others because a primitive idea in one case does not necessarily coincide with the concepts or conclusions derived in different approaches and labelled by the same names. The most typical examples are entropy and temperature.

Some of the semantic difficulties are unavoidable but can be minimised if their origin is seen in perspective. Thermostatics gains interest and real value in this way. First, because a wealth of generally agreed evidence and usefulness exists for thermostatics; second, because any thermodynamic theory must recover known results of thermostatics as asymptotic limits.

The contribution of thermostatics to the clarification of thermodynamics is enhanced if some present day difficulties are taken into account. For this, an unconventional discussion seems useful and one is proposed here.

This presentation has the specific purpose of attempting to aid understanding of apparently diverging views in the conviction that macroscopic thermodynamics has suffered from persistently overlooking the basic structure of thermostatics expressed in axiomatic bases, such as those of Tisza[1] and Callen[2].

Because the main objective is to find a basis for convergence among different lines of thought in thermodynamics, the other branches of classical physics, for example, mechanics, will be taken as primitive. We take the view that their structure and formulation are well accepted and will denote them by the abbreviation CP.

The dichotomy between CP and thermodynamics is somewhat artificial and does not correspond exactly to historical evolution. Nevertheless it reflects a trend, typical in physics.

The principle of energy conservation is one of the main achievements of classical thermodynamics, and an essential link between thermodynamics and CP. That principle will be taken as basic. The other essential contribution of classical thermodynamics† was the concept of entropy.

Entropy is, presently, one of the controversial points. To take entropy as a primitive concept, or to start, as in CKC, from temperature, would raise similar objections. To avoid these objections a different basis is here sought. The proposed dichotomy between thermodynamics and CP, is along this line. Furthermore, the primitive concept of an adiabatic wall allows a definition of heat by exclusion.

Those assumptions are plausible and generally acceptable. However, they are not enough to formulate thermodynamics, which must express the fundamental empirical evidence loosely expressed by such statements as

† By classical thermodynamics is meant the thermodynamics typified by Clausius–Kelvin–Carathéodory, which, following Tisza[1], will be briefly called CKC thermodynamics. The Gibbs treatment is obviously excluded as the Macroscopic Thermodynamics of Equilibrium (MTE) of Tisza and Callen.

impossibility of perpetual motion or *unavoidable existence of dissipation in real systems*, and the *flow of heat from hot to cold*, etc. All thermodynamic theories take these statements as basic and try to give them a precise meaning. Entropy is one result of such an attempt; absolute temperature is another.

In equilibrium, or thermostatics, both are accepted. The questions to be answered are: are concepts of entropy and absolute temperature, originated in CKC, the only ones able to express those basic facts concerning dissipation and direction of heat flow, and do they apply to nonequilibrium situations? The answers to these questions will vary with the author, his concepts, and even with the philosophical attitude to physics. Our own attitude is that they are not the only ones, and that they do not necessarily apply to all nonequilibrium situations, at least without increasing or changing somewhat their traditional content.

In some modern schools of thermostatics, the Clausius–Duhem inequality is taken as a starting point for systems in nonequilibrium. The same inequality is accepted in CKC and the different meanings sometimes attributed to *entropy* and *temperature* merely reflect different backgrounds and motivations.

Behind the different approaches lies the essential impossibility of direct access to microscopic knowledge of the system. At most, there are models, concepts, theories, but none of them is able fully to explain macroscopic behaviour in all circumstances.

Two radical attitudes can be taken in macroscopic thermodynamics. One is to assume a system without memory and possessing properties that are process independent. The other is to assume memory and properties that are process dependent. Both attitudes have the same basic limitations from a practical point of view because, even if the system has intrinsic properties, they can be demonstrated only in some types of processes. For instance, a gas will show properties in shock waves which are not revealed in flows at low subsonic speeds. Solid materials which behave as elastic for certain experiments will show viscoelasticity or plasticity in a different experiment. In a pure macroscopic phenomenological theory, those properties and conditions of occurrence will not be known before the experiment is performed. The attitude which considers properties process dependent, does not aim at the intrinsic nature of the system but at its behaviour in given processes. If all processes can be identified the predictive value of the theory, which is the main aim, is achieved. Of course, for a process to be possible in a physical system it must satisfy some basic conditions, one being the condition of dissipation. This attitude lends itself naturally to a mathematical expression by functionals; we call it the FU approach. However, functionals are not the attribute of one or other approach.

An important departure between FU and the *intrinsic* approach, which we will call LS, lies in the number of independent variables; this number is smaller in FU and has been assumed to be advantageously substituted by a knowledge of all past processes undergone by the system.

A simple example will explain better an essential difference. Let us take a system, which undergoes the processes of compression and expansion, and comprises an ideal gas. If a pure mechanical view is assumed, the system is described with only pressure (P) and volume (V) as variables. By performing experiments on the system it would become clear that pressure and volume alone would not suffice to describe its behaviour which would show different relationships between P and V depending on the rate of volume change, even keeping the environment constant. In the simplest approach, it would be necessary to describe its behaviour by $P = V(\mathrm{d}V/\mathrm{d}t)$. This relationship would not suffice for all kinds of experiments, so, a greater generality would be reached assuming that behaviour at time t would be a functional of all the past history expressed by P, V, and their time rates at each time. There is no doubt that a complete prediction of the system's behaviour would be possible by this approach.

The other way of looking at the experimental results would be to assume that P and V were insufficient to describe the system. Then, a new variable (temperature $= T$) would be advanced, and a relationship $f(P, V, T) = 0$ would be assumed as characteristic of the system.

Both attitudes are, in principle valid. In the example, the FU approach would possibly be rejected on practical grounds. In more complex systems, however, no such practical evidence can be claimed and the choice is a matter of opinion, though it appears more intuitive and logical to seek continuity from the traditional lines of thought.

To extend classical thermodynamics to systems, which show the so called *memory effects*, the concept of hidden coordinates was proposed and is becoming widely used. Initially, it was introduced in analogy with chemical reactions. Presently, it is used in an autonomous and somewhat arbitrary way to advance proposals for new theoretical frameworks. However, it becomes increasingly apparent that neither a principle nor even a rule exists to guide in the choice or proposal of such hidden variables or coordinates. This weakens the usefulness of the approach. No remedy is presented here although some motivation is given for the choice of direction. This motivation comes from thermostatics when considered as an asymptotic limit of thermodynamics and taking into account that a microscopic structure exists. The proposal is an inference from a phenomenological point of view. For this, we consider entropy as an integral degree of freedom which, in thermostatics, reflects equilibrium among a much greater number of internal degrees of freedom. In nonequilibrium, entropy—which is an additive property—must be separated into those groups of internal degrees of freedom among which equilibrium prevails or can be assumed to prevail. The minimum number of such partial groups necessary to describe a process, depends on the process. In one limit (thermostatics) only one group is necessary and the internal degrees of freedom reduces to entropy; in the other limit, no equilibrium among groups of internal variables exists and all are necessary. Of course, thermodynamics makes sense only when a small number of internal degrees of freedom is necessary; this is its strength but is, paradoxically, also a weakness which appears sometimes to be overlooked.

1.2 Thermostatics

A thermodynamic system is a portion of matter enclosed by a surface. The surface has specific attributes which define its physical nature. In thermodynamics such a surface is usually called a wall. An adiabatic surface or wall is a perfect heat insulator. It is assumed that

(1) energy is conserved, and
(2) all other branches of classical physics (CP) are known.

Assume a thermodynamic system on which experiments are performed. Our first aim is to characterise completely the system and its interactions with the outside through CP forms of energy. To ensure that only CP energy is exchanged, suppose that the system is enclosed by an adiabatic wall.

Exchanges of CP energy can only be accomplished through the degrees of freedom, which, by definition, are the independent extensive variables, $X_1, \ldots X_n$. Those variables are called *external variables* because they can be defined and measured independently of the contents of the system. The identification and measurement of $X_1, \ldots X_n$ belongs to CP rather than to thermodynamics. The same is true for the energy exchange through the adiabatic surface. This elementary energy exchange is given by†

$$\tau_i \, \mathrm{d}X_i \tag{1.1}$$

where τ_i is the *generalised force* associated with X_i. τ_i is measured at the surface from outside the system. Because of energy conservation, this exchange equals the change of energy in the system, that is

$$(\delta E)_{\mathrm{ad}} = \tau_i \, \mathrm{d}X_i \tag{1.2}$$

† Sum is always implied in a repeated subscript.

Generally, the τ_i will depend explicitly on time. From the set of all experiments which can be performed on the system a subset can be defined for which a closed path exists such that†

$$\oint F_i \, dX_i = 0 \tag{1.3}$$

Processes which have property 1.3 are called *reversible processes of the first kind.*

For reversible processes of the first kind

$$dE = dU = F_i \, dX_i \tag{1.4}$$

Because the X_i are degrees of freedom they can be varied independently and the definition of F_i implies that

$$F_i = \frac{\partial U}{\partial X_i} \tag{1.5}$$

$$U = U(X_1, \ldots X_n, \lambda) \tag{1.6}$$

The λ in equation 1.6 are arbitrary parameters of integration. From equations 1.2 and 1.5 the *postulate of dissipation* can be expressed by

$$(\tau_i - F_i) \, dX_i \geqslant 0 \tag{1.7}$$

for all thermodynamics processes.

It should be noted, regarding the inequality 1.7, that the signs of τ_i or F_i are not arbitrary because they depend on the sign of dX_i, and dE. The sign given to the energy exchange when received by the system is arbitrary and a matter of convention. The same is true for the sign of any particular X_i. However, the signs of τ_i and F_i are a consequence of those for dX_i and dE.

Once the CP energy exchange of the system is characterised an inquiry into other forms of energy exchange can be considered. To prevent a flow of CP energy it is a necessary and sufficient condition to keep the X_i constant. Keeping the X_i constant and removing the adiabaticity of the surface, exchanged energy cannot be of a CP form. This energy exchange is called *heat.* Heat is the energy exchanged while keeping constant the external coordinates. However, if energy can be exchanged keeping constant the external coordinates, that energy can only come from another thermodynamic system.

By definition, a *heat reservoir* is a thermodynamic system which is able to exchange energy while keeping the external coordinates constant. If a heat

† Note that either τ_i or F_i are measured from outside. When the X_i are varied, and energy is transferred, a force appears associated with X_i. This force would be, generally, not only a function of the X_i but also of its time change. Among all the possible time changes of X_i, a particular subset exists which enjoys property 1.3. The particular force which corresponds to this subset is F_i and is itself a subset of τ_i.

reservoir exchanges energy with the system this means, by energy conservation, that

$$(\mathrm{d}E)_{X_i} = \mathrm{d}Q_h = -\mathrm{d}U_h \tag{1.8}$$

where U_h is the energy of the heat reservoir.

When the system exchanged CP energy, an external degree of freedom was necessarily changed. By analogy, internal degrees of freedom, ξ_m, and internal generalised forces, π_m, can be introduced such that

$$(\mathrm{d}E)_{X_i} = -\mathrm{d}Q_h = \pi_m \,\mathrm{d}\xi_m$$

In contrast to the X_i and F_i, which were external and accessible to measurement, the ξ_m and π_m are internal and not accessible to direct macroscopic measurement. If no special reason exists, at this level, to distinguish between the ξ_m and π_m, the first step will be to assume that internal behaviour can be described by only one set, and to write

$$(\mathrm{d}E)_{X_i} = T\,\mathrm{d}S \tag{1.9}$$

thus

$$T = \left(\frac{\partial E}{\partial S}\right)_{X_i} \tag{1.10}$$

Naturally, assuming that the internal state is described by only one internal coordinate implies some type of homogeneity. In particular T, being a generalised force, must be assumed uniform and the driving force for Q. This induces a direct correspondence of T with θ, the empirical temperature ($T \geqslant 0$)†. To maintain consistency, the concept of T and S must apply to the heat reservoir. The relation between them is imposed by conservation of energy, for example

$$\mathrm{d}Q = T\,\mathrm{d}S = -T_h\,\mathrm{d}S_h = -\mathrm{d}Q_h \tag{1.11}$$

and

$$\left(\frac{1}{T}-\frac{1}{T_h}\right)\mathrm{d}Q = \mathrm{d}S+\mathrm{d}S_h \tag{1.12}$$

We can now express the second fundamental inequality: if *heat* flows from the *hotter* to the *colder* body, we have the equivalent inequalities

$$\left(\frac{1}{T}-\frac{1}{T_h}\right)\mathrm{d}Q \geqslant 0 \tag{1.13}$$

or

$$\mathrm{d}S+\mathrm{d}S_h \geqslant 0 \tag{1.14}$$

The last inequality shows that S is not conserved unless $T = T_h$.

† The choice $T \geqslant 0$ is of course not arbitrary. The classical arguments can be used, in a similar way, to distinguish between the empirical temperature (θ) and the absolute temperature (T). It does not seem necessary to repeat the argument here.

Processes for which $T = T_h$ are defined as *reversible processes of the second kind*: otherwise they are irreversible of the second kind in which case

$$dS + dS_h > 0$$

Consider now a general thermodynamic process in which both internal and external coordinates can vary. For those processes in which equations 1.3 and 1.10 apply, which means reversibility of the first kind and a description by only one internal degree of freedom, total exchange of energy is given by

$$dE = dU = F_i \, dX_i + T \, dS \tag{1.15}$$

Equations 1.3 and 1.10 also imply the existence of

$$U = U(X_1, \ldots X_n, S) \tag{1.16}$$

This equation is called the *fundamental thermostatic equation* of the system, and is characteristic of its material properties.

The fundamental equation presented above expresses the energy exchanged with the system in terms of $X_1 \ldots X_n$ external coordinates and only one internal coordinate. So, in relation to an arbitrary level reflected in the integration constants, U is the energy *contained* in the system. The question to answer now is: can equation 1.16 also represent the energy when the system has undergone, in relation to the arbitrary level, interactions through the X_i other than the reversible ones of the first kind?

In a general adiabatic evolution, the true energy exchanged by the system is

$$dE = \tau_i \, dX_i \tag{1.17}$$

However, if $U = U(X_1 \ldots, S)$ can represent an internal energy and if, going from X_i' to X_i'', the total energy received was ΔE it is formally possible to have

$$\Delta E = U(X_1'', \ldots X_n'', S'') - U(X_1', \ldots X_n', S') \tag{1.18}$$

In this relation, the X_i are known because they are external and S has to be adjusted so as to satisfy the principle of conservation of energy. Equation 1.16 can always be written if S is restricted, in this context, to an adjustable parameter.

If ΔE is sufficiently small it can be expressed as

$$\Delta E = \left(\frac{\partial U}{\partial X_i}\right)_{X_i = X_i'} (X_i'' - X_i) + \left(\frac{\partial U}{\partial S}\right)_{S = S'} (S'' - S') + \ldots \tag{1.19}$$

or

$$dE = F_i \, dX_i + T \, dS \tag{1.20}$$

It must be stressed that for equations 1.19 and 1.20 to be possible, it is only necessary that $\partial U / \partial X_i$ and $\partial U / \partial S$ exist at the point X_i', S'. This is certainly true if $U(X_i, S)$ exists for itself. At this stage, equations 1.19 and

1.20 do not imply that F_i, T, or S correspond to any real τ_i or T existing during the evolution. The only correspondence which already exists is for the $\mathrm{d}X_i$ because these are external coordinates. As a consequence equation 1.20 is a Pffafian expression, not necessarily an exact differential of E.

Now combining equations 1.17 and 1.20 yields

$$(\tau_i - F_i)\,\mathrm{d}X_i - T\,\mathrm{d}S = 0 \tag{1.21}$$

and using the first fundamental inequality

$$(\tau_i - F_i)\,\mathrm{d}X_i \geqslant 0 \tag{1.22}$$

leads to

$$T\,\mathrm{d}S \geqslant 0 \tag{1.23}$$

Because $T \geqslant 0$, by definition

$$\mathrm{d}S \geqslant 0 \tag{1.24}$$

So, if the internal variable S exists it can only increase in a general adiabatic process.

The description of the system by a single internal variable necessarily implies some homogeneity and internal equilibrium. A *thermostatic system* is defined as the system whose behaviour can be described by only one internal degree of freedom. This degree of freedom is called entropy. For a thermostatic system, $U(X_i, S)$ always exists so S' in equation 1.18 is the value of S in the initial state and S'' in the final one.

Real systems do not in general obey the rules of thermostatics. However, if a system can be considered thermostatic for small perturbations, the fundamental equation will describe any end states provided they are *equilibrium states*, and the law of increase of entropy in any adiabatic process is then applicable to them.

1.3 Discussion on the Structure of Thermostatics

The derivations and conclusions presented so far were outlined to stress a fundamental structure and its limitations. Some of these are direct consequences of the basic assumptions. Thus we note that the discussion was restricted to closed systems and to the possibility of assigning an energy to the system itself, excluding implicity any form which results from the interaction with the outside except if that interaction can be expressed by a constant.

The restriction to closed systems is easily removed. The exclusion of *long range* forces is typical of traditional thermodynamics and is still an unsettled subject.

Even accepting the basic assumptions as physically meaningful, the postulated existence of equation 1.3 may appear somewhat arbitrary. Essentially, it postulates the possibility of reversible transformations through any external degree of freedom. CKC theories devote considerable discussion to this aspect and attempt to define the so-called state variables by the concept of the reversible process. To motivate them, direct appeal to experience is used and the concept of quasistatic processes introduced. The existence of equation 1.3 could have been defined with reference to experiments performed on the system, and certainly this must be done if a particular system is involved and application of the theory is required. There is, however, an essential difference in logical approach and concept between the present approach and CKC theories. A first difference lies in the use of external degrees of freedom as fundamental variables. These are additive and independent: the primitive variables used in CKC are not. As a direct consequence, the use of Pffafians is not needed here for the mathematical development.

From a logical point of view, it can be argued that the first task of the experimenter is to identify all the possible ways of energy exchange with the system. This means identifying *external* degrees of freedom whose measure is not dependent, in fact, on the contents of the system, nor their state. In contrast, the generalised force associated with the external degree of freedom depends on the system because it is its *reaction* to the process. Furthermore, it is an experimental fact that this reaction depends on the time rate of the process.

Recognising this as a universal fact only two fundamental approaches can be taken, as indicated in the introduction. One is to consider the system as having intrinsic properties which are process independent: the other that properties depend on the process. The first attitude can be identified with all thermostatic theories and is the traditional attitude to thermodynamics. This can be synthethised by postulating equation 1.3. In the present approach, equation 1.3 was extended to all external degrees of freedom. This is not the case with existing theories of thermostatics which exclude purely dissipative degrees of freedom. However, it can be argued that a completely dissipative process is also an idealisation and that F_i in equation 1.3 can be conceived as vanishingly small. For a strict thermostatic theory, such an extension of equation 1.3 to all X_i has no practical value: it can have when extension to real systems is involved.

It has already been stated that *dissipation* is a universal fact. Its precise definition is, however, not so obvious unless some common background is assumed. Expression 1.7 is a clear definition if the entities involved are agreed upon. As in Newtonian mechanics, it can also be accepted that expression 1.7 defines the entities themselves. Around this question, and equivalent ones, metaphysical discussions can become endless.

The approach followed here was to assume a knowledge of CP and to extract the consequences. The knowledge of CP is generally accepted in a postulational basis and it appeared natural to use that formulation without further discussion. In practical terms, the characterisation of a real system and the process it undergoes from an experimental viewpoint cannot be done in an absolute way without an underlying theory and a conceptualisation of the experiment.

To decide experimentally if a process is reversible or not is an impossible task unless a conceptual reference already exists for the limiting, idealised process which can only be introduced by postulation. This means, ultimately, that no experimental means exist to decide if a force associated with X_i in a process is τ_i or F_i, because no experimental evidence is possible to quantify exactly the dissipation. As a consequence, the fundamental equation here deduced or the equations of state in CKC are ultimately postulated. They can be verified within experimental error. Quantitatively, dissipation depends on them.

The recognition that, in real processes, the real force is different from the reversible one is unequivocally expressed by equation 1.7; dissipation is then expressed by the inequality sign which in itself expresses the impossibility of predicting quantitatively τ_i without further assumptions.

The universal fact of dissipation is usually expressed by the principle of entropy increase in isolated systems. The equivalence of statements was shown with the further assumptions implied. The use of one approach or another is open to discussion. However, entropy is a derived concept which expresses the universal facts already discussed regarding dissipation and heat flow, and is only undisputably accepted in equilibrium situations. Once the concept of entropy is at stake, it appears natural to reconsider it in the light of those facts which originated it.

No discussion was presented for the particular interpretation of the X_i. It does not appear essential at this level. The X_i used depend on the particular system whose interactions with the outside must be identified before the thermodynamic formalism is used. Identification of all those possible exchanges is the task of the experimenter within the scope of CP. Once they are identified so are the X_i.

One of the X_i deserves further comment—the one associated with its *extension.* In CKC theories, this basic variable is an external measure—volume—which involves only geometry and no material properties. The other basic variable is pressure. In CKC, pressure has a central role and belongs to the class of primitive ideas like temperature. Its historical role in the genesis of CKC is easily understood, as a result of its direct physical appeal. In nonequilibrium situations, only habit made it an easily used concept.

Pressure is defined here, following Tisza[1], that is, as the derivative of the fundamental equation in relation to volume, apart from a conventional sign.

The definition immediately implies that volume is one of the external degrees of freedom. This definition agrees with the usual results for liquids and gases where exchange of mechanical energy involves only changes of volume, not shape. This is also the case where a microscopic interpretation is easily established.

Not taking the pressure as a fundamental variable (as in CKC theories) avoids two immediate difficulties. One is the introduction of equilibrium and homogeneity from the outset, the other a mixing of truly independent variables with dependent ones. In fact, it is impossible to vary the volume without changing the pressure if all other variables are kept constant. The mixing implied, in CKC, the use of Pffafians and its orientation to integrating factors which lead to entropy.

In deriving the fundamental equation, the τ_i can be considered either as forces applied to the system or the reaction of the system to these forces. The discussion involves only algebraic signs. Conceptually, the transition is nevertheless important because the reactions are already system dependent and as such are material properties. So, the transition from *outside* to *inside* comes from the generalised forces. In contrast with CKC, however, attention is focussed on the interior of the system itself when considering heat flow.

The elaboration presented here aims at deriving the fundamental equation for the thermostatics system, as an intrinsic property, independent of processes or surroundings. The fundamental equation contains all the usual equations of state as particular cases. Conversely, the fundamental equation can be obtained if all equations of state are known. This essential geometrisation of thermostatics, initiated by Gibbs, is so well documented in the work of Tisza and Callen that no further discussions seem necessary at this point.

1.4 Thermostatics to Thermodynamics

In section 1.2, page 7, only one degree of freedom was assumed as a first step to describe the internal state of the system. This implied some internal equilibrium or macroscopic homogeneity. All thermostatic theories have this assumption. In CKC theories there are no practical means of insuring that a particular state is an equilibrium one. In the approach of Tisza that objection can be removed, at least in a conceptual way. This, however, can only be done with the calculation of entropy in the gas state which implies a microscopic theory.

Having in mind the possibility shown by Tisza of staying at a non-experimental level, a *thermostatic system* was defined as one described by only one internal degree of freedom. This definition stresses an ideal system which can represent all systems when in equilibrium. In contrast, a *thermodynamic system* is defined as one possessing more than one internal degree of freedom.

Assuming M internal degrees of freedom, ξ_κ, implies (compare section 1.2)

$$(\mathrm{d}U)_{X_i} = \pi_\kappa \xi_\kappa = -\mathrm{d}Q_h \tag{1.25}$$

it is further assumed that

$$\pi_\kappa = \frac{\partial U}{\partial \xi_\kappa} \tag{1.26}$$

and thereby,

$$U = U(X_1, \ldots X_n, \xi_1, \ldots \xi_m) \tag{1.27}$$

which is called the *fundamental thermodynamic equation*. Its specific functional form is characteristic of the material properties of the system. This equation will be valid regardless of the process involved.

The motivation for equation 1.27 has already been discussed. If accepted, it is only required to postulate its properties in order to comply with the obvious facts of dissipation and heat flow. This is best done through postulates which closely parallel those of Callen for thermostatic systems. In these postulates, the external and internal degrees of freedom are supposed known and, by definition

$$S = \sum_1^M \xi_\kappa \quad \text{where} \quad \xi_\kappa > 0 \tag{1.28}$$

Postulate 1—The internal energy of a macroscopic thermodynamic system, U, is a non-negative, continuous and differentiable function of all degrees of freedom, additive over the constituent subsystems with the property

$$\sum_\kappa \left(\frac{\partial U}{\partial \xi_\kappa}\right)_{X_i} \cdot \xi_\kappa > 0$$

Postulate 2—The values assumed by the degrees of freedom are those which maximise S over the manifold of constraints.

Postulate 3—For

$$\frac{\partial U}{\partial \xi_\kappa} = 0, \qquad \xi_\kappa = 0$$

Postulate 4—Internal time-dependent constraints can not decrease S.

If the system is enclosed by an adiabatic wall and the X_i are constant, the system is isolated. If no internal constraints are imposed, the internal variables assume the values which maximise S. These are found from

$$\text{maximise } S = \sum_1^M \xi_\kappa$$

subject to

$$U = U(X_1, \ldots X_n, \xi_1 \ldots \xi_n) = \text{constant}$$

Using the method of Lagrange multipliers, the problem is transformed into the unconstrained maximisation of

$$\psi = S + \lambda U \tag{1.29}$$

with λ to be considered as a constant. Stationarity implies

$$\mathrm{d}\psi = 0 = \left(\frac{\partial S}{\partial \xi_\kappa} + \lambda \frac{\partial U}{\partial \xi_\kappa}\right)\mathrm{d}\xi_\kappa + \left(\frac{\partial S}{\partial X_i} + \lambda \frac{\partial U}{\partial X_i}\right)\mathrm{d}X_i \tag{1.30}$$

Because $\mathrm{d}X_i = 0$, $\mathrm{d}\xi_\kappa$ is arbitrary, and $\partial S/\partial \xi_\kappa = 1$, then

$$\frac{\partial U}{\partial \xi_\kappa} = \pi_\kappa = \frac{1}{\lambda}$$

or

$$\pi_1 = \pi_2 \ldots = \pi_\kappa = T$$

as a necessary condition for stationarity.

If the system only exchanges heat with a heat reservoir, the system and the heat reservoir form a composite thermodynamic system.

At each time, we will have to find the ξ_κ as follows:

$$\text{maximise } \xi_h + \sum_1^M \xi_\kappa$$

subject to

$$U(X_1, \ldots X_n, \xi_1, \ldots \xi_n) + U_h = \text{constant}$$

where the subscript h refers to the heat reservoir. Again, there results immediately

$$\pi_1 = \ldots = \pi_M = \pi_h$$

The heat reservoir is a thermostatic system by definition, so

$$\mathrm{d}U_h = -\mathrm{d}Q_h = \pi_h \,\mathrm{d}\xi_h = -T_h \,\mathrm{d}S_h$$

and because no internal constraints were assumed

$$\pi_1 = \ldots = \pi_M = T = T_h$$

$$\mathrm{d}Q_h = \sum_\kappa \pi_\kappa \,\mathrm{d}\xi_\kappa = T \sum_\kappa \mathrm{d}\xi_\kappa = T\,\mathrm{d}S$$

The same argument can be used to show that the absence of internal constraints always reduces the results to those obtained by thermostatics, as they should. In those cases, there is no need to distinguish between internal degrees of freedom because postulate 2 imposes equality of internal generalised forces, so

$$\pi_\kappa \, \mathrm{d}\xi_\kappa = T \, \mathrm{d}S$$

and only one entropy and temperature are needed to describe the behaviour of the system.

In real systems, the internal degrees of freedom are subject to time-dependent constraints. These can be thought of as rate relations among themselves and the external degrees of freedom. Those relations are (dynamic) constitutive equations. They are to be postulated separately if a time description of the process is sought.

The absence of internal constraints and the postulates also imply that U is a monotonically increasing function of S. In fact

$$\left(\frac{\partial U}{\partial S}\right)_{X_i} = \frac{\pi_\kappa \, \mathrm{d}\xi_\kappa}{\mathrm{d}\xi_\kappa}$$

In the absence of internal constraints, the internal generalised forces assume the common value

$$\pi_1 = \ldots = \pi_\kappa = T$$

because

$$\xi_\kappa > 0, \qquad \frac{\partial U}{\partial \xi_\kappa} \cdot \xi_\kappa \geqslant 0$$

and

$$\frac{\partial U}{\partial \xi_\kappa} = T \qquad T \geqslant 0$$

so

$$\left(\frac{\partial U}{\partial S}\right)_{X_i} = T \geqslant 0$$

It is noted that postulate 1 by itself does not insure a unique value of U if only S is specified. With postulate 2, the nonuniqueness of S is removed. However, it stresses clearly that the final dependence of U on S depends on the constraints.

It was already shown that $\partial U/\partial S = T$, T being the absolute temperature if no internal constraints exist. Naturally, it is to be asked what is temperature if there are internal constraints. Knowing the fundamental equation, partial temperatures can be defined as the π_κ. The measured macroscopic temperature in the usual sense is not an absolute quantity. It depends on the instrument used because temperature is *measured* by secondary effects. The instrument itself is a thermodynamic system. That secondary effect can be computed from the postulates and the fundamental equations of the system and the *thermometer*. With a suitable thermometer the π_κ are measured likewise.

Postulate 3 is equivalent to the Nernst postulate. At zero absolute temperature, entropy is zero, and so are the ξ_κ. The advantage and implications of this postulate are discussed in Tisza[1].

1.5 Stability

The postulates impose restrictions on the possible forms of the fundamental equation. Other restrictions are a consequence of the physical meaning of the equation.

By postulate 2, the values assumed by the degrees of freedom are those which maximise S. If a maximum does not exist, the fundamental equation cannot describe a physical system.

In thermostatics these conditions are expressed as intrinsic stability conditions. Here, two aspects must be considered and result from the existence of more than one internal degree of freedom. First, a system which is kept with external coordinates constant must be able to attain a thermostatic type of equilibrium with itself, the implication being that any system can be subdivided by conceptual walls into arbitrary subsystems without altering its state. As will be shown, the second condition implies the first when internal degrees of freedom are unconstrained.

Given a system, divide it into two arbitrary subsystems A and B by a conceptual wall restrictive to one of the X_i and called X_l. This wall transforms the system into a composite one whose global entropy and energy will be

$$S = S_{\mathrm{A}} + S_{\mathrm{B}} \qquad U = U_{\mathrm{A}} + U_{\mathrm{B}}$$

The maximisation problem reduces to the maximisation of S subject to

$$\begin{aligned} U &= U_{\mathrm{A}} + U_{\mathrm{B}} = C_1 \\ X_i^{\mathrm{A}} + X_i^{\mathrm{B}} &= C_2 \qquad (i \neq l) \\ X_l^{\mathrm{A}} &= C_3 \\ X_l^{\mathrm{B}} &= C_4 \end{aligned}$$

with C_1, C_2, C_3, C_4 as given constants.

Substituting the last two relations into S and U, and using again the method of Lagrange multipliers, the problem is again reduced to the unconstrained maximum of

$$\psi = S_{\mathrm{A}} + S_{\mathrm{B}} + \lambda_0[U_{\mathrm{A}} + U_{\mathrm{B}}] + \lambda_i(X_i^{\mathrm{A}} + X_i^{\mathrm{B}}) \qquad i \neq l$$

The condition of stationarity is given by

$$d\psi = 0 = (1+\lambda_0\pi_\kappa^A)\,d\xi_\kappa^A + (1+\lambda_0\pi_\kappa^B)\,d\xi_\kappa^B + \left(\lambda_0\frac{\partial U^A}{\partial X_i^A}+\lambda_i\right)dX_i^A + \left(\lambda_0\frac{\partial U^B}{\partial X_i^B}+\lambda_i\right)dX_i^B$$

Because $d\xi_\kappa$ and dX_i are arbitrary, the relation above implies

$$\pi_\kappa^A = -\frac{1}{\lambda_0} = \pi_\kappa^B = T$$

Eliminating now the X_i from the equations of constraint

$$\frac{\partial U^A}{\partial X_i^A} = \frac{\partial U^B}{\partial X_i^B}$$

as should be expected.

The maximum condition is now expressed by

$$d^2\psi \leqslant 0$$

This condition has a more clear expression if the consequence of additivity imposed by postulate 1 is used. This postulate implies that U^A and U^B are homogeneous of first order. As a consequence $\partial U^A/\partial X_i^A$ and $\partial U^B/\partial X_i^B$ are homogeneous of order zero. Besides, corresponding to subdivisions of the same system, their functional dependence on the X_i and ξ_κ is the same.

Introducing the specific quantities

$$u_A = \frac{U^A}{X_l^A}, \qquad u_B = \frac{U^B}{X_l^B}, \qquad x_i = \frac{X_i}{X_l}, \qquad \xi_\kappa^* = \frac{\xi_\kappa}{X_l}$$

and taking into account the condition of stationarity, $d^2\psi$ can be expressed as

$$d^2\psi = -\frac{1}{T}\left\{\frac{\partial^2 u}{\partial\xi_m^*\,\partial\xi_n^*}\,d\xi_m^*\,d\xi_n^* + \frac{\partial^2 u}{\partial x_q\,\partial x_r}\,dx_q\,dx_r\right\}$$

where $u = \dfrac{U}{X_l}$ and $q, r \neq l$

which can also be written as

$$d^2\psi = -\frac{1}{T}\frac{\partial^2 u}{\partial\phi_i\,\partial\phi_j}\,d\phi_i\,d\phi_j$$

ϕ representing either ξ or x.

Because $T > 0$†

† If $T = 0$, $S = 0$ by the postulates, so this case need not be considered.

S is a maximum if

$$\frac{\partial^2 u}{\partial\phi_i\,\partial\phi_j} \geqslant 0$$

which means that the quadratic form must be positive definitive. If

$$\frac{\partial^2 u}{\partial\phi_i\,\partial\phi_j}\,\mathrm{d}\phi_i\,\mathrm{d}\phi_j = 0$$

for arbitrarily small $\mathrm{d}\phi_i$, $\mathrm{d}\phi_j \neq 0$, the condition is transferred to

$$\mathrm{d}^3 u = 0$$

$$\mathrm{d}^4 u \geqslant 0$$

and so on.

Generally $\mathrm{d}^2 u > 0$, and so no higher order differentials are necessary. The condition $\mathrm{d}^2 u > 0$ is the intrinsic stability criteria. Using now the theory of quadratic forms it is easily shown that a necessary condition for

$$\frac{\partial^2 u}{\partial\phi_i\,\partial\phi_j}\,\mathrm{d}\phi_i\,\mathrm{d}\phi_j \geqslant 0$$

is

$$\frac{\partial^2 u}{\partial\xi_m^*\,\partial\xi_n^*}\,\mathrm{d}\xi_m^*\,\mathrm{d}\xi_n^* \geqslant 0$$

as was stated before.

The intrinsic stability criteria was established in terms of maximisation of S, subject to U being constant, besides the other constraints. A dual formulation is possible. It consists in minimising U subject to S constant, and conserving the other constraints. Using again the method of Lagrange multipliers it is a simple matter to show that the same condition in terms of U will result, that is

$$\frac{\partial^2 u}{\partial\phi_i\,\partial\phi_j}\,\mathrm{d}\phi_i\,\mathrm{d}\phi_j \geqslant 0$$

The interesting fact to be stressed is that this is a known condition of stability for CP. This shows the consistency of thermodynamics as formulated here with the other branches of classical physics. Note that S and not ξ_κ are assumed constant in CP.

The duality also shows that the maximum postulate on S could have been substituted by a postulate of minimum internal energy, this formulation having, probably, more physical appeal to all those who come to thermodynamics from continuum mechanics.

The unity of interpretation is still enriched when the Lagrange transforms of the fundamental equations are considered, which bring into discussion the classical thermodynamic potentials. That unity becomes almost obvious when thermodynamics is formulated in the way presented here. Besides, the intrinsic stability itself introduces the domain of validity of the fundamental equation. This means that the formalism followed here sets its own limits or, at least, warns about eventual loss of physical meaning. The importance of intrinsic stability for discussion of phase transitions and critical points must also be mentioned and the work of Tisza[1] is once more referred to.

So far, no internal constraints have been explicitly considered. The methodology to be followed would be the same, albeit with added complexity. It must be noted, however, that imposing internal constraints can give rise to intrinsic stability which otherwise would not exist. If these constraints are time dependent, no thermostatic equilibrium would be possible.

1.6 Thermodynamics of Continuous Systems

No explicit reference to system extension has so far been made. However, it appears natural to assume that a unit volume or mass can be considered as a basic scaling factor for the fundamental equation. As a result of the first order homogeneity of the fundamental equation, it becomes of zero order homogeneity when referred to unit mass or volume. What scaling factor is more appropriate will depend on the situation. We will then have

$$u = u(x_1 \ldots, \phi_1 \ldots)$$

it being understood that

$$u = \frac{U}{L} \qquad x_i = \frac{X_i}{L} \qquad \phi_\kappa = \frac{\xi_\kappa}{L}$$

L being the scaling factor.

Once the scaling factor is known, U, X_i, ξ_κ are recovered.

In continuous systems, u, x_i, ϕ_κ, are field variables if the fundamental thermodynamic equation is assumed to apply in vanishingly small mass or volume elements. This is the usual local state argument. Using the local state reasoning the ξ_i are few. Physically they are easily interpreted as partial entropies associated with peculiar types of microscopic structure. Their number depends on the level at which description is aimed. They can have a classical or quantum-mechanical interpretation and according to the number they can lose completely their macroscopic character to become *coordinates* of the most elementary particles.

The chief difference with traditional LS theories lies in the vanishingly small system being thermodynamic. The motivation behind the traditional

LS, which uses thermodynamic subsystems was that relaxation time would depend only on size. Later, relaxation was introduced by reference to chemical reactions and, by analogy, hidden coordinates were postulated. This construction would preserve the thermodynamic structure and concepts of temperature and entropy. It does not seem to have succeeded without artificiality, and present day discussions show it clearly.

Taking the vanishingly small subsystem as thermodynamic, the identification of x_i with the components of strain in continuous systems, seems obvious if mechanical energy is the only CP energy form. The ξ_i and the internal constraints will depend on the material. Balance equations will be set down in the usual way. However, it must be stressed that more than one *heat flow* can exist simultaneously, each one associated with the corresponding ξ_i. Furthermore, different relaxation times can exist between the ξ_i in neighbouring subsystems and within the subsystem itself. For instance, if ξ_1 can be exchanged among subsystems, and $\xi_2 \ldots$ cannot, the coupling regarding ξ_2 will come through ξ_1, etc.

1.7 Conclusions

A postulational formulation of thermodynamics has been presented which generalises thermostatics. It reduces to thermostatics when internal constraints do not exist. The formulation results directly from those experimental facts which inspired CKC theories.

The basic approach was to separate clearly other branches of classical physics from thermodynamics and to assume them primitive. By analogy with CP theories, internal degrees of freedom were postulated. As a consequence, the usual concept of entropy in nonequilibrium situations does not unequivocally describe the internal behaviour, unless internal constraints are absent. In general situations, partial entropies can be considered with corresponding temperatures.

Characteristic of the formulation, is the existence of a fundamental equation which closely resembles Gibbs function for thermostatics. Further restrictions on the fundamental equation ensure compatibility with thermostatics and a recovery of all its results. It must be stressed particularly that a dual formulation exists and conditions for intrinsic stability are clearly set down. These conditions are essential for the physical existence of the system. Phase transitions can be discussed on this formalism using pure mathematical arguments.

On application to continuous systems and the formulation of constitutive equations, the postulates are fundamental restrictions on the possible forms they can assume, besides those which result from frame indifference, material symmetry, etc. No reference to Clausius–Duhem inequalities is involved, such type of restriction being already embodied in the basic postulates which are defined in terms of clearly defined quantities. No reference to equilibrium is needed. Results associated with equilibrium are direct consequences of the postulates.

In applications to practical systems, the same practical difficulties exist as in LS or FU approaches and result from the basic lack of knowledge of what is inside the system. If this is inferred from microscopic theories, the theory here presented easily encompasses it.

No attempt has been made to present or discuss particular continuous systems, or materials. However, a general conceptual framework was developed which appears able to provide a smooth transition from classical thermodynamics to present applications in continuous systems. No claim of rigorous mathematical proofs was made: rather, a logical motivation was sought taking for granted familiarity with the Tisza and Callen formulations for MTE.

Acknowledgements

The work reported here was performed with the support of Instituto de Alta Cultura, Research Project TLE 2.

References

1. L. Tisza. *Generalised Thermodynamics*, MIT Press (1966)
2. H. B. Callen. *Thermodynamics*, Wiley, New York (1960)
3. J. Meixner. *Thermodynamics of Processes*, Lectures at Lehigh University (1969/70)
4. A. G. Portela. Estabilidade intrinseca e condicionada de sistemas termostáticos *Técnica* (1960)
5. C. Truesdell. *Rational Thermodynamics*, McGraw-Hill, New York (1969)
6. J. Kestin. *A Course in Thermodynamics*, Blaisdell (1968)
7. J. J. D. Domingos. As equações fundamentais em mecânica de fluidos e transmissão de calor. *Rev. Port. Química*, **8** (1966), 88
8. J. J. D. Domingos. O mínimo de produção de entropia no escoamento uniforme dum fluido newtoniano. *Técnica*, no. 362 (1966)
9. J. J. D. Domingos. Métodos variacionais em mecânica dos fluidos e transmissão de calor. *Técnica*, no. 371 (1967)
10. J. J. D. Domingos. Stationary states with minimum entropy production and non constant phenomenological coefficients. *Portugalie Physica*, **5** (1969), 139
11. J. J. D. Domingos. *Lições de Termodinâmica no I.S.T.* (1972)

2. From Thermostatics to Thermodynamics; Discussion Paper

Ingo Müller†

2.1 Prologue on Temperature

On 7th February, 1615 the Venetian diplomat Giovanfrancesco Sagredo wrote a letter to Galileo Galilei in which he reported what he had read off from his thermoscope: that 'well water is actually colder in winter than in summer' and he muses 'that our senses judge differently'‡

Beginning at that time and progressing at a painfully slow pace the concept of *temperature as an empirical measure for hot and cold* transpired. Even today there is often mistrust in 'the physical sense of temperature' in thermodynamics, and one purpose of this prologue is to suggest that we should not endorse that mistrust. Let us be like the above-mentioned Sagredo who obviously—in making his statement—realised that some thermometers are better than others and used his common sense to make a choice between different ones.

As long as one characteristic of a body is its being hot or cold, it *does* make sense to talk about temperature as a measure of that characteristic. To be sure though, this empirical temperature need not be the absolute temperature of thermostatics and, in particular, it can be positive and negative, as indeed it is according to most empirical scales, and it can range from $-\infty$ to $+\infty$.

I stress this point, because in Professor Domingos' paper, from which in this discussion I take my clues, I felt that the distinction between the empirical temperature and the absolute temperature was not given the emphasis it deserves, although that distinction was made.

2.2 The Objectives of Thermodynamics and of the Constitutive Theory

Thermodynamics is a field theory and its ultimate objective is the determination of the fields

$\rho(x_n, t)$—density

$v_i(x_n, t)$—velocity

$\vartheta(x_n, t)$—empirical temperature

† The Johns Hopkins University, Baltimore, Maryland, USA.

‡ According to W. E. Knowles Middleton[1].

in a body. The necessary field equations are based upon the equations of balance of

$$\begin{array}{ll} \text{mass} & \dot{\rho}+\rho v_{i,i}=0 \\ \text{momentum} & \rho\dot{v}_i-t_{ij,j}=\rho f_i \\ \text{internal energy} & \rho\dot{\varepsilon}+q_{i,i}-t_{ij}v_{i,j}=\rho r \end{array} \tag{2.1†}$$

and field equations in fact result, if constitutive equations are known which relate the specific internal energy ε, the heat flux q_i and the stress t_{ij} to the thermodynamic fields in a materially dependent manner. I shall consider a *simple heat conducting fluid* which is characterised by constitutive equations of the form

$$\begin{aligned} \varepsilon &= \varepsilon(\rho, \vartheta, \dot{\vartheta}, \vartheta_{,i}) = \varepsilon(\rho, \vartheta, \dot{\vartheta}, g) \\ q_i &= q_i(\text{———}) = -\kappa(\text{———})\vartheta_{,i} \\ t_{ij} &= t_{ij}(\text{———}) = -p(\text{———})\delta_{ij}+Q(\text{———})\vartheta_{,i}\vartheta_{,j} \end{aligned} \tag{2.2}$$

where $g \equiv \vartheta_{,i}\vartheta_{,i}$ and where the representations are the result of the requirement of material objectivity with respect to Galileï transformations; p is called the pressure and κ the heat conductivity.

While for the material characterised by equation 2.2 linear irreversible thermodynamics would assume that the constitutive relations for ε, κ, p and Q be those of equilibrium, no such *assumption of local equilibrium* is made here. In other words, I allow ε, κ, p and Q to depend on $\dot{\vartheta}$ and g as well as on ρ and ϑ.

Insertion of the constitutive relations into the equations of balance leads to a set of five field equations for the five thermodynamic fields and every solution of these equations is called a *thermodynamic process* in a simple heat conducting fluid.

So far neither entropy nor absolute temperature needed to be mentioned, but then—in talking about field equations—I have pretended that we know the functions

$$\varepsilon(\rho, \vartheta, \dot{\vartheta}, g), \quad \kappa(\rho, \vartheta, \dot{\vartheta}, g), \quad p(\rho, \vartheta, \dot{\vartheta}, g), \quad Q(\rho, \vartheta, \dot{\vartheta}, g) \tag{2.3}$$

and in reality we do not; not for a *single* material. Therefore, the most pressing problem of thermodynamics lies in the *constitutive theory* which strives to find the form, or at least restrict the generality of the constitutive functions; entropy and absolute temperature come into thermodynamics as auxiliary quantities of the constitutive theory.

Like every other *discussor*, according to the instructions we received, I am supposed 'to introduce controversy, agreement and expansion' and I comply

† The specific body force f_i and the specific supply r of internal energy (through radiation) are taken to be given fields.

by offering the theory of a simple heat conducting fluid as a model for the thermodynamic method. There are no unidentified variables here, rather there is a conceptually clear mathematical problem of finding solutions to a set of partial differential equations, and there is the wish to learn more about the differential equations that govern the behaviour of a particular body under consideration; that is, there is the wish to learn more about the constitutive functions. Thermostatics pursues that same wish and, although that theory achieves little compared to our need, it achieves something and I fully concur to Professor Domingos' emphasis on the value of the study of thermostatics for the direction into which thermodynamics should move.

2.3 The Limited Contribution of Thermostatics to the Constitutive Theory

Thermostatics is concerned with thermodynamic processes of uniform temperature for which the constitutive relations in equation 2.2 for simple heat conducting fluids read

$$\begin{aligned} \varepsilon &= \varepsilon(\rho, \vartheta, \dot{\vartheta}) \\ q_i &= 0 \\ t_{ij} &= -p(\rho, \vartheta, \dot{\vartheta})\delta_{ij} \end{aligned} \tag{2.4a}$$

and for which the equations of balance of mass and internal energy combine to give

$$r = \dot{\varepsilon} - \frac{p}{\rho^2}\dot{\rho} \tag{2.4b}$$

If the rate of temperature is so small that the values of internal energy and pressure become independent of $\dot{\vartheta}$, the constitutive relations and the energy equation assume the forms

$$\begin{aligned} \varepsilon &= \varepsilon|_E(\rho, \vartheta) \\ q_i &= 0 \qquad \text{and} \qquad r = \dot{\varepsilon}|_E - \frac{p|_E}{\rho^2}\dot{\rho} \\ t_{ij} &= -p|_E(\rho, \vartheta)\delta_{ij} \end{aligned} \tag{2.5†}$$

A *thermostatic process* is a pair of fields $\{\rho(x_n, t), \vartheta(t)\}$ which satisfies the energy equation 2.4*b* and in particular a thermostatic process is called *slow*, if it satisfies the energy equation 2.5; we notice that every thermostatic process is possible given the proper supply r to satisfy the energy equation.

† The index E refers to equilibrium, defined as a thermodynamic process with uniform and time-independent fields of velocity and temperature and with time-independent density.

A theorem by Euler ensures that $\dot{\varepsilon}|_E-(p|_E/\rho^2)\dot{\rho}$ has integrating factors and we write

$$\dot{\eta}_\Lambda(\rho, \vartheta)=\Lambda(\rho, \vartheta)\left\{\dot{\varepsilon}|_E-\frac{p|_E}{\rho^2}\dot{\rho}\right\} \tag{2.6}$$

This is the first step toward entropy: the existence of integrating factors and of potentials to the expression $\varepsilon|_E-(p|_E/\rho^2)\dot{\rho}$. Although Clausius did not know this, nothing is needed but mathematics to arrive at equation 2.6 in the present case of two variables. If there are more than the two variables ϑ and ρ, the existence of integrating factors is no longer a matter of course, and this is where Carathéodory's inaccessibility argument becomes important, because it ensures the existence of integrating factors in the case of three or more variables.

In any case, little has been achieved by deriving equation 2.6, and nothing useful concerning the constitutive theory. But now one makes use of the empirical knowledge that two bodies in contact are equally hot in equilibrium—that is, that their temperatures are equal—and shows that *one* of the integrating factors is a *universal* function of temperature alone. We denote *that* integrating factor by $1/T(\vartheta)$, the corresponding potential by $\eta|_E$ and call $\eta|_E$ the specific entropy in equilibrium. Thus we have

$$\dot{\eta}|_E=\frac{1}{T(\vartheta)}\left\{\dot{\varepsilon}|_E-\frac{p|_E}{\rho^2}\dot{\rho}\right\} \tag{2.7}$$

$\eta|_E$ and $\varepsilon|_E$ are both functions of ρ and ϑ and, when the differentiations indicated in equation 2.7 are performed, we obtain the equation

$$\left(\frac{\partial\eta|_E}{\partial\vartheta}-\frac{1}{T}\frac{\partial\varepsilon|_E}{\partial\vartheta}\right)\dot{\vartheta}+\left(\frac{\partial\eta|_E}{\partial\rho}-\frac{1}{T}\frac{\partial\varepsilon|_E}{\partial\rho}+\frac{p|_E}{\rho^2 T}\right)\dot{\rho}=0 \tag{2.8}$$

which must hold for all slow thermostatic processes, hence, in particular, for arbitrary values of $\dot{\vartheta}$ and $\dot{\rho}$. Therefore, we could easily violate equation 2.8 unless that equation were identically satisfied by the conditions

$$\frac{\partial\eta|_E}{\partial\vartheta}=\frac{1}{T}\frac{\partial\varepsilon|_E}{\partial\vartheta} \quad \text{and} \quad \frac{\partial\eta|_E}{\partial\rho}=\frac{1}{T}\left(\frac{\partial\varepsilon|_E}{\partial\rho}-\frac{p|_E}{\rho^2}\right) \tag{2.9}$$

which we summarise in the form of a Gibbs equation

$$\mathrm{d}\eta|_E=\frac{1}{T(\vartheta)}\left\{\frac{\partial\varepsilon|_E}{\partial\vartheta}\mathrm{d}\vartheta+\left(\frac{\partial\varepsilon|_E}{\partial\rho}-\frac{p|_E}{\rho^2}\right)\mathrm{d}\rho\right\} \tag{2.10}$$

The Gibbs equation implies the integrability condition

$$\frac{\partial \ln T}{\partial \vartheta} = \frac{\dfrac{\partial p|_E}{\partial \vartheta}}{\rho^2 \dfrac{\partial \varepsilon|_E}{\partial \rho} - p|_E} \tag{2.11}$$

and this relation represents the contribution of thermostatics to the constitutive theory. It concerns the two functions $p|_E = p(\rho, \vartheta, 0, 0)$ and $\varepsilon|_E = \varepsilon(\rho, \vartheta, 0, 0)$ and states that the combination on the right-hand side of equation 2.11 not only is a function of ϑ alone, but that it is the *same* function for *all* fluids. Important though it is, this result is obviously a rather limited contribution to the constitutive theory; we should like the theory to impose restrictions on all four functions ε, κ, p, and Q of four variables each.

Certainly the integrability condition, equation 2.11, is not the result at all that has physicists intrigued with thermomechanics to the extent that they feel entropy to be the passe-partout to theoretical physics. Rather that feeling is based on two corollaries of Carathéodory's and Clausius' arguments

(1) If two bodies in contact are in equilibrium, the entropy of the compound body is the sum of the entropies of the parts†.

(2) In a rapid thermostatic process between two equilibria at times t_1 and t_2 the change of entropy must conform to the inequality‡

$$\eta(t_2) - \eta(t_1) \geqslant \int_{t_1}^{t_2} \frac{r\,dt}{T}.$$

An interesting sideline, but a sideline nonetheless is provided by the fact that, from equation 2.11 and the known constitutive relations for ideal gases (say), $T(\vartheta)$ can be calculated and is found to be a monotone and non-zero function of ϑ, so that it becomes suitable as a measure for temperature. $T(\vartheta)$ by convention is taken to be positive and is said to measure the *absolute temperature.*

Turning back to the introduction of controversy, I wish to comment on the common practice to *define* the absolute temperature as the differential quotient $\partial\varepsilon/\partial\eta$. As far as continuum thermodynamics is concerned, this procedure does not seem advantageous. First of all, to apply it, one must know the form of the entropy and usually one does not, and secondly there is no guarantee that $\partial\varepsilon/\partial\eta$ in fact is a measure for hot and cold; I know of

† From Carathéodory[2]: 'This additive property of entropy . . . has motivated many physicists, to consider entropy as a physical quantity which, like mass, pertains to every body.'

‡ While Clausius obtains this result by the consideration of rapid cycles from the requirement that internal energy cannot 'all by itself' pass from a colder to a warmer body, Carathéodory, from his inaccessibility argument, obtains only the special case that results from setting $r = 0$.

one case, in relativistic thermodynamics, where this latter point certainly becomes debatable; see Alts and Müller[3].

2.4 The Proposition of Entropy in Thermodynamics

To use entropy in thermodynamics is a venture and it is that no less for Coleman and Truesdell now than it was before for Meixner, Eckart, Jaumann and Duhem. Leaving much unsaid with regard to details of motivation and differences of presentation I remark that basically all these authors have assumed the validity of a balance of entropy in the form of the Clausius–Duhem inequality†

$$\rho\dot{\eta}+\left(\frac{q_i}{T}\right)_{,i}-\frac{\rho r}{T}\geqslant 0$$

for every thermodynamic process, where η is a constitutive quantity.

I believe that I have mentioned all results of thermostatics that have served to motivate the Clausius–Duhem inequality. Apart from that, some motivation is found in the kinetic theory of one-atomic gases, but that is already dubious motivation for this particular inequality, because the kinetic theory furnishes an entropy flux which is by no means equal to heat flux over absolute temperature. I realised that in my thesis‡ and was subsequently led to the idea that the entropy flux—for the purposes of continuum thermodynamics—should be given by a constitutive relation so that the Clausius–Duhem inequality would be replaced by the more general inequality

$$\rho\dot{\eta}+\Phi_{i,i}-\frac{\rho r}{T}\geqslant 0$$

Even this inequality in the specific form of its supply term still bears the mark of thermostatics and clearly the kinetic theory does not offer any help with respect to that term. Therefore, in order to be on the safe side, I have more recently (for example, Müller[4]) proposed to delete that supply term entirely, to consider supply-free bodies and assume the validity of the inequality‖

$$\rho\dot{\eta}+\Phi_{i,i}\geqslant 0 \quad \text{with} \quad \begin{aligned} \eta &= \eta(\rho, \vartheta, \dot{\vartheta}, \vartheta_{,i}) = \eta(\rho, \vartheta, \dot{\vartheta}, g) \\ \Phi_i &= \Phi_i(\text{———}) = \varphi(\text{———})\vartheta_{,i} \end{aligned} \tag{2.12}$$

in every thermodynamic process in a supply-free body, that is for every solution of the field equations that are based on the equations of balance

† The supply term $\rho r/T$ is not usually to be found in the older literature.

‡ I. Müller. *Ausbreitungsgeschwindigkeit von Stoerungen in Kontinuierlichen Medien.* Thesis, Aachen (1966).

‖ The constitutive relations for η and Φ_i are appropriate for a simple heat-conducting fluid; see also equation 2.2.

$$\dot{\rho}+\rho v_{i,i}=0$$
$$\rho\dot{v}_i-t_{ij,j}=0 \tag{2.13}$$
$$\rho\dot{\varepsilon}+q_{i,i}-t_{ij}v_{i,j}=0$$

I remark that no specific assumptions concerning entropy flux and entropy supply have entered the inequality 2.12.

The requirement that the fields $\rho(x_n, t)$, $v_i(x_n, t)$ and $\vartheta(x_n, t)$ that satisfy the inequality must be solutions of the field equations may be thought of as a constraint on these fields; now in Liu[5] it is proved that these constraints may be eliminated by use of *Lagrange multipliers* so that the new inequality

$$\begin{aligned}\rho\dot{\eta}+\Phi_{i,i}-\Lambda^{\rho}(\dot{\rho}+\rho v_{i,i})-&\\ -\Lambda^{v_i}(\rho\dot{v}_i-t_{ij,j})-&\\ -\Lambda(\rho\dot{\varepsilon}+q_{i,i}-t_{ij}v_{i,j})\geqslant 0&\end{aligned} \tag{2.14}$$

must hold for *all* (analytic) fields $\rho(x_n, t)$, $\vartheta(x_n, t)$, $v_i(x_n, t)$. The Lagrange multipliers Λ^{ρ}, Λ^{v_i} and Λ according to Liu may depend on ρ, ϑ, $\dot{\vartheta}$, $\vartheta_{,i}$ and v_i in general and they join η and Φ_i as auxiliary quantities of the thermodynamic constitutive theory which eventually must either be determined or eliminated from the results.

Insertion of the constitutive relations 2.2 and 2.12 into the inequality 2.14 leads to an expression on the left-hand side that is linear in the (arbitrary) derivatives

$$\dot{v}_i,\ \dot{\rho},\ \ddot{\vartheta},\ \rho_{,i},\ \vartheta_{,il},\ \dot{\vartheta}_{,i},\ v_{i,l}$$

so that the inequality could be violated unless the terms with those derivatives vanish; therefore they *must* vanish and the conditions for that are the following ones†

$$\Lambda^{v_i}=0 \tag{2.15}$$

$$\frac{\partial\eta}{\partial\rho}-\Lambda\frac{\partial\varepsilon}{\partial\rho}-\frac{1}{\rho}\Lambda^{\rho}=0 \tag{2.16}$$

$$\frac{\partial\eta}{\partial\vartheta}-\Lambda\frac{\partial\varepsilon}{\partial\vartheta}=0 \tag{2.17}$$

$$\frac{\partial\Phi_i}{\partial\rho}-\Lambda\frac{\partial q_i}{\partial\rho}=0 \tag{2.18}$$

$$\frac{\partial\Phi_{(i}}{\partial\vartheta_{,l)}}-\Lambda\frac{\partial q_{(i}}{\partial\vartheta_{,l)}}=0 \tag{2.19}$$

† Note the similarity of this argument to the corresponding argument in thermostatics, that in the one that led to equation 2.9.

$$\frac{\partial \Phi_i}{\partial \vartheta} - \Lambda \frac{\partial q_i}{\partial \dot{\vartheta}} + \rho\left(\frac{\partial \eta}{\partial \vartheta_{,i}} - \Lambda \frac{\partial \varepsilon}{\partial \vartheta_{,i}}\right) = 0 \tag{2.20}$$

$$\left(\frac{\partial \Phi_i}{\partial \dot{\vartheta}} - \Lambda \frac{\partial q_i}{\partial \dot{\vartheta}}\right)\vartheta_{,l} - \rho^2\left(\frac{\partial \eta}{\partial \rho} - \Lambda \frac{\partial \varepsilon}{\partial \rho}\right)\delta_{il} + \Lambda t_{il} = 0 \tag{2.21}$$

Thus Λ^{v_i} is identically zero while Λ^ρ and Λ are seen to be independent of the velocity v_i. Now, with $\Phi_i = \varphi\vartheta_{,i}$ and $q_i = -\kappa\vartheta_{,i}$ the relation 2.19 reads

$$(\varphi + \Lambda\kappa)\delta_{il} + 2\left(\frac{\partial \varphi}{\partial g} + \Lambda \frac{\partial \kappa}{\partial g}\right)\vartheta_{,i}\vartheta_{,l} = 0$$

whence we conclude, since this equation must hold for all $\vartheta_{,i}$

$$\varphi = \Lambda\kappa \qquad \text{and} \qquad \frac{\partial \Lambda}{\partial g} = 0 \qquad \text{so that} \qquad \Phi_i = \Lambda(\rho, \vartheta, \dot{\vartheta})q_i$$

Equation 2.18 then implies that Λ is independent of ρ as well and we have

$$\Phi_i = \Lambda(\vartheta, \dot{\vartheta})q_i. \tag{2.22}$$

With this we eliminate Φ_i from equations 2.15 to 2.21 and obtain results that may be summarised in two formulae

$$\frac{\partial \ln \Lambda}{\partial \dot{\vartheta}} = \frac{Q}{\kappa} \tag{2.23}$$

$$d\eta = \frac{\partial \eta}{\partial \vartheta} d\vartheta + \Lambda(\vartheta, \dot{\vartheta})\left\{\left(\frac{\partial \varepsilon}{\partial \rho} - \frac{p}{\rho^2}\right)d\rho + \frac{\partial \varepsilon}{\partial \dot{\vartheta}} d\dot{\vartheta} + \left(\frac{\partial \varepsilon}{\partial g} + \frac{Q}{2\rho}\right)dg\right\} \tag{2.24}$$

The argument that led to equations 2.15 to 2.21 has also left us with the residual inequality

$$\rho\left(\frac{\partial \eta}{\partial \vartheta} - \Lambda \frac{\partial \varepsilon}{\partial \vartheta}\right)\dot{\vartheta} + \frac{\partial \Lambda}{\partial \vartheta} q_i \vartheta_{,i} \geqslant 0$$

whose left-hand side assumes a minimum, namely zero, for equilibrium† so that of necessity we must have

$$\frac{\partial \eta|_E}{\partial \vartheta} = \Lambda|_E \frac{\partial \varepsilon|_E}{\partial \vartheta} \tag{2.25}$$

$$\frac{\partial \Lambda|_E}{\partial \vartheta} \kappa|_E \leqslant 0 \tag{2.26}$$

$$\frac{\partial \Lambda|_E}{\partial \vartheta} \frac{\partial \varepsilon}{\partial \dot{\vartheta}}\Big|_E \geqslant \frac{\partial \Lambda}{\partial \dot{\vartheta}}\Big|_E \frac{\partial \varepsilon|_E}{\partial \vartheta} \tag{2.27}$$

† Here again equilibrium means a time-independent thermostatic process (with uniform and time-independent velocity).

From equations 2.25 and 2.24 we conclude, because η in equilibrium is independent of $\dot{\vartheta}$ and g

$$\mathrm{d}\eta|_E = \Lambda(\vartheta, 0)\left\{\frac{\partial\varepsilon|_E}{\partial\vartheta}\mathrm{d}\vartheta + \left(\frac{\partial\varepsilon|_E}{\partial\rho} - \frac{p|_E}{\rho^2}\right)\mathrm{d}\rho\right\} \tag{2.28}$$

and, since among all integrating factors of

$$\frac{\partial\varepsilon|_E}{\partial\vartheta}\mathrm{d}\vartheta + \left(\frac{\partial\varepsilon|_E}{\partial\rho} - \frac{p|_E}{\rho^2}\right)\mathrm{d}\rho$$

there is in general only one that depends on temperature only, namely the reciprocal of the absolute temperature, we conclude that (see equation 2.10)

$$\Lambda|_E = \Lambda(\vartheta, 0) = \frac{1}{T(\vartheta)} \tag{2.29}$$

and this is a *universal* function of ϑ†. This conclusion permits us to rewrite the two inequalities 2.26 and 2.27 as follows

$$\kappa|_E \geqslant 0 \qquad -\frac{1}{T^2}\frac{\mathrm{d}T}{\mathrm{d}\vartheta}\frac{\partial\varepsilon}{\partial\dot{\vartheta}}\Big|_E \geqslant \frac{\partial\varepsilon}{\partial\vartheta}\Big|_E\frac{\partial\Lambda}{\partial\dot{\vartheta}}\Big|_E \tag{2.30}$$

the first one requires positivity of the heat conductivity in equilibrium, while the second one permits a finite speed of propagation of disturbances in temperature, as I have shown elsewhere (Müller[4]).

From the expression 2.24 for $\mathrm{d}\eta$ we obtain integrability conditions which do not contain the auxiliary quantity η any more

$$\frac{\partial \ln\Lambda}{\partial\vartheta} = \frac{\dfrac{\partial p}{\partial\vartheta}}{\rho^2\dfrac{\partial\varepsilon}{\partial\rho} - p} = \frac{2\dfrac{\partial p}{\partial g}}{\kappa - \rho\dfrac{\partial\kappa}{\partial\rho}} = -\frac{\dfrac{\partial Q}{\partial\vartheta}}{2\rho\dfrac{\partial\varepsilon}{\partial g} + Q} = \frac{Q}{\kappa}\,. \tag{2.31}$$

This string of equations represents a contribution of the entropy principle to the thermodynamic constitutive theory, because it implies that the four terms on the right-hand side are functions of ϑ and $\dot{\vartheta}$ only.

I emphasise the similarity of the argument which led to equation 2.31, to the procedure in thermostatics, where the restriction for the constitutive theory also resulted from an evaluation of an entropy relation and from an integrability condition for the entropy. One aspect, however, of the thermostatic result is so far missing in thermodynamics, namely the universal character of the restriction, and now I proceed to show that indeed $\Lambda(\vartheta, \dot{\vartheta})$ is a universal function, or again, at least the same function for all fluids of the considered type!

† At least, it is the same function for all fluids.

To that end we must place one fluid in contact with another one; the interface between them shall be represented by a singular surface for the purpose of the mathematical description, and for the jump of the heat flux and the stress across the interface we have the conditions

$$[q_i e_i] = 0 \qquad \text{and} \qquad [t_{ij} e_j] = 0 \tag{2.32}$$

which represent the equations of balance of energy and momentum at the interface. The square brackets $[\Psi]$ denote the difference $\Psi^{I} - \Psi^{II}$, where the indices I and II characterise the two fluids and e_i is the unit normal vector of the interface†. In terms of the representations 2.2 the two jump conditions imply

$$[\kappa \vartheta_{,\perp}] = 0 \qquad \text{and} \qquad [Q \vartheta_{,||} \vartheta_{,\perp}] = 0 \tag{2.33}$$

where $\vartheta_{,\perp}$ and $\vartheta_{,||}$ are the normal and tangential components of the temperature gradient respectively.

Let us now look at an interface at which the temperature is continuous at all times so that $[\vartheta(x_n, t)] = 0$ for all x_n on the interface.

Obviously $\dot{\vartheta}$ and $\vartheta_{,||}$ are then also continuous and the conditions 2.33 imply

$$[\kappa \vartheta_{,\perp}] = 0 \qquad \text{and} \qquad [Q \vartheta_{,\perp}] = 0$$

these two relations can both be true for all $\vartheta^{I,II}_{,\perp}$ only if

$$\frac{Q}{\kappa}\Big|_{I} = \frac{Q}{\kappa}\Big|_{II}$$

holds and by equation 2.31 this means that $\partial \ln \Lambda / \partial \dot{\vartheta}$ must have the same value on both sides of the interface. Because $\partial \ln \Lambda / \partial \dot{\vartheta}$ is a function of the variables ϑ and $\dot{\vartheta}$ only, which are both continuous at the interface, we conclude that $\partial \ln \Lambda / \partial \dot{\vartheta}$ is a universal function of ϑ and $\dot{\vartheta}$. In fact, Λ itself is a universal function, since $\Lambda(\vartheta, 0)$ is the universal absolute temperature as we saw earlier. In Müller[6] I have called $\Lambda(\vartheta, \dot{\vartheta})$ the *coldness*.

In conclusion we now see that the four terms on the right-hand side of equation 2.32 are the *same* functions of ϑ and $\dot{\vartheta}$ in *all* simple heat conducting fluids. Also it may be of interest to remark that the universal character of the coldness together with equation 2.22 and the first relationship of equation 2.32 ensure that the normal component of the entropy flux is continuous at the interface, if the temperature is. Conversely, had we *assumed* that continuity of the entropy flux, when $[\vartheta] = 0$ holds, we should also have concluded that $\Lambda(\vartheta, \dot{\vartheta})$ is a universal function. (see Müller[4,6]).

† For the validity of the jump conditions in equation 2.32 the tangential velocities on either side must have the same value (for example, they may both vanish). But apart from that these jump conditions are as general as they can be, if we want to stop short of treating the interface as a separate body with its own thermodynamic properties like surface tension, surface energy, etc.

I am afraid in the presentation of this chapter I may have strayed rather far from a discussion of Professor Domingos' contribution. I apologise for that and point to what seems to be a rather basic difference in our attitude toward thermodynamics, reflecting, I suppose, two different schools of thought. While for one of these schools the basic formalism of thermostatics remains germane to thermodynamics because of the assumption of local equilibrium in which the equilibrium Gibbs equation holds, the other school makes no such assumption and gets different results even in the near-equilibrium range of linear irreversible thermodynamics.

Remarks

Were thermodynamic experimentation easier than it is, we might be able to run an experimental check on the results of the previous chapter. But as it is, with little experimental evidence on rapid and strongly nonuniform processes, we are left to speculate on whether the universal coldness in fact exists and whether the consequences it predicts are real.

I have talked here about the entropy principle, nearly exclusively, and that was because I thought that I might have something constructive to say about it. However, I do not wish to give the impression that I regard the entropy principle as the centrepiece of thermodynamics; in fact, in most cases its consequences are few and certainly fewer than the consequences of invariance requirements on the constitutive functions, such as the *principle of material frame-indifference with respect to accelerated translations and rotations.* About that principle now, I should have nothing constructive to say, indeed to the contrary. That principle is contradicted by the kinetic theory of one-atomic gases† even, which so beautifully lends its support to the concept of entropy.

Also, there are crucial areas in thermodynamics where we have no guiding principles at all. For instance, which constitutive class will correspond to a given class of materials? Or more specifically: is there any fluid whose behaviour conforms to the constitutive relations of a simple heat conducting fluid defined earlier? In fact, recent research seems to indicate that, if $\dot{\vartheta}$ is a variable, so should $\dot{\rho}$ and $\rho_{,i}$ be. On that count simple heat conducting fluids provide an oversimplified, although suggestive model for modern thermodynamics.

Acknowledgement

This work was supported by a grant from the National Science Foundation to The Johns Hopkins University.

† For substantiation of this remark, see Müller[7].

References

1. W. E. Knowles Middleton. *A History of the Thermometer and its Use in Meteorology*, Johns Hopkins Press, Baltimore, Md. (1966)
2. C. Carathéodory. Untersuchungen ueber die grundlagen der thermodynamik. *Mathematische Annalen*, **67** (1909), 355. See also: *Gesammelte Mathematische Schriften*, Beck'sche Verlagsbuchhandlung, Muenchen (1955), 131
3. T. Alts and I. Müller. Relativistic thermodynamics of simple heat conducting fluids *Arch. Rat. Mech. Anal.*, **48** (1972), 245
4. I. Müller. Entropy, coldness and absolute temperature. *Proc. CISM*, Udine, Italy (1971)
5. I-Shih Liu. Method of Lagrange multipliers for the exploitation of the entropy principle. *Arch. Rat. Mech. Anal.*, **46** (1972), 131
6. I. Müller. Die kaeltefunktion, eine universelle funktion in der thermodynamik viskoser waermeleitender fluessigkeiten. *Arch. Rat. Mech. Anal.*, **40** (1971), 1
7. I. Müller. On the frame dependence of stress and heat flux. *Arch. Rat. Mech. Anal.*, **45** (1972), 241

Discussion

PRIGOGINE

In the presentation of the principles of thermodynamics an important role is often played by pedagogical considerations. This is generally a matter of taste. The interesting presentation given by Professor Domingos may certainly be useful; it seems to me, however, that it is not easy to extend it to open systems which are of great interest today. Also the physical basis of his relation 1.28 is not clear to me. If the ξ_κ represent internal parameters, some conversion factors should at least appear in equation 1.28.

DOMINGOS

The extension to open systems can be done through the concept of internal constraints in a way similar to the approach of Tisza and Callen. A global system is supposed divided by internal walls with specific properties, for instance, impervious to mass flow. To each subsystem a Gibbsian description is applicable assuming them in equilibrium. Consider, for example, only two such subsystems. Removing the constraint of the internal wall, if they were not in mutual equilibrium, a mass flow arises among them; they are open regarding each other but closed regarding the outside. Through this device, we can reduce the study of open systems to closed composite systems by the appropriate choice of mass reservoirs.

It is this introduction of internal constraints which makes Tisza's thermodynamics essentially different from Gibbs' thermodynamics. This concept is implied throughout our exposition. I would also like to stress that in this construction, the usual *reservoirs* in classical thermodynamics are not external to *our* thermodynamic system but one of its composite parts. Without unnecessary details, this stresses that interaction with the particular thermodynamic system under study comes from other thermodynamic systems which usually have different fundamental equations. Of course, in the development of this theory, equivalence with the usual construction is easily shown.

Regarding relation 1.28, it merely represents a split of entropy into several parcels, so no conversion factors are needed. The ξ_κ are not hidden coordinates in the usual sense and were introduced as degrees of advancement of reaction. This is why we called them internal coordinates. The main idea behind the splitting of total entropy into parts, comes from the concept that if global microscopic equilibrium does not exist, we can nevertheless think of equilibrium among groups of internal degrees of freedom. Each one of these could then be characterised by macroscopic parameters which we call the ξ_κ. Each one has the meaning of a *partial entropy*. The total entropy of the system will be their sum. This introduction of the ξ_κ adds a new capability to the description of thermodynamic behaviour and can be useful in unusual situations.

It should be noted that the ξ_κ collapse into the usual entropy if no internal constraints exist, (internal means here inside a subsystem, not among subsystems in the sense of Tisza). In that case we will have the usual thermodynamics and the fundamental equation reduces to the usual Gibbs equation in which the usual hidden coordinates parallel degrees of advancement of reaction.

To summarise, we split the usual entropy into parts. Relations among these parts are dynamic constitutive relations, which express time-dependent restrictions to internal equilibrium at the subsystem level. All the thermodynamic variables will usually depend on them. If no such internal restrictions exist, no distinction among them is possible and, as a consequence of the postulates, we have only one temperature and one entropy.

TISZA

I very much appreciate the fact that Professor Domingos has chosen to develop thermostatics in a version that I have advanced some years ago under the name of MTE. Generally speaking this theory covers the same range of phenomena as traditional thermostatics but it may be in order for me to call attention to a feature for which this is not entirely true.

It is usual to say that thermostatics deals with closed systems whereas open systems belong to irreversible thermodynamics (TIP). By contrast, in MTE, an open system in contact with a reservoir is treated on an equal footing with a closed system; irreversible processes are initiated by the relaxation of constraints in composite systems and they are treated as transitions from one equilibrium to another. Such elementary discrete steps may be lined up in long sequences leading a rudimentary description of irreversibility with a qualitative temporal ordering. In order to obtain a true theory of irreversibility this qualitative ordering ought to be made quantitative. This calls for a substantial broadening of the basis of the theory.

DOMINGOS

I certainly agree with the comments of Professor Tisza, and refer to chapter 1, references 7 and 8, where broadening of the theory was attempted. Whether this extension is or not in the spirit of MTE as put forward by Professor Tisza is a question not to be answered by me. I think that the extension is valid and, moreover, that it emphasises the logical and conceptual value of the original formulation of MTE.

PRIGOGINE

Professor Müller assumes the validity of the Clausius–Duhem inequality. This would mean that there exists a Liapounoff function (the entropy function) which can be expressed through *macroscopic variables.* Near equilibrium in the range of TIP this is indeed so as indicated by statistical considerations I shall summarise in chapter 5. However, further away from equilibrium, the assumption of an entropy function whose associated flow and source have a macroscopic meaning (that is, can be expressed in terms of the quantities which appear in the macroscopic field equations) is a supplementary new principle for which at the moment I see no justification.

MÜLLER

First let me point out that I have used an entropy inequality that is more general than the Clausius–Duhem inequality. But Professor Prigogine is right, I have indeed *assumed* that the entropy and its flux both exist and are given by general constitutive relations. I agree that one might want to discuss these assumptions but I insist that they are weaker than the assumptions that are commonly made concerning the entropy and the entropy flux, since these involve the idea of local equilibrium and a specific relation between the entropy flux and the heat flux. The results derived from my assumptions, therefore, should be viewed with more confidence than the classical results and they *are* different even in the near equilibrium range of TIP.

RIVLIN

I would like to ask Professor Müller four questions and I think it would perhaps be advantageous if we could deal with them one at a time.

The first question relates to the measurement of empirical temperature. How does he propose to measure it and how does he ensure that his measurements describe the system he is dealing with, rather than an interaction between the system and the thermometer.

MÜLLER

For the measurement of empirical temperature I should use any quickly reacting thermometer, whose reading quantifies our sensation of hot or cold. To exclude the influence of the other thermodynamic fields on the reading I should have to know how this influence arises in order to be able to speculate on how an experimentalist would contrive to eliminate it.

RIVLIN

I am somewhat doubtful that it would in fact be possible, in strongly irreversible situations, to devise an empirical thermometer whose reading could be meaningfully related to thermodynamic quantities defined in a more fundamental way. However, for obvious reasons, I cannot prove that this is so.

Professor Müller has used the principle of equipresence. While, I have no objection to his use of the same set of independent variables in each of his constitutive equations, I would like to point out that, in doing so, he is making an arbitrary physical assumption—and he may well be justified in doing this. However, his need to do so is not mandated by any principle. The so-called *principle of equipresence* is, in fact, a quite meaningless statement, which is violated by many fundamental theories in Physics.

MÜLLER

To my thinking, the principle of equipresence renders explicit our lack of knowledge about the constitutive theory and, if I use the same variable in every constitutive relation, I am motivated by the feeling that it would be the lack of uniformity among these equations that would require motivation, rather than the uniformity itself. If I may draw an analogy to statistical mechanics I should compare the situation here to the situation a physicist finds himself in if he is asked about the probability of different microstates that correspond to the same macrostate. In that situation he assumes equal probability for everything he has no knowledge about and in the same spirit I assume equipresence of variables in constitutive relations.

RIVLIN

I find myself in complete accord with Professor Müller's remarks since in them he recognises that he is indeed making an assumption which is convenient for the purposes he has in mind. The main purpose of my question was, in fact, to register some protest against the frivolous use of the word *principle* which has become so common in modern continuum mechanics.

My next question refers to Professor Müller's use of the *principle of material frame indifference*. The principle, in so far as it requires invariance of the constitutive equations under reflection–transformation of the reference system, can lead to erroneous results. The correct restriction is one which involves only rotations, and possibly translations, of the reference frame.

MÜLLER

I have specifically mentioned that I apply a principle of material frame indifference with respect to Galilei transformations. In my case of a fluid this implies that the constitutive relations are isotropic functions with respect to the orthogonal group. But I agree with Professor Rivlin that, in general, if constitutive functions are isotropic with respect to reflections, this reflects a material symmetry rather than a universal law of nature.

RIVLIN

Finally, I would like to ask Professor Müller how he defines entropy and entropy flux and, having defined them, what is his evidence that these quantities satisfy an inequality of the type that he envisages? In asking this question, I would like to underline my concern with the widespread propagation of thermodynamic theories in which such quantities as entropy and temperature are introduced as primitive concepts, without any attempt to explain how they are to be measured, or related to physical models of the matters with which they are concerned. I would like to ask Professor Müller whether he considers such theories to be meaningful? Specifically I would be glad if he would express his views on the Coleman theory of this type.

MÜLLER

I should like to break up my answer to Professor Rivlin's question into four parts

(1) Indeed I consider the empirical temperature as a primitive concept, and this—I think—is now amply clear from my talk and my answer to Professor Rivlin's first question. I am perfectly happy with that; I am less happy, I admit, that as far as continuum thermodynamics goes I have to consider nonequilibrium entropy as a primitive concept, but I do not see any alternative to that at the present state of the art.

(2) Of course both in the kinetic theory of gases and in statistical mechanics there is ample motivation for the assumption of a nonequilibrium entropy in the form of the various $\mathscr{H}$-theorems. This evidence of statistical mechanics to my mind establishes the existence of the entropy as an additive property in all bodies.

(3) While I thus accept the entropy in nonequilibrium, I try to minimise the assumptions that go with this quantity. Therefore, I have taken the entropy flux as an arbitrary constitutive quantity (within this class of materials) and I have not introduced the absolute temperature along with entropy. The existence of this universal function and, indeed, of the coldness *follows* from the argument.

(4) While it is thus clear that I do not accept Coleman's form of the entropy principle I *am* following Coleman's way of thinking in insisting that we should look upon the entropy principle as a restrictive condition on the constitutive functions.

NEMAT-NASSER

I must first thank Professor Müller for his contribution which has many points in common with mine (chapter 14). It is, moreover, complementary to mine, in the sense that he treats the conduction problem excluding deformation, and I treat deformation excluding conduction. However, I have a number of specific questions which are narrow in scope, unlike those posed by Professors Prigogine and Rivlin.

(1) You motivated the concept of entropy and absolute temperature by means of what you called *thermostatics*, and then you wrote down the Clausius–Duhem inequality which you subsequently modified on certain grounds. While I appreciate the motivation and agree fully with the thermostatic results, I cannot see (i) where you showed the existence of entropy at nonequilibrium states; (ii) granting that it exists, where you showed its extensive property; (iii) granting that quality, where you examined its uniqueness or the lack of its uniqueness. In fact, within the framework that you presented, it is easy to show that the entropy which satisfies the Clausius–Duhem or your modified version of the Clausius–Duhem inequality, is not unique.

(2) You mentioned that thermostatics provided only *small contribution* to the constitutive relations. I feel that this is because of the mode of representation you have chosen for these relations. I see absolutely no reason for insisting to represent constitutive relations *explicitly* in terms of thermokinetic variables, as you have done. The *implicit* representation by means of additional subsidiary variables, appears more natural, has added attributes, and makes the contribution of thermostatics much more meaningful and significant, as I will discuss in chapter 14.

(3) Since you dealt with heat conduction, the heat absorption by radiation must be a significant ingredient of your work. Even with my naive understanding of physics. I can see that radiation needs to be treated quite carefully, since one can envisage many modes of energy exchange that may be involved. I think this will involve questioning some of the basic assumptions that you have used, for example the nature and multiplicity of empirical temperature.

MÜLLER

I have assumed that the entropy exists as an additive constitutive quantity that is used as an auxiliary quantity for the thermodynamic constitutive theory. While these assumptions cannot be proved, there is motivation for them in thermostatics and in statistical mechanics. Since the entropy drops out of all results—as is fitting for an auxiliary quantity—the question of uniqueness is immaterial.

I have no objection to the use of subsidiary variables, if they are identified and if field equations are laid down for them.

There are certainly processes where a body does not absorb or emit heat and these I have considered for the derivation of restrictions on constitutive functions. According to the customary understanding such restrictions remain valid when radiation *is* present.

MILLER
Professor Müller has served as a lightning rod for criticisms. I would like to comment on some of them.

First, I think his programme has substantial value in this sense: it is always useful to look at the consequences of differing sets of *macroscopic* hypotheses for comparison with alternate theories, such as Onsager's irreversible thermodynamics.

Second, there were criticisms that the *entropy* and *temperature* or *coldness* quantities do not seem to be measurable. However, the same criticism can be levelled at well-known formulations of classical thermodynamics, such as Professor Callen's, which take the thermostatic entropy as a primitive concept. This entropy cannot be measured directly either, precisely because there is no such thing as an entropy meter.

Third, the use of the *principle of equipresence* was severely criticised. Equipresence is really just an expression of Murphy's law for the variables which have to be considered in constitutive equations. In other words, it is to be expected that the worst will always happen (that is, all the possible variables will be required everywhere) unless we can prove differently by symmetry, invariance, or thermodynamic conditions. The same idea is present in the linear laws of Onsager's theory (of which I am a partisan), where one insists on including all the possible cross-terms. Without cross terms, for example, thermoelectric effects would not exist. Later discussion raised the point that *principle* is a strong word and that words like *should* or *must* are equally strong. However, most of us will agree that trying out the *hypothesis* of equipresence can be of great help in discovering what interaction terms should be looked for experimentally. An example is the need for cross term diffusion coefficients to explain diffusion in three or more component systems.

3. Statistical Thermodynamics of Equilibrium: STE

Laszlo Tisza†

Abstract

Starting from MTE a heuristic procedure is used to deepen the theory to STE. The main idea is a sharpening of the Boltzmann–Einstein principle according to which the probability of a fluctuation state is given by the exponential of its *entropy cost*. The sharpening consists mainly in the more precise calculation of this quantity for fluctuations within a closed system and for fluctuations in an open system through coupling with the environment. The theory is valid for systems of any size, and the continuity of the thermodynamic formalism in the space of intensive variables is shown to be consistent with the molecular and quantal discontinuities in ordinary space.

3.1 Introduction

In a fundamental paper Einstein[1] developed a theory of fluctuations by considering the thermodynamic quantities rather than the phase space coordinates of the particles as random variables. His point of departure was Boltzmann's relation

$$S - S_0 = k \ln W/W_0 \tag{3.1}$$

connecting entropy and *probability*[2]. However, instead of reducing the entropy to probabilities defined in microscopic terms (or, rather, to numbers of microstates), Einstein obtained the probabilities of fluctuation states in terms of differences of entropy

$$W/W_0 = \exp(\Delta S/k) \tag{3.2}$$

Here ΔS is the difference of entropy between the fluctuation state and the equilibrium state. I shall refer to it briefly as the *entropy cost* of the fluctuation.

The basic idea underlying the formalism based on equation 3.2 will be called the Boltzmann–Einstein (B–E) principle, a method widely used in the literature for the computation of fluctuations under a variety of conditions. This acceptance of the B–E principle for computations contrasts with the lack of appreciation of its potential for the discussion of conceptual problems. Yet in spite of its close formal relation to Boltzmann's theory, the new departure has some radically new conceptual aspects. Einstein does not

† Massachusetts Institute of Technology, Cambridge, Mass., USA.

observe the traditional division between *thermodynamics*, a *phenomenological macroscopic nonstatistical continuum theory* on the one hand, and *statistical mechanics*, a *speculative microscopic* theory operating with *discontinuous mathematics*, on the other. He clearly has the best of both worlds: he calculates fluctuations without confining himself to the discussion of ideal gases, and maintains the full generality of thermodynamic systems. In this of course, he was anticipated by Gibbs[3], but he avoids the pitfall of the equipartition theorem that had been an irreducible stumbling block for any theory that evaluates equation 3.1 on the basis of classical mechanics. All this is achieved without explicitly invoking the quantum theory!

Einstein's paper appeared in 1910. Molecules had just become accepted as observable physical objects and Boltzmann's constant k became a measurable physical quantity†. Whereas in the last century the continuum conception of matter seemed safely phenomenological, now the tables were turned, the material continuum without fluctuations turned out to be inconsistent with the claim to be phenomenological, *provided this term means, as it should, closeness to experimental facts.*

The simplest solution of this difficulty, accepted—at least implicitly—by most physicists, is to stop claiming a fundamental role for thermodynamics and to consider it only as a macroscopic approximation to the fundamental molecular mechanics.

Einstein's theory suggests, however, the possibility of another option. Instead of considering the crisis in the foundations of thermodynamics as a cause for retrenchment, one might view it as a challenge and opportunity for expansion: what really matters is that thermodynamics is a *phenomenological* theory of the conversions of matter and energy, a *theory of measurement.* The insistence on the macroscopic limitation was necessary only as long as the state of the experimental art was thus limited. Modern physics indeed abounds in phenomenological theories on all levels. To put this microscopic extension of phenomenological thermodynamics on a systematic basis is the philosophy behind the programme that I have been pursuing for a number of years under the name of *generalised thermodynamics*, briefly GTD. This programme consists of three major stages.

(1) MTE (macroscopic thermodynamics of equilibrium). The scope of this theory is, by and large, identical to that of classical thermostatics, but it is structured differently, and it spells out explicitly some of the hidden assumptions of the latter. First we have the specification of the constitutive equations in terms of the fundamental equation, and second the distinction between thermodynamic *processes* and *operations*, namely the manipulation

† The subtle change of status of the constant k is described in Planck's autobiographic notes. See p. 157–8 of reference 4.

of constraints. This is a practical manifestation of the programme to consider thermodynamics as a theory of measurement.

(2) STE (statistical thermodynamics of equilibrium).

(3) A theory to deal with the interplay of statistics with correlations stemming from microscopic dynamics. The foundations of this theory have not yet been sufficiently clarified.

Although the value of GTD ultimately will be judged by the measure of success of stage (3), the already completed parts have contributed to the clarification of concepts within their scope. In the case of MTE this was greatly furthered by the monograph of Herbert Callen[6]. For a considerable improvement of the theory of critical points see Griffith and Wheeler[7].

My purpose in this paper is to explain and interpret the main results of STE. This theory was developed by Tisza and Quay[8]. However, my exposition will take a somewhat different turn. Originally we started from a few probabilistic postulates utilising the theory of additive independent random variables, and established STE without making use of the entropy concept of MTE. At present I propose to proceed in a fashion that is—I believe—more in the spirit of this conference: starting with a concise summary of the relevant aspects of MTE I shall deepen these in a heuristic vein to arrive at STE.

The central idea is to sharpen the B–E principle in more than one way. Einstein *replaced* equation 3.1 by equation 3.2, because the evaluation of the former on the basis of classical mechanics was in conflict with experiment (equipartition law). The fact that these difficulties were avoided by using equation 3.2 within the context of thermodynamics, points towards a hidden harmony between quantum mechanics and thermodynamics. At present we are in a position to make this implicit harmony explicit by evaluating equation 3.1 in accordance with quantum mechanics, and by using it jointly with equation 3.2. Consistency requires, however, that both relations be restated in a more precise form. This will be done in the next section; the main points involved are as follows.

To begin with I note that the use of the same symbol W in both equations produces a conceptual fuzziness. In equation 3.1 W is not a probability in the precise sense of the word and the ratio W/W_0 is usually justified as such only in the limit of large systems.

I will show that a somewhat more careful handling of the conceptual situation enables one to forego this restrictive assumption. This programme leads in a natural way to the Gibbsian theory of ensembles, but not as abstract mathematical models, but as close conceptual descriptions of actual experimental situations.

As mentioned above my interest is not in fluctuations as such—these have been calculated already in entirely satisfactory ways—but in setting up a statistical thermodynamic formalism that is both pedagogical and precise. As a byproduct, I also wish to clarify a few conceptual problems.

First there is the question: how do we reconcile the molecular and quantal discontinuities of matter with the continuity of the differential geometrical formalism of MTE? This question will be fully answered. The gist of the matter is that the continuity of the thermodynamic surface is understood in the abstract space of intensive parameters, and this is fully consistent with the above mentioned granularity of matter in ordinary space.

The second problem concerns the extent to which quantum mechanics is allowed to enter STE.

The replacement of classical point mechanics by quantum mechanics disposed of the difficulties stemming from the equipartition theorem and the lack of stability of classical systems. This is sufficient grounds to reconsider the blanket injunction against the introduction of mechanical concepts into thermodynamics. Yet not all problems have been solved by quantisation and, in fact, some new ones may have been added. All I need add at this point is that STE contains only simple and clear quantum mechanical connections without explicit references to models, and all subtler problems have been relegated to the, as yet, unfinished theory listed above under (3). It is by no means obvious that this 'chasing the wolves to the neighbouring County' has to be successful. That it is, hinges on the fact that it is possible to carve out of quantum mechanics a set of problems governed by the time-independent Schrödinger equation. This is all we shall be concerned with in STE, and even here we shall not be dealing with the explicit solution of the equation, but only with the gross description of the spectrum in terms of the so-called structure function defined in the next section.

Section 3.3 deals with the further development of the programme claiming that GTD is a theory of measurement. Section 3.4 deals with the so-called thermodynamic limit. The last section contains the discussion of the results obtained and suggestions for further work.

3.2 From MTE to STE

The fundamental theorem of MTE can be stated somewhat loosely as follows: systems left under constant external conditions tend to a state of *thermodynamic equilibrium* determined from the *entropy maximum* principle.

I have suggested that this proposition be called the *principle of thermostatic determinism.*

In order to put this principle to practical use we have to know first of all the fundamental equation of the system

$$S = S(X_1, X_2, \dots V) = S(X, V) \tag{3.3}$$

expressing the entropy as a function of the additive variables such as the energy U, the mole numbers of chemical species (or independent components) contained in the volume V.

There are two simple limiting situations in which the constancy of the external conditions is conveniently realised.

(1) *Closed systems* (often called isolated systems) are sheltered by adiabatic impermeable rigid walls from exchanging additive quantities with the surroundings. (I assume the absence of long range interactions.)

Let us impose a partition of the system into two subsystems

$$V = V' + V'' \tag{3.4}$$

The corresponding partition of the quantities

$$X = X^{0\prime} + X^{0\prime\prime}$$
$$S(X) = S'(X^{0\prime}) + S''(X^{0\prime\prime})$$

is determined from the entropy maximum principle stating that any deviation from this partition leads to a decrease of the total entropy ΔS_{cl} (where the subscript is short for *closed*)

$$\Delta S_{\mathrm{cl}} = S'(X') + S''(X'') - S(X) \leqslant 0 \tag{3.5}$$

For single-phase systems the result is simply stated: the quantities X and S are distributed with uniform *density*

$$X^{0\prime} = X(V'/V) \qquad S^{0\prime} = S(V'/V) \tag{3.6}$$

The quantities involved are *extensive.*

(2) *Open systems* in contact with an infinite environment (reservoir) of constant intensive parameters, or briefly *intensities.*

The intensities conjugate to the X are defined by

$$\pi = \frac{1}{k}\frac{\partial S}{\partial X} \tag{3.7}$$

where k is an arbitrary constant of the dimension of the entropy. In STE k is identified with Boltzmann's constant. Its formal introduction at this point serves to unify our notation.

The equilibrium values of the X are now determined from equation 3.7 by requiring the constancy of the *intensities.* We shall say that the intensities π of the reservoir and the conjugate quantities X (or their densities) are *matched.* The entropy maximum principle is expressed now as follows

$$\Delta S_{\mathrm{op}} = S(X) - S(X^0) + \Sigma\pi(X^0 - X) \leqslant 0 \tag{3.8}$$

The subscript is short for *open*. The π, X^0 are matched while π, X are arbitrary unmatched values of the parameters.

Introducing the (generalised) Massieu function

$$\Phi(\pi) = \frac{1}{k} S(X^0) - \Sigma \pi X^0 \tag{3.9a}$$

with

$$\frac{\partial \Phi}{\partial \pi} = -X^0 \tag{3.9b}$$

we have

$$\Delta S_{\text{op}} = S(X) - \Phi(\pi) - \Sigma X \pi \leqslant 0 \tag{3.10}$$

Note that equations 3.7 and 3.9*b* are the necessary conditions that ΔS_{op} be an extremum on varying X and π respectively.

We turn now to the microscopic re-interpretation of the foregoing sketch to be carried out in three steps dealing with *molecular*, *quantal* and *statistical aspects* respectively.

(a) The *mole* numbers appearing in equation 3.3 can be scaled by Avogadro's number to yield the number of *molecules*, or any other particles which may be involved. Thus all symbols in that equation have a meaning in a microscopic theory except for the entropy, to which we now turn.

(b) Consider a system of composition $N_1, N_2, \ldots$ in the volume V. We define the structure function

$$G(U, N_1, N_2, \ldots V) = G(X, V)$$

as the number of linearly independent solutions of the Schrödinger equation which have an energy eigenvalue $E \leqslant U$. We denote by $\mathrm{d}G$ the number of states within a narrow energy interval. This is a convenient notation that enables us to handle uniformly the cases of a continuous spectrum $\mathrm{d}G = g(U)\,\mathrm{d}U$ and a discrete spectrum $\mathrm{d}G = g_n$, respectively.

Note that G depends on the same set of independent variables as the entropy in equation 3.3. Actually $\ln \mathrm{d}G$ has entropy-like properties and we define

$$\tilde{s}(X, V) = k \ln \mathrm{d}G(X, V) \tag{3.11}$$

as the *microcanonical entropy*. This relation is the promised restatement of equation 3.1. Its precise meaning calls for some comments.

The introduction of the absolute entropy instead of entropy differences is due to Planck[4]. However, I wish to put in a plea against the tradition of calling $\mathrm{d}G$ a *probability*. The number $\mathrm{d}G$ is usually large and fails to display the properties of a normalised probability; it is inferred from the solution of a differential equation, and is used only indirectly to establish two important probability distribution functions as shown in the next subsection.

I wish to express a reservation also concerning the interpretation of $\tilde{s}$ on the left-hand side of equation 3.11. We are dealing only with the raw material for the construction of the entropy of STE. Note that these subtleties are of little importance in the limit of large systems, but they are essential for the present programme.

Before proceeding with the discussion it might be in order to reassure the purist that this intrusion of quantum mechanical elements does not impair the phenomenological character of the theory. What is involved is only a displacement of the boundary between the phenomenological theory on the one hand and the theory of models on the other.

Setting up the Schrödinger equation involves the Hamiltonian of the system in terms of its particles and their interactions. All this is outside the scope of STE and so are the procedures yielding the solution which almost always involve approximations. What we need in STE is only the simple assumption that the solution can be expressed in terms of a structure function which no longer involves explicit references to the underlying mechanical model.

(c) The central postulate that conveys the transition of MTE to STE requires the weakening of the principle of thermostatic determinism.

In MTE the trial distributions of the entropy maximum principle are not considered to be *physical*, their role is only to determine the *physical* equilibrium state leading to thermostatic determinism.

We proceed now to STE by recognising the comparison states as fluctuations and we use the Boltzmann–Einstein principle to establish the probability distribution functions (d.f.) as exponentials of the *entropy cost*.

However, the present discussion has some refinements stemming from the distinction of fluctuations in closed and open systems. Thus each of the entropy costs given in equations 3.5 and 3.10 leads to a distinct distribution function.

We have the microcanonical d.f.

$$\mathrm{d}f(x'\,|\,x, V', V) = \exp\left[\Delta S_{\mathrm{cl}}/k\right] \qquad (3.12)$$

and the canonical d.f.

$$\mathrm{d}F(x\,|\,\pi, V) = \exp\left[\Delta S_{\mathrm{op}}/k\right] \qquad (3.13)$$

To the right of the vertical bar are the parameters that are fixed experimentally and that control the distribution of the random variables to the left. We use the symbol x to denote a specific value of the random variable X.

In order to evaluate these expressions in microscopic terms we rewrite equations 3.5 and 3.10 in terms of the microcanonical entropy

$$\Delta S_{\mathrm{cl}} = \tilde{s}'(x') + \tilde{s}''(x'') - \tilde{s}(x) \qquad (3.5a)$$

and

$$\Delta S_{\mathrm{op}} = \tilde{s}(x) - \Phi(\pi) - \Sigma x\pi \qquad (3.10a)$$

By using equation 3.11 and inserting into equation 3.12 we obtain the microcanonical d.f.

$$\mathrm{d}f(x'|x, V', V) = \frac{\mathrm{d}G'(x'V')\,\mathrm{d}G''(x''V'')}{\mathrm{d}G(x, V)} \tag{3.14}$$

The condition of normalisation of the probability yields the composition rule for the structure function

$$\mathrm{d}G(x) = \int_{x'} \mathrm{d}G'(x')\,\mathrm{d}G''(x-x') \tag{3.15}$$

where we have dropped the obvious references to the volume.

Thus the composition of the structure functions is obtained by convolution which we denote conventionally as

$$\mathrm{d}G(x) = \mathrm{d}G'(x') * \mathrm{d}G''(x-x') \tag{3.15a}$$

By inserting equation 3.10*a* into equation 3.13 and by using equation 3.11, we obtain the canonical d.f.

$$\mathrm{d}F(x|\pi, V) = \mathrm{d}G(x, V)\exp[-\Phi - \Sigma\pi X] \tag{3.16}$$

The normalisation condition yields

$$\exp[\Phi] \equiv Z = \int \exp[-\Sigma\pi X]\,\mathrm{d}G(x, V) \tag{3.17}$$

Thus $$Z \equiv \ln\Phi \tag{3.18}$$

is the Laplace transform of $G(x, V)$. More precisely we speak of Laplace–Stieltjes transform, since it is the Stieltjes integral that renders the uniform handling of the continuous and the discrete spectrum possible.

For a completely discrete spectrum we write

$$Z = \sum_n g_n \exp[-\Phi - \Sigma\pi x_n] \tag{3.17a}$$

or $$Z = \sum_i \exp[-\Phi - \Sigma\pi x_i] \tag{3.17b}$$

where the first sum is over levels x_n of degeneracy g_n, the second over each nondegenerate state x_i. It is the discrete representation that is responsible for the conventional term: partition sum for Z.

From the point of view of probability theory the function $\Phi(\pi)$ is the moment generating function of the canonical d.f. We have, in particular

$$\bar{x} = -\frac{\partial\Phi}{\partial\pi} \tag{3.19}$$

$$\langle \Delta x_i \Delta x_k \rangle = \frac{\partial^2 \Phi}{\partial \pi_i \partial \pi_k} \tag{3.20}$$

Let us consider now a composite system: $V = V' + V''$, $x = x' + x''$. It is well-known that the composition rule of equation 3.15 is consistent with the multiplicative composition for the Laplace transform

$$Z'Z'' = Z \quad \text{or} \quad \Phi' + \Phi'' = \Phi \tag{3.21}$$

It is evident from the foregoing formalism that the π and the $\bar{x}$ can be considered as conjugate parameters in the sense of MTE.

The entropy expression of this formalism is obtained from equation 3.9 by substituting $\bar{x}$ for X^0

$$\frac{1}{k} S(\bar{x}) = \Phi(\pi) + \Sigma \pi \bar{x} \tag{3.22}$$

It is plausible to introduce a random entropy function.

$$\frac{1}{k} s(x) = \Phi(\pi) + \Sigma \pi x \tag{3.23}$$

The entropy of the system in contact with the reservoir $R(\pi)$ is then simply $s(\bar{x})$.

Note that the expression $\eta = -s(x)/k$ plays an important part in Gibbs' statistical mechanics where it goes under the name of *index of probability.*

From equation 3.17*b* we obtain for a nondegenerate quantum state x_i

$$\frac{1}{k} s(x_i) = -\ln f_i \tag{3.24}$$

and the entropy of the open system is

$$s(\bar{x}) = -k \sum_i f_i \ln f_i \tag{3.25}$$

It is well-known that this expression can be considered as a functional corresponding to an arbitrary normalised distribution function

$$\Sigma f_i = 1 \tag{3.26}$$

and

$$s(\tilde{f}) = -k \sum_i \tilde{f}_i \ln \tilde{f}_i \tag{3.27}$$

is maximised if $\tilde{f} = f$ is the canonical d.f. This theorem is sometimes chosen as a point of departure for a very direct derivation of the canonical d.f.

The best known among these theories is that of Jaynes[9]. In this approach the expression 3.27 for the entropy has to be justified from the principles of information theory or the theory of statistical estimation.

It is worth noting that in the present context this result follows from the sharpened form of the Boltzman–Einstein principle.

Jaynes' theory is only one in a series that emphasise the close relation of thermodynamics to probability theory and mathematical statistics. While these theories agree in their opposition to the traditional polarisation of phenomenological thermodynamics against statistics, they do differ among themselves in a number of subtle points. I cannot enter into the discussion of details, but I wish to indicate the underlying idea of the derivation of Tisza and Quay[8] who discussed also some of these subtle differences.

Let us consider a composite system in contact with the reservoir $R(\pi)$. By using equations 3.14, 3.17 and 3.21 one verifies at once the relation

$$\mathrm{d}F'(x'|\pi, V')\,\mathrm{d}F''(x''|\pi, V'') = \mathrm{d}f(x'|x, V, V')\,\mathrm{d}F(x|\pi, V, V') \qquad (3.28)$$

The derivation of the distribution functions in reference 8 is based on the fact that this argument can be inverted. The functional equation 3.28 can be justified on the basis of qualitative probabilistic assumption and then solved to recover the explicit forms of equations 3.14 and 3.16 for the distribution functions. The method followed is the modification of one devised by Szilard[10].

However, before accepting this close tie between statistics and thermodynamics without reservations we have to explain the consistency of continuum thermodynamics with molecular and quantal discontinuities. The key to this problem is in equation 3.17. The structure function may refer to a single molecule and may be discontinuous because of quantal effects. Yet the Laplace–Stieltjes transform Z and its logarithm Φ are continuous and differentiable any number of times[11]. Note that $\Phi(\pi)$ represents a smooth surface in the space of intensities rather than in ordinary space. We see from equation 3.20 that this surface is convex.

The same situation can be described also in somewhat different terms. The function $\Phi(\pi)$ is the moment generating function of the canonical distribution function. STE is fundamentally a method of describing a probabilistic problem in terms of its moment generating function.

Another point is that the functional form of the fundamental equation of MTE remains rigorously valid provided the parameters are properly interpreted. This is an important proviso which is easily overlooked if one confines oneself to dealing with the thermodynamic limit.

Thus intensities should be assigned in a rigorous sense only to reservoirs, whereas finite systems are described only in terms of averages of extensive parameters, or densities.

In view of the far-reaching symmetry between conjugate extensive and intensive parameters, one may ask whether there is a way to deal with sharp values of the extensive quantities and accept a corresponding diffuseness in the intensities. This is indeed the case as will be seen in the next section.

3.3 The Thermodynamic Theory of Measurement

The most obvious interpretation of the canonical d.f. is that it predicts the temporal random sequence of the observed additive quantities (densities) of a system that is in contact with an environment of constant known intensities.

There is, however an inverse problem of equal practical importance: measure the distribution of the additive quantities and draw inferences on the unknown intensities of the environment. Within MTE the rigorous match between reservoir intensities and system densities renders this problem trivial from the theoretical point of view, although it is of considerable practical interest. Thus one measures, say, the energy of a finite system and infers the temperature of the environment with which it has been in equilibrium. The finite system can be considered as a thermometer. The *indicator property*, such as the length of a fluid column, can, of course, be calibrated in terms of energy differences. Whereas the discussion of diverse indicator properties is very important from the practical point of view, only the energy measurement is significant in the present context.

Measurements which belong in the same general class arise also under more interesting conditions. Thus we may use the known magnetic moment of the proton to probe an unknown magnetic field in the laboratory or in interstellar space.

Also sedimentary rocks and fossil objects may enable us to estimate the temperature and composition of the archaic ocean.

In STE where the deterministic intensity density match is weakened into a statistical one the problem becomes nontrivial even from a theoretical point of view.

I shall demonstrate the procedure in terms of thermometry. Let us consider the d.f. canonical in the energy.

$$dF(u|\beta) = dG(u)\exp[-s(u, \beta)/k] \tag{3.29}$$

with

$$s(u, \beta)/k = \Phi(\beta) + u\beta \tag{3.30}$$

where u is a specific value of the energy U and

$$\beta^{-1} = kT$$

Suppose our system has been in contact with an environment $R(\beta)$ of unknown temperature. We cannot infer the value of β from a single measurement yielding the value u, but it would be reasonable to obtain an average of several measurements and ask for the (reciprocal) temperature β that yields a canonical average identical to the empirical one

$$\langle u(\beta)\rangle_{\text{can}} = \langle u\rangle_{\text{emp}} \tag{3.31}$$

This is a satisfactory answer, but I propose to obtain the same result in a different way, because, as a byproduct, I shall arrive at the other interpretation of the canonical formalism alluded to at the end of the last section.

Suppose I have only a single measurement u and ask for the value β that maximises the probability of obtaining the value u that was actually found. It is conventional to write the condition of maximisation in terms of

$$\ln \mathrm{d}F = \ln \mathrm{d}G(u) - s(u, \beta)/k \tag{3.32}$$

$$\frac{\mathrm{d}(\ln \mathrm{d}F)}{\mathrm{d}\beta} = -\frac{1}{k}\frac{\mathrm{d}s(u, \beta)}{\mathrm{d}\beta} = 0 \tag{3.33}$$

Or, by using equation 3.30

$$\frac{\mathrm{d}\Phi}{\mathrm{d}\beta} + u = 0 \tag{3.34}$$

Suppose this relation is satisfied for $\beta = \hat{\beta}$.

The maximum of the probability corresponds to the minimisation of $s(u, \beta)$. Hence we have

$$\left(\frac{\mathrm{d}^2\Phi}{\mathrm{d}\beta^2}\right)_{\beta=\hat{\beta}} \geqslant 0 \tag{3.35}$$

We denote the corresponding value of the entropy function as

$$\frac{1}{k}\hat{s} = \min\{\Phi(\beta) + \beta u\} = \Phi(\hat{\beta}) + \hat{\beta} u \tag{3.36}$$

Since $\hat{\beta}$ can be expressed from equation 3.34 in terms of u, we obtain from here a function

$$\hat{s} = \hat{s}(u) \tag{3.37}$$

From equations 3.34, 3.36 and 3.37 we obtain

$$\frac{1}{k}\frac{\mathrm{d}\hat{s}}{\mathrm{d}u} = \hat{\beta} + \left(\frac{\mathrm{d}\Phi}{\mathrm{d}\hat{\beta}} + u\right)\frac{\mathrm{d}\hat{\beta}}{\mathrm{d}u} = \hat{\beta} \tag{3.38}$$

Thus equation 3.37 can be considered a fundamental equation in the sense of MTE with the conjugate parameters u and $\hat{\beta}$.

It is easy to show (see section IVC of reference 8) that the definition of $\hat{s}$ (equation 3.36) can be used to establish the entropy maximum principle of MTE.

The preceding formalism beginning with equation 3.32 is a special case of what is called in mathematical statistics the method of maximum likelihood[12]. That thermometry can be considered as an instance of this method of estimation has been recognised by Mandelbrot[13].

We may summarise these results as follows:

The MTE formalism based on $S = S(U)$ and $\partial s/\partial u = k\beta$ can be interpreted in STE for systems of any size in terms of two different choices for the pairs of conjugate variables:

(a) $\bar{u}, \beta$ (b) $u, \hat{\beta}$

It is remarkable that the functional form is the same for both instances. This simplicity depends critically on our specific structuring of the theory; it is easily lost on apparently minor modifications.

Say, we decided to estimate the temperature by requiring

$$\max \mathrm{d}F(u|\beta) = \langle u \rangle_{\mathrm{emp}} \tag{3.31a}$$

instead of equation 3.31. This means we seek the most probable value of the d.f. in equation 3.16 rather than the maximum of the likelihood. Maximising $\ln \mathrm{d}F$ with respect to u we obtain the condition

$$k\frac{\partial (\ln \mathrm{d}G)}{\partial u} + \beta = 0$$

In such a way we arrive at a formalism in terms of the conjugate parameters

$$\tilde{s} = k \ln \mathrm{d}G_{,\beta}$$

It is apparent from equation 5.12 of reference 8, that, in general, the functional form of $\tilde{s} = \tilde{s}(u)$ is different from that of the canonical formalism obtained above.

In the so-called thermodynamic limit all three formalisms coalesce in the single formalism of MTE. This asymptotic case is briefly considered in the next section.

3.4 The Thermodynamic Limit

The thermodynamic limit is attained in principle for infinite systems for which the fluctuations tend to zero. In this limiting case the random variables assume their thermostatic values with probability one. In other words the distribution functions become δ-functions. Inserted into equation 3.14 this yields

$$\mathrm{d}G(x'+x'') = \mathrm{d}G'(x')\,\mathrm{d}G''(x'') \tag{3.39}$$

provided that the partition maintains the constant density stipulated in equation 3.6. This is indeed the standard product rule used in conjunction with Boltzmann's entropy definition. This approximation to the correct convolution relation precludes the application to small systems.

Turning to open systems we rewrite the canonical d.f. as follows

$$\mathrm{d}F = \exp\left[\ln \mathrm{d}G - s(x, \pi)/k\right] \tag{3.40}$$

In the thermodynamic limit we set $x = \bar{x}$ and obtain $\mathrm{d}F \to 1$. Thus

$$s(\bar{x}, \pi) \approx k \ln \mathrm{d}G \tag{3.41}$$

and the microcanonical and canonical entropies become identical, as expected. This argument is very sketchy because the choice of the differential $\mathrm{d}G = g(x)\,\mathrm{d}x$ must be subject to some restrictions. For a more careful discussion I refer to section V of reference 8. I may note, however, that the simplified discussion is justified under all practical conditions.

3.5 Discussion

In the Introduction, I defined STE as the theory arising out of MTE by means of the sharpened Boltzmann–Einstein principle.

This programme involves the extension of the scope of thermodynamics in the microscopic direction, leading to the inclusion of material usually handled within statistical mechanics; also these results are established under more general conditions than customary and without assuming that the system of interest has many degrees of freedom.

The simplest way to characterise STE is to state that it is a particular branch of quantum mechanics as explained in terms of the following instructions. Consider the time-independent Schrödinger equation, the solutions of which are characterised by the structure function. It is sufficient to assume that a structure function exists, without regard to the details of the mechanical model or to the method of solution. Once the structure function is known, we arrive at the generalised Massieu function by means of the Laplace transformation, equation 3.17. Hence one obtains the microcanonical and the canonical distribution functions 3.14 and 3.16. The entire Gibbsian ensemble theory follows, and each type of ensemble corresponds closely to a particular type of experimental situation. In the limit of large systems, different ensembles give numerically coincident results, and they appear merely as different mathematical models without physical distinction.

One of the important results of STE is that the continuous analytical character of its formalism in thermodynamic phase space is consistent with the discontinuities of the material systems under study. This means the opening up of atomic phenomena to description with thermodynamic methods.

Judging from STE we may say that this description is characterised by precise mathematical and conceptual techniques, always in close contact with experiment, but only for questions within the legitimate range of the theory. It is therefore in order to close this discussion with a few remarks concerning the directions in which STE can be generalised to extend the range of phenomena covered.

It is generally recognised that thermodynamics ought to consider also the linear and angular momenta as admissible additive integrals. While usually of little interest for large systems, we know that these quantities play a paramount role in the quantum mechanics of particles. I am currently engaged in extending STE to include angular momentum and it is apparent already that the harmony between thermodynamics and quantum mechanics emerging in the present paper becomes much more pronounced in the process.

A second avenue for generalisation deals with the transition from problems of thermostatics to those of thermodynamics. These questions have been the object of numerous investigations, but in spite of the wealth of relevant results the situation is still far from satisfactory. This is true particularly under the more exacting microscopic conditions envisaged within GTD. Conversely, it may be stated also that it is in these developments that the real advantages of the microscopic extension of thermodynamics promise to become manifest.

References

1. A. Einstein. *Ann. Physik*, **33** (1910), 1275
2. L. Boltzmann. *Vorlesungen zur Gastheories*, Barth, Leipzig (1896)
3. J. W. Gibbs. *Collected Works*; vol. I. *Thermodynamics*; vol. II. *Elementary Principles in Statistical Mechanics.* Scribner, New York (1902). (Reprinted by Yale Univ. Press, New Haven, 1948)
4. M. Planck. *Naturwiss*, **31** (1943), 153
5. L. Tisza. *Generalised Thermodynamics*, M.I.T. Press (1966)
6. H. B. Callen. *Thermodynamics.* Wiley, New York (1960)
7. R. B. Griffith and J. C. Wheeler. *Phys. Rev.*, **A2** (1970), 1047
8. L. Tisza and P. M. Quay. *Ann. Phys. (N.Y.)*, **25** (1963), 48. Reprinted in reference 5
9. E. T. Jaynes. *Phys. Rev.*, **106** (1957), 620; **108** (1957), 171
10. L. Szilard. *Z. Physik*, **32** (1925), 753. Also in *Collected Works*, vol. I, M.I.T. Press (1972), p. 34; English translation p. 70
11. D. V. Widder. *The Laplace Transform*, Princeton Univ. Press, Princeton, N.J. (1941), p. 57
12. H. Cramer. *Mathematical Methods of Statistics*, Princeton Univ. Press, Princeton, N.J. (1946), p. 498
13. B. Mandelbrot. *Symp. Inform. Theory*, M.I.T., September 1956; *IRE Trans. Inform. Theory*, IT–2 (1956); *Ann. Math. Statist.*, **33** (1962), 1921

Discussion

PRIGOGINE

While I sympathise with the attempt of Professor Tisza to bring together dynamics and thermodynamics, I do not see any element in his method to do it in a concrete fashion. Thermodynamic behaviour is only to be expected in larger systems when precise additional assumptions are satisfied. On the contrary, Tisza seems to deal with small or large systems on an equal footing. If the small systems are coupled to reservoirs this coupling, as well as the Hamiltonian of the reservoirs, has to appear explicitly except in the case of weak coupling.

TISZA

Professor Prigogine does not seem to appreciate that my programme is complementary to his: instead of subsuming thermodynamics to dynamics, I am engaged in extending thermodynamic methods to certain microscopic situations. I describe the system—large or small—by a Hamiltonian, but the environment only in terms of its intensities.

'Bringing together dynamics and thermodynamics' lacks precise meaning unless we specify the *model year* of the dynamics. Thus Einstein minimised his reliance on *D* (1900) in his theory of fluctuations in order to avoid the equipartition difficulties. The less than total commitment to this branch of dynamics on the part of the quantum generation was a prerequisite for discovering *D* (1930). In my paper, I modernised Einstein's procedure by using some *D* (1930), but not too much, in order to preserve the model independence of thermodynamics, and maybe even to pave the way towards a hypothetical *D* (?) of elementary particles.

CALLEN

I would like to comment on certain aspects of the *Third Law*. That law, or postulate, is a particularly weak element in the foundations of continuum thermodynamics.

It has often been asserted that Planck's form of the Nernst postulate, to the effect that the entropy vanishes at zero temperature, implies non-degeneracy of the ground state. Casimir[a], Klein[b], and Griffiths[c]†, have refuted this assertion, demonstrating instead that the postulate reflects a restriction on the density of states in some interval above the ground state. Their conclusions rest on the observation that the ground state degeneracy g_0

† See references at end of this section.

contributes a zero-temperature *entropy-per-particle* of only

$$\frac{1}{N} \ln g_0$$

which vanishes in the thermodynamic limit ($N \to \infty$) even if $g_0 = 0(N)$; it should be recalled that the Dulong–Petit value of the entropy-per-particle is of order unity. Secondly, the various authors above stress that the two limits ($N \to \infty$, and $T \to 0$) must be taken in this order (the $N \to \infty$ limit first) in order to accord with experimental procedures, and that (as we shall see shortly) the interchange of limits drastically alters the conclusions to be reached.

The proper order of the limiting procedures reflects a fascinating circularity, characteristic of the foundations of physics. The absolute zero of temperature is inaccessible (because of the Nernst theorem!). Hence experimenters make measurements at non-zero temperatures and extrapolate to $T = 0$. At each temperature they first extract the extensive part of the measured entropy (eliminating surface effects, etc.) by finding that part of the entropy which scales with N (operationally taking the $N \to \infty$ limit). If the Nernst theorem were not true, and if the $T = 0$ state were accessible, their measurements would be made at $T = 0$ and the opposite order of limits would be relevant!

My purpose here is to refer to a theorem[d], which relates the Planck form of the Nernst theorem to the density-of-states-spectrum. Let $G_N(E)$ be the *structure function*, as introduced in Professor Tisza's lecture. That is $G_N(E)$ is the number of states with energy less than or equal to E, in a system of N particles. The theorem then states that the Nernst theorem will be violated if there exists some $\varepsilon_0 > 0$ and some $b < 1$ such that

$$\lim_{N \to \infty} \frac{1}{N} \ln G_N(\varepsilon_0 N^b) = c > 0 \tag{3.42}$$

The proof is simple. The entropy per particle $s(T)$ is given by

$$s(T) = \lim_{N \to \infty} \frac{1}{N} \frac{\partial}{\partial T} \left[T \ln \int_0^\infty \exp(-\beta E) \, \mathrm{d}G_N(E) \right] \tag{3.43}$$

whence, carrying out the differentiation, taking the $T \to 0$ limit, and dropping an intrinsically, positive term on the right-hand side,

$$s(0) \geqslant \lim_{\beta \to \infty} \lim_{N \to \infty} \frac{1}{N} \ln \int_0^\infty \exp(-\beta E) \, \mathrm{d}G_N(E) \tag{3.44}$$

whence

$$s(0) \geqslant \lim_{\beta \to \infty} \lim_{N \to \infty} \frac{1}{N} \ln \left\{ e^{-\beta \varepsilon_0 N^b} \int_0^{\varepsilon_0 N^b} \mathrm{d}G_N(E) \right\} \geqslant c \tag{3.45}$$

Hence equation 3.42 implies a lower bound of c for the entropy-per-particle (but note the crucial role in equation 3.45 of the order of the limiting procedures !).

Intuitively, the theorem has the following interpretation. The condition

$$\operatorname*{Lim}_{N\to\infty} \frac{1}{N} \ln G_N = c$$

implies that G_N varies asymptotically like $(1+a)^N$, with $a > 0$. A number of states $G_N \sim (1+a)^N$ can be referred to as a *combinatorial number of states*; it requires such a number of states to make a significant contribution to the entropy. Equation 3.42 specifies how high in the energy spectrum we must go to accumulate such a combinatorial number of states. If we must go to an energy of the order of $\varepsilon_1 N$ (that is, to a definite energy per particle ε_1) then the Nernst theorem is obeyed. But if we accumulate a combinatorial number of states as an energy $\varepsilon_0 N^b$ with $b < 1$ then the Nernst theorem is violated. It should be noted that the energy $\varepsilon_0 N^b (b < 1)$ is an infinite energy in the thermodynamic limit, but one corresponding to a vanishing energy per particle. Clearly a spectrum with a combinatorial number of states at finite energy $[$such as $G_N(E) = g_0 + g_1(E/E_1)^N]$, violates the Nernst theorem. Contrary conclusions which have been asserted in the literature can be traced to the inversion of the limiting procedures.

One can conjecture on the plausibility of the restriction on physical structure functions imposed by the Nernst postulate, and on possible physical origins of this restriction. I have engaged in this seductive exercise elsewhere[d]. It remains an unsolved problem of the foundations of thermodynamics.

References

a. H. B. G. Casimir. *Z. Physik*, **171** (1963), 246
b. M. J. Klein. *Rendiconti S. I. F.*, X Corso (1960), **1**
c. R. B. Griffiths. In *A Critical Review of Thermodynamics*, ed. by E. B. Stuart, B. Gal-Or and A. J. Brainard, Mono, Baltimore (1970)
d. H. Callen. In *Modern Developments in Thermodynamics*, ed. by B. Gal-Or, Keter, Jerusalem (1973)

4. A Symmetry Interpretation of Thermodynamics†

Herbert Callen‡

Abstract

An interpretation of the conceptual basis of thermodynamics is advanced. This interpretation is meant to identify the essential origins of thermodynamics, to clarify its character, and to indicate the plausible directions of its potential generalisations. It is suggested that thermodynamics can be viewed as the study of those properties of macroscopic matter which follow from the symmetry properties of physical laws, mediated through the statistics of large systems.

4.1 Introduction

Professors Domingos and Tisza, in chapters 1 and 3, have discussed the logical foundation of thermodynamic theory. Their emphasis was in a classical tradition[1,2,3,4] stressing rigour, minimising the number of independent postulates, and unmasking hidden implicit assumptions. My interest here is in a very different spirit, complementary to that formal tradition. I shall be concerned with relatively subjective issues of interpretation. I undertake to explore such questions as 'Why does thermodynamics exist?', or 'What is its conceptual content?'. In short, I intend to discuss the *meaning* of thermodynamics. Necessarily, the discussion will be looser in form, allusive rather than formally constructive, and certainly open-ended.

I shall undertake to convince you that the seminal concept underlying thermodynamics is the concept of symmetry. Fundamental physical laws generally are subject to a variety of symmetry transformations. Quite independent of the detailed content of the basic laws, their symmetry properties alone impose restrictions on the possible properties of matter. The study of these symmetry-induced restrictions is the nexus of thermodynamics. In short, my thesis is that *thermodynamics is the study of those properties of macroscopic matter which follow from the symmetry properties of physical laws, mediated through the statistics of large systems.*

† This work was supported by the National Science Foundation and by a Fellowship Grant, in 1972–73, of the John Simon Guggenheim Memorial Foundation. It is adapted from a paper to be published in *Foundations of Physics*, Jan. 1974.

‡ Department of Physics, University of Pennsylvania, Philadelphia, Pa., USA.

Two considerations contribute at least to the *a-priori* plausibility of this construction. Firstly, it rationalises the peculiar nonmetrical quality of thermodynamics. It explains the model-independence and the sweeping generality of thermodynamics. It clarifies why thermodynamics has no characteristic *equations* in its postulatory structure, analogous to the Schrödinger equation of quantum mechanics, or to Newton's laws of classical mechanics, or to Maxwell's equations of electromagnetic theory. Secondly, the symmetry interpretation of thermodynamics anticipates the unique form of the *results* of thermodynamic theory. These results do not consist of the quantitative predictions which we expect from other fields of physics. Instead, thermodynamics culminates only in the prediction of equality between apparently unrelated quantities, as, for instance

$$(\partial\mu/\partial P)_N = (\partial V/\partial N)_P$$

Or, in the Onsager extension to coupled irreversible processes, that $L_{12} = L_{21}$. Such results of thermodynamics theory are of the type that might reasonably be expected of a theory based on symmetry. They would not be considered as satisfactory results of the more conventional, metric theories of physics, and they emphasise the distinction between thermodynamics and these other theories.

4.2 Noether's Theorem and Physical Symmetry Principles

Preparatory to a discussion of thermodynamics proper, I shall first recall certain relevant aspects of symmetry principles.

The primary theorem relating symmetry considerations to physical consequences is Noether's theorem. According to this theorem every continuous symmetry transformation, under which the Lagrangian of a given system remains invariant, implies the existence of a conserved function (of the micro-coordinates and their derivatives). *That is, every continuous symmetry of a system implies a conservation theorem, and vice versa.*

The most primitive class of symmetries[5] is the class of *continuous space–time transformations*. The (presumed) invariance of physical laws under time translation implies energy conservation, spatial translation symmetry implies conservation of momentum, and rotational symmetry implies conservation of angular momentum.

The discrete space–time symmetries (of time-reversal, spatial inversion and charge conjugation) appear to be rigorous symmetries of the strong and electromagnetic interactions, although they are violated by the *weak interaction*. Accordingly, they are applicable to common thermodynamic systems in which weak interaction processes (for example, beta decay) play no significant role. Thermodynamic theory would require appropriate modifications for astrophysical systems in which weak interaction processes might be important[6].

An important class of symmetries has been termed *dynamical*[5]. The symmetry of the electromagnetic equations under gauge transformation is the prototype of the class of dynamical symmetries. It refers to a particular mathematical transformation of the electromagnetic equations (acting on the scalar and vector potentials and on the operators of the matter field) which leaves the equations invariant. This abstract mathematical quality is characteristic of dynamical symmetries; they are 'formulated in terms of the laws of nature', in contrast to the geometrical symmetries which can be 'formulated in terms of the events themselves'[5]. Thus the geometrical symmetry principle of spatial translation can be stated in terms of the equivalence of two processes occurring at different places, but no such physical interpretation can be given to the changes in the scalar and vector potentials which leave Maxwell's equations invariant.

The conserved quantity corresponding to gauge symmetry is the electric charge.

Other dynamic symmetries give rise to the conservation of baryon number and of lepton number.

Many additional symmetries exist, such as the symmetries giving rise to the conservation of strangeness and isospin in strong interactions. Because the associated nuclear processes generally do not occur in conventional thermodynamic systems these symmetries do not play a role in current thermodynamic theory.

4.3 Broken Symmetry and Goldstone's Theorem

Another important area of symmetry considerations centres on the concept of *broken symmetry*[7,8,9]. We summarise the relevant aspects, following the review of Grib, Damaskinskii and Maksimov[7].

A system *may* exhibit the full symmetry of its Lagrangian, but it is characteristic of infinitely large systems that they also may *condense* into states of lower symmetry. As has been stressed also by Anderson[9], this leads to an essential difference between infinite systems and finite systems, such that the former do not satisfy the laws of quantum mechanics in the simple manner of finite systems[7].

The broken symmetry state is distinguished by the appearance of a *macroscopic order parameter*. This macroscopic order parameter obeys the laws of classical physics, as distinct from the laws of quantum mechanics.

Whereas all quantum states of a finite system lie within a single Hilbert space, the appearance of a macroscopic order parameter determines a continuum of disjoint Hilbert spaces. To each macroscopically-distinct value of the order parameter there is a separate Hilbert space. All the states in one such Hilbert space are orthogonal to all the states in another. The transformation from one Hilbert space to another is not unitary, and in each space the micro-observables are described by operators which realise unitarily nonequivalent representations of the observables. These facts manifest themselves physically in the absence of interference between states with different values of the macroscopic order parameter.

The breaking of the symmetry establishes a multiplicity of *vacuums* or ground states, related by the transformations of the (broken) symmetry group. The various values of the macroscopic order parameter are in a many-to-one correspondence with the several ground states (for example, each value of the vector magnetic moment of a spherical ferromagnet is associated with that ground state with the same direction of its magnetic moment). According to Coleman's theorem this ground state exhibits the maximal lowering of the symmetry of all its associated macrostates, or 'everything broken for the world is broken for the vacuum'[7].

Finally, broken symmetry systems are subject to Goldstone's theorem[10,7], which states that if the broken symmetry group is a continuous group whose generators can be written as integrals of local densities, and if the interaction falls off sufficiently rapidly with distance, then there exists a branch of elementary excitations for which the energy goes to zero in the long wavelength limit.

4.4 Thermodynamic Coordinates; Conserved Coordinates

The scope of thermodynamics is determined by the criteria for selection of the variables of the theory. The criteria are suggested, but not demanded, by the nature of conventional macroscopic measurements.

Macroscopic measurements generally are exceedingly slow with respect to the atomic scale of time, (typically, of the order of 10^{-15} s) and exceedingly coarse with respect to the atomic scale of distance ($\simeq 10^{-7}$ mm). Futhermore, macroscopic measuring devices usually yield spatially-integrated responses; they respond additively to the subregions within their region of sensitivity. Accordingly, *thermodynamic coordinates are defined as spatially homogeneous, extensive (additive), and time-independent.* This definition severely limits the states to which thermodynamics can apply and it excludes all dynamical considerations.

The most obvious candidates for thermodynamic coordinates are those extensive quantities which are *conserved*, this being the most obvious way (but *not* the only way) of achieving time-independence. Each such conserved coordinate bespeaks an underlying physical symmetry.

The most immediately evident conserved coordinate is, of course, the *energy* (time-translation symmetry). Its relevance as a thermodynamic coordinate underlies the *first law* of thermodynamics.

Time-translation, spatial translation, and spatial rotation symmetries are interrelated in a single class of continuous space–time symmetries. The symmetry interpretation of thermodynamics immediately suggests, then, that energy, linear momentum and angular momentum should play fully analogous roles in thermodynamics. The equivalence of these roles is rarely evident in conventional treatments, which appear to grant the energy a misleadingly unique status. The momentum and the angular momentum are generally suppressed by restricting the theory to systems at rest, constrained by external *clamps*. Nevertheless, it is evident that, in principle, the linear momentum does appear in the formalism in a form fully equivalent to the energy, for relativistic considerations[11,12] imply that the energy in one frame appears partially as linear momentum in another frame. Similarly, the angular momentum is only occasionally introduced explicitly into thermodynamic formalisms (as in astrophysical applications to rotating galaxies); it appears for instance in the *Boltzmann factor*, $\exp(-\beta E - \beta \mathbf{\Lambda} \cdot \boldsymbol{L})$, additively and symmetrically with the energy.

To stress these facts we might well amend the first law to read that 'the extended first law of thermodynamics is the symmetry of the laws of physics under space and time translations and under spatial rotation'.

The equality of status of the energy, the momentum, and the angular momentum dispels the separate and unique role generally accorded to the energy. Thermodynamics is not appropriately characterised as 'the science of energy and of its transformations'. This fact can be dramatised by devising specific models (see Appendix, p. 76) for which a full thermodynamic theory can be formulated, but in which the energy is totally absent as a relevant variable. Familiar central formulae such as $\mathrm{d}S = \mathrm{d}Q/\tau$ remain in such theories, although $\mathrm{d}Q$ does not have the significance of heat or energy.

4.5 Other Conserved Coordinates

We have identified conserved quantities as one class of physical variables satisfying the criteria for thermodynamic coordinates. More specifically, we have identified that particular set of conserved variables which originate in the continuous space–time symmetries of physical laws. Other symmetry principles result in additional conserved parameters.

In a system of particles undergoing the full range of possible nuclear interactions the *composition* of the system would be described by the conserved baryon and lepton numbers. These are the fundamental compositional coordinates of thermodynamics. In practice, however, much stronger approximate conservation theorems apply. The number of atoms of each atomic species, or the number of molecules of each molecular species, may be approximately conserved. In such cases the *mole numbers* are appropriate compositional coordinates.

Even where the conservation rules underlying the compositional coordinates are only approximate, they are generally grounded in symmetry considerations[13]. An instructive example is the case of ortho and parahydrogen. Parahydrogen molecules have antiparallel nuclear spins and orthohydrogen molecules have parallel nuclear spins; they are antisymmetric and symmetric respectively under permutation of nuclei. This difference in symmetry gives rise to a *selection rule*; the two molecular species thereby are individually conserved, and the proper thermodynamic coordinates include the mole numbers of orthohydrogen and of parahydrogen *separately*. Only by including both mole numbers as independent variables can agreement between thermodynamic theory and experiment be attained. However, addition of a small admixture of water vapour or of oxygen alters the situation drastically. The magnetic field of the paramagnetic oxygen ions distorts the symmetry of the hydrogen ions and thereby destroys the selection rule. Ortho and parahydrogen then freely intraconvert, and a proper thermodynamic description includes only a single compositional variable—the mole-number of hydrogen. Thus, the proper choice of the thermodynamic coordinates describing the composition of a thermodynamic system is based on conservation theorems reflecting underlying symmetry considerations.

Under appropriate conditions all the conservation theorems of physics would be reflected in associated thermodynamic coordinates. The total charge and the total *strangeness*, for instance, would join the energy, angular momentum, hyperon numbers, etc., as independent variables in the thermodynamic fundamental equation.

4.6 Broken Symmetry Coordinates

We continue the survey of variables which qualify as thermodynamic coordinates (knowing full well that we must eventually arrive at the familiar list U, V, $\boldsymbol{M}$, N_1, $N_2, \ldots$). The energy U is the prototype of variables conserved by virtue of the continuous space–time symmetries; the mole numbers $N_1 \ldots N_2$ are the prototypes of variables conserved by virtue of various other symmetries. In addition to these there are yet additional variables which, though not conserved, nevertheless are time-independent. These are the broken symmetry coordinates discussed in section 4.3. The prototypes of these variables are the electric dipole moment $\boldsymbol{P}_E$, or the magnetic dipole moment $\boldsymbol{M}$, or the volume V.

Broken symmetry coordinates are associated with the order parameters of condensations from states with the full symmetry of the Lagrangian to states with a lesser symmetry. They are classical parameters, obeying classical mechanics, and determining disjoint Hilbert subspaces of the full Hilbert space of the system[7].

The macroscopic role of the broken symmetry coordinates has been explored most fully by Halperin and Hohenberg[14], and by Martin, Parodi, and Pershan[15]. These authors first observe that the macroscopic dynamics of systems is describable in terms of certain long-lived degrees of freedom or modes. They state[15] that 'the existence of such modes can always be traced either to conservation laws or, in the case of ordered systems, to "continuous broken symmetries".' The macroscopic dynamics then can be characterised by *hydrodynamic considerations*, which they define[14] as theories 'utilising only the conservation laws for the Hamiltonian, the symmetry properties of the ground state, and assumptions that one can expand certain quantities in powers of the gradients and magnitudes of the deviations from equilibrium'. The thermodynamic theories in which we are interested are the static limits of these hydrodynamic theories.

Consider specifically the magnetic moment of a ferromagnet. The Hamiltonian of an isolated system is necessarily rotationally symmetric, but at a particular *Curie temperature* the elementary magnetic moments of a system may *condense* into a state of broken symmetry. The system then develops a *macroscopic* magnetic moment, in some arbitrary direction (taken as the z-axis). Assume the magnitude of the magnetic moment to be $M = mM_0$, where M_0 is the saturation value of the magnetisation. Rotation of any *finite* number of spins does not alter the value of m (in the $N \to \infty$ limit) but the corresponding states define a Hilbert space. All states in this space are orthogonal to all states corresponding to some other value of m, which differ by rotation of an *infinite* number of spins[7]. In addition, all states excited from the ground state along z are orthogonal to all states excited from the ground state oriented at some angle θ, for the scalar product of the two states is proportional to $(\cos\theta)^N$, which vanishes as $N \to \infty$. Both the direction and magnitude of the magnetisation are classical variables by virtue of the properties conferred on them by the principles of broken symmetry.

We shall see later that the Goldstone spectrum of excitations underlies the unique properties of the phase transitions at which broken symmetry coordinates make their appearance.

The multiplicity of ground states of a ferromagnet (oriented in various directions) is another common feature of broken symmetry coordinates. *This ground-state degeneracy does not contribute to the entropy at zero temperature, however, because of the noninterference of states with distinct order parameters.*

Thus a variety of important thermodynamic properties are linked to the broken symmetry origin of thermodynamic coordinates, such as the magnetic moment.

It should be mentioned in passing that in a common model, consisting of an array of interacting electron spins, the magnetic moment is *conserved* by virtue of angular momentum conservation. This accidental and misleading property never applies to a real system. If the system contains both electron spins and orbital moments, each with a different g-factor, or if the electron spins interact with the lattice through spin–orbit coupling, the magnetic moment is *not* a conserved coordinate.

The electric dipole moment is another broken symmetry coordinate, closely analogous to the magnetic moment.

The number of particles (or mole numbers) in the condensed phase of a superfluid[9], the sublattice magnetisation of an antiferromagnet[8], and the order parameter of a binary alloy are additional broken symmetry coordinates.

Finally, the *volume* must be understood as a broken symmetry coordinate. A finite volume of a solid or liquid system breaks the continuous translational symmetry of space. A gas has no intrinsic value of the volume; again the translational symmetry of space must be broken by the solid system which contains the gas. Perhaps more fundamentally, any finite density of particles defines an unitarily disjoint Hilbert space, and it breaks the symmetry under Galilean transformations[7].

The broken symmetry origin of the volume is evident in the characteristic properties of the condensation of a solid or liquid system. Such a second order transition is fully analogous to the ferromagnetic transition, exhibiting similar critical behaviour. The Goldstone excitations are the longitudinal phonons (analogous to the spin waves of a ferromagnet), and it is the infinite fluctuations of these excitations which dominate the transition.

The role of the volume as a broken symmetry coordinate is revealed even more clearly in the thermodynamics of anisotropic crystals. There the components of the (finite) strain tensor (relative to some arbitrary reference system) play the role of thermodynamic coordinates. They define the anisotropic shape of the system, and they clearly are broken symmetry coordinates. In simple fluid systems the off-diagonal elements necessarily vanish and the diagonal elements are equal; only the trace of the strain tensor remains as an independent variable. That trace is the volume.

It is convenient that the conventional *simple systems* discussed in elementary thermodynamics have one prototype of each of the three characteristic classes of thermodynamic coordinates; coordinates conserved by the continuous space–time symmetries (U), coordinates conserved by other symmetry principles (N), and nonconserved, broken symmetry coordinates (V).

4.7 The Separate Roles of Conserved and Broken Symmetry Coordinates

In this synoptic survey of thermodynamics I implicitly adopt the logical framework of the postulational approach[16]. That is, the extensive coordinates $U, V, N, \ldots$ are taken as fundamental, in agreement with our understanding that such coordinates are mechanical rather than statistical; they can be defined in principle for every microstate, or for nonequilibrium macrostates, and they can be represented by quantum mechanical operators. Of course these reasons lie outside macroscopic phenomenology, but the logical exercise of erecting a theory without external references is not my present purpose.

The postulatory formulation then confronts the archtypical problem of thermodynamics. Suppose two isolated systems, with parameters $U_1^0, V_1^0, N_1^0, \ldots$ and $U_2^0, V_2^0, N_2^0, \ldots$ are brought into diathermal and semi-permeable contact; that is, the energy U and the partial mole number N are permitted to redistribute between the two systems, whereas the volumes, the mole numbers of other components, and all other coordinates are maintained separately constant. *It is postulated that the solution of such problems has the form characteristic of most areas of theoretical physics—namely that the solution is provided by an extremum principle.*

To recapitulate the consequences briefly, it is postulated that there exists an extensive function of the extensive coordinates (called the entropy) which is maximum in the equilibrium state. Then to solve the problem above we write (by the extensivity property of the entropy) that

$$S = S_1(U_1, V_1^0, N_1^0, ..) + S_2(U_2, V_2^0, N_2^0, ..) \tag{4.1}$$

By the extremum principle

$$\partial S = \frac{1}{T_1}\partial U_1 - \frac{\mu_1}{T_1}\partial N_1 + \frac{1}{T_2}\partial U_2 - \frac{\mu_2}{T_2}\partial N_2 = 0 \tag{4.2}$$

where, *by definition,*

$$\frac{1}{T} \equiv \frac{\partial S}{\partial U}; \qquad \frac{\mu}{T} \equiv \frac{\partial S}{\partial N} \tag{4.3}$$

Conservation of energy and of mole number implies

$$\delta U_1 + \delta U_2 = 0; \qquad \delta N_1 + \delta N_2 = 0 \tag{4.4}$$

or

$$\delta S = \left(\frac{1}{T_1} - \frac{1}{T_2}\right)\delta U_1 - \left(\frac{\mu_1}{T_1} - \frac{\mu_2}{T_2}\right)\delta N_1 = 0 \tag{4.5}$$

It follows that the temperatures of the two systems are equal ($T_1 = T_2$) and that the chemical potentials of the permeable component are equal ($\mu_1 = \mu_2$).

The equations of state 4.3, determine the quantities T_1, T_2, μ_1 and μ_2 as functions of the extensive parameters, permitting evaluation of the values of these extensive parameters in the equilibrium state. A byproduct of the formalism is the identification of the quantity T (introduced formally as a partial derivative of the fundamental equation) with the intuitive notion of the temperature.

Now this particular method of introducing the entropy and the intensive parameters is only one of many alternative approaches, most of which proceed inversely, in the much more difficult direction from processes to state functions. The postulatory framework is *not* essential to the symmetry interpretation which is our present interest. Nevertheless, its unique simplicity makes it particularly convenient for a discussion of the nature of thermodynamics, and specifically at this moment for the roles of different classes of thermodynamic coordinates.

In the problem above each of the two free coordinates (energy and mole number) are conserved rather than broken symmetry coordinates. In contrast, consider two systems with magnetic moments M_1 and M_2. A problem analogous to that above does not make physical sense. We do not normally have a problem of *interchange* of magnetic moment between two interacting systems, and certainly not subject to a conservation theorem on the total magnetic moment. The analogue of the problem above does not arise for the electric dipole moment, for the order parameter of superfluid helium, or for any other broken symmetry coordinate.

Now the volume might at first seem to be an exception to these statements. A standard problem of thermodynamics involves two gases separated by a movable piston, contained within a common cylinder. Motion of the piston then leads to $\delta V_1 = -\delta V_2$, and an analysis identical to equations 4.1 to 4.5 leads to equality of temperature and pressure. The *conservation* equation ($V_1 + V_2 = \text{const}$) here is *not* of a fundamental nature, however. Suppose that gas #1 is in a cylinder of cross section A_1, closed by a movable piston; gas #2 is in a *different* cylinder of cross section A_2, also fitted with its own piston. We connect the two pistons by a rigid bar. Then the *conservation* relation is replaced by

$$\frac{\delta V_1}{A_1} = -\frac{\delta V_2}{A_2} \tag{4.6}$$

The solution leads to the selfevident result $P_1 A_1 = P_2 A_2$.

Hence we see that broken symmetry coordinates are subject to very different auxiliary conditions than are conserved coordinates. In some cases, as in equation 4.6, we are free to devise various constraints on a broken symmetry coordinate. In the case of the magnetisation of a ferromagnet we can control the intensive parameter (the magnetic field); the auxiliary condition is then that the partial derivative $(\partial S/\partial M)_{U,V,N}$ must have a specified value. In the case of an antiferromagnet the intensive parameter (a staggered field) is not subject to control, and the auxiliary condition is that the derivative $(\partial S/\partial M)_{\text{subl}} = 0$. Similarly, the intensive parameter corresponding to the quantity of superfluid component in liquid helium has no physical realisation and must be set equal to zero. *In each case a broken symmetry coordinate is subject to an external auxiliary condition, in contrast to conserved coordinates which are determined by universal conservation conditions.*

4.8 The Entropy-Maximum Principle and 'Unitary Symmetry'

We have stressed, with more than usual emphasis, the physics underlying the initial choice of variables of thermodynamic theory. That choice is a fateful one. A very few variables meet the criteria of extensivity and time-independence required for macroscopic measurability. Those which qualify do so by virtue of one or another symmetry consideration. All other microscopic variables thereby are consigned to a class of incoherent, nonobservable modes, which underlie the concept of heat. Analysis of the symmetry origin of the thermodynamic coordinates has led us also to the first law of thermodynamics. Now we must probe more deeply into the second and third laws, examine the emerging theory of second order phase transitions, and explore the origin of the Onsager extension to irreversible processes.

The thermodynamic form of the entropy principle, as distinct from the statistical mechanical form, is based on the *equal a-priori probability of states.* The thermodynamical principle is purely static. It is rooted in the principle that *in equilibrium* all permissible microstates contribute equally to the macrostate, and that the entropy is simply $k_B \ln W$, where W is the number of permissible microstates.

Mechanisms of irreversibility, or of entropy increase, are *dynamical,* and they lie outside the scope of equilibrium thermodynamics. Professor Prigogine will discuss the broken symmetry aspects of irreversible dynamics in chapter 5.

The equal *a-priori* probability of states is already in the form of a symmetry principle, even before we trace its origin to deeper principles. The entropy depends *symmetrically* on all permissible states. This principle, if accepted, determines the functional form of the entropy; the only symmetric function of a set (in this case a set of states) is the number in the set, or a function of the number. The particular function $S = \ln W$ is determined completely then by symmetry over the set of states and by the requirement of extensivity.

However, we still seek the origin of the equal *a-priori* probability of states in a deeper symmetry. It would appear that the fundamental symmetry is a *dynamical* symmetry[5], specifically, the invariance of the equations of statistical mechanics under a rotation in the physical Hilbert space (that is, under arbitrary unitary transformations among the physically-permissible microstates). *The conserved quantity resulting from this symmetry is the volume in phase space W* (or the ln of W).

The conservation of the (*fine grained*) phase space volume under an internal unitary transformation is, of course, the famous Boltzmann $\mathscr{H}$-theorem. That theorem is usually stated in terms of one particular unitary transformation—the time translation operation—but it depends only on the unitarity of the transformation.

It is interesting to reflect on the significance of the conservation of W. An arbitrary (*fine grained*) phase space distribution propagates with time, flowing through phase space without either coalescing or diffusing. The probability density tends neither to coalesce around particular favoured states in phase space, nor does it diffuse to avoid particular unfavoured states. *There are no favoured states in quantum mechanics, and no unfavoured ones, and this impartiality is a dynamical symmetry of the quantum mechanical formalism.*

Unitarity is often characterised simply as *conservation of probability*, but it is considerably more. A transition matrix of the form

$$\begin{matrix} 1/2 & 1/2 \\ 0 & 1 \end{matrix}$$

conserves probability; a system in state #1 either remains in state #1 or makes a transition to state #2, each with probability 1/2; a system in state #2 necessarily remains in that state. Probability is conserved, but the second state is favoured over the first, and an arbitrary probability density coalesces entirely into the second state. The unitarity symmetry of quantum mechanics (or of classical mechanics) disbars such asymmetrical transition matrices.

Given unitary symmetry, or the impartiality of quantum mechanics among the microstates, it follows that a uniform probability density in phase space remains uniform under the intrinsic dynamics of the system.

Furthermore, a uniform distribution is the only distribution which is both stationary and *stable with respect to random, external perturbations.*

It follows that a system in equilibrium, stationary in time and stable under random fluctuations of its environmental interactions, is represented by a distribution function which is uniform in the permissible region of phase space. This is the crux of the thermodynamic entropy principle.

4.9 Time-Reversal Symmetry

It may contribute to clarity to restate some of the foregoing observations in the illuminating (but nonrigorous) formalism of the Pauli master equation[17,18]

$$\frac{d\rho_i}{dt} = \sum_j (\omega_{ij}\rho_j - \omega_{ji}\rho_i) \tag{4.7}$$

Here ρ_i is the probability of occupation of state i (ρ_i is the diagonal element of the density matrix) and ω_{ij} is the transition probability from state j to state i. (All off-diagonal elements of ρ are neglected.) The unitarity condition on the S-matrix (the ω_{ij} are squares of the S matrix elements) requires

$$\sum_j \omega_{ij} = \sum_j \omega_{ji} \tag{4.8}$$

It follows immediately that a solution of equation 4.8 is the uniform probability distribution

$$\rho_i = \text{constant} \tag{4.9}$$

As has often been pointed out, time-reversal symmetry, or the condition

$$\omega_{ij} = \omega_{ji'} \tag{4.10}$$

is a stronger condition than unitarity, and it leads *independently* to the same solution. We shall not enter into a discussion of the conditions for time-reversal symmetry[19]. But we stress that *the interchangeability of the unitarity condition*, equation 4.8, *and time-reversal symmetry*, equation 4.10, (when the latter is applicable) *demonstrates that unitarity is properly viewed as a symmetry condition.* Either of these symmetry conditions underlies the equal *a-priori* probability of states, equation 4.9, and thence the entropy-maximum principle of thermodynamics.

4.10 Phase Transitions and Broken Symmetry

Much of the conventional wisdom of thermodynamics has been shaken by recent developments in the theory of phase transitions[20]. The unexpected singularities of thermodynamic functions at critical points and the universality of the critical point exponents challenge the scope of classical theory.

Second order transitions are associated with the breaking of the symmetry of the Lagrangian of the system, and with the appearance of broken symmetry coordinates. Phase transitions therefore are a central and fundamental aspect of the thermodynamic formalism, directly coupled to the very existence of the basic thermodynamic coordinates.

For simplicity of discussion we consider a second-order transition in a crystal, thinking for instance of the onset of a ferroelectric moment. Above the transition the charge density in the crystal is invariant under some symmetry group $\mathscr{G}$. In the classical theory of Landau[21] one expands the charge density in a set of basis functions of the irreducible representations of the group $\mathscr{G}$.

$$\rho(\boldsymbol{r}) = \rho_0(\boldsymbol{r}) + \sum_{\Gamma,m}{}' \rho_{\Gamma,m}\, \Phi_{\Gamma,m}(\boldsymbol{r}) \tag{4.11}$$

Here $\rho_0(\boldsymbol{r})$ belongs to the fully symmetric representation, the sum is over all *other* representations Γ, and over the row index m of each representation. The $\Phi_{\Gamma,m}(\boldsymbol{r})$ are the basis functions. The free energy can then be considered as a function of the coefficients $\rho_{\Gamma,m}$. The form of the function is dictated by the symmetry $\mathscr{G}$; it must be composed of invariant combinations of the $\rho_{\Gamma,m}$ whence

$$F = F_0 + \sum_{\Gamma,m}{}' A_\Gamma(T, P, \ldots)\rho_{\Gamma,m}^2 + \text{4th order invariants} + \ldots\ldots \tag{4.12}$$

At high temperatures the stability of the symmetric state implies that all the A_Γ coefficients must be positive. Landau postulated that, as the temperature is lowered to some *critical* value T_c, some particular one of the coefficients A_Γ passes through zero. Below the temperature T_c the coefficient $A_\Gamma(T, P; N)$ is negative. Then minimising the free energy equation 4.12 leads to non-zero values of the quantities $\rho_{\Gamma m'}$ the actual values depending on the higher-order terms in equation 4.12. It is well-known that this theory leads to singularities of a form which disagrees with experiment [22].

A. Michelson[23] has emphasised that the symmetry argument above is fatefully over-simplified in that it assumes that a single coefficient A_Γ vanishes alone. This is, in fact, forbidden by the continuity within the symmetry group of a real system. That symmetry group is a *space group*, containing both translational and rotational (or reflection) elements[21]. The translational sub-group is Abelian, with one-dimensional representations labelled by the wave-vector $\boldsymbol{k}$. Then equation 4.12 becomes

$$F = F_0 + \sum_k A_k(T, P\ldots)\rho_k^2 + \sum_{(k_1 k_2 k_3 k_4)} B_{1234}(T, P\,..)\rho_{k_1}\rho_{k_2}\rho_{k_3}\rho_{k_4} + .. \tag{4.13}$$

Restrictions imposed by the space group symmetries imply that A_k and B_{1234} are symmetric under various rotations or reflections in k-space. Assume that the instability occurs at $k = 0$, which is the case of most general interest[21]. Then the coefficient A_0 passes through zero, and the continuity of the A_k insures that neighbouring coefficients have neighbouring zeros. As the temperature is lowered, additional A_k continually became unstable, and the singularity is formed by the confluence of a sequence of singular points.

Expanding the coefficients around zero wave-vector ($A_k = A_0 + A'k^2 + ..$) and recasting equation 4.13 in real space

$$F = F_0 + \int d^3r\{A'[\nabla\rho(\mathbf{r})]^2 + A_0\rho^2(\mathbf{r}) + B\rho^4(\mathbf{r})\} \tag{4.14}$$

This, of course, is the Ginzburg–Landau free energy functional[24] on which the Wilson theory[20] is based. The essential singularity precludes the steepest-descent evaluation of the partition function (or the minimisation of the free energy function). It will be recalled, however, that the more fundamental canonical average which is required is the result of an application to open subsystems of the basic principle of equal *a-priori* probabilities of states[25].

The intrusion of the various *modes* $\rho(\mathbf{k})$ into thermodynamic theory, demanded by the symmetry analysis, is rooted in even-deeper symmetry origins. These modes are, of course, the Goldstone excitations[7–10] associated with the broken symmetry coordinate emerging at the transition.

The consequences of the canonical averaging are realised in a specific functional structure of the free energy in the vicinity of the transition point. The divergent part of the free energy is shown to be a generalised homogeneous function of its variables (the *scaling form*). From this functional form all the scaling relationships and the critical exponents follow[22,20]. Even the specific evaluation of the canonical average is not essential to all the results, and it is of interest to note that many of the results can be obtained by group theoretical methods, using the concepts of the *renormalisation group*[20].

4.11 Onsager Reciprocity

Except for the *third law*, the seminal principles of equilibrium thermodynamics now have been discussed. Each derives from underlying symmetry considerations. The third law remains somewhat of a mystery. In its most naive form, expressed in terms of ground state degeneracy, it is suggestive of a symmetry statement, as degeneracy in quantum mechanics is always associated with symmetry[26]. But as careful analysis reveals, the third law depends on the form of the density-of-states function at non-zero energy. The *law* remains an unexplained postulate.

In 1931 Onsager[27] extended thermodynamic theory beyond the realm of equilibrium, to include steady-state, linear processes. It is too well-known to require elaboration here that Onsager based that extension on a single additional principle—the time-reversal symmetry of physical laws. He associated macroscopic processes with the decay of spontaneous fluctuations in an equilibrium system, and he assumed equality of the two time-reversed correlation functions

$$\langle x_1(0)x_2(t)\rangle = \langle x_1(0)x_2(-t)\rangle \tag{4.15}$$

From this he was able to show the famous reciprocity relationship between the mutual interference of two linear processes. The association of linear irreversible response with spontaneous fluctuations was later validated formally through the fluctuation–dissipation theorem, and independent derivations of the Onsager reciprocity were given in terms of quantum statistical perturbation theory. In all of these derivations it was shown that the central basis of the Onsager theory is the time-reversal symmetry of physical laws.

4.12 Conclusion

In this sketchy outline I have attempted to probe the various germinal laws of thermodynamics. Two underlying principles consistently emerge. The bases of macroscopic thermodynamic laws lie in the symmetries of microscopic physical laws. And the irrelevant details of specific systems are blurred by the properties of large statistical collections (in analogy with the obliteration of detail under the central limit theorem). I submit that thermodynamics can be viewed as the study of those properties of macroscopic matter which follow from the symmetry properties of physical laws, mediated through the statistics of large systems.

Appendix

To emphasise the lack of uniqueness of the energy in thermodynamics I shall demonstrate a model in which the energy plays no relevant role. The model is, of course, *contrived*, but its implications should not thereby be compromised.

Consider a system with N noninteracting spins, each of which can be *up* or *down*, and each carrying one unit of angular momentum (in units of $\hbar/2$). The system has a moment of inertia I and an angular frequency of net rotation ω, so that the total angular momentum (z-component) is

$$L = L_m + n_\uparrow - n_\downarrow \tag{4.A1}$$

where

$$L_m = I\omega \tag{4.A2}$$

and

$$n_\uparrow + n_\downarrow = N \tag{4.A3}$$

Assume the moment of inertia to be infinitely large and ω to be infinitely small, so that $I\omega$ is finite. Then the kinetic energy of rotation $\frac{1}{2}I\omega^2$ vanishes. Furthermore, the electron spins are noninteracting. Hence *all states of the system have zero energy, and the energy is not a relevant variable.*

The total angular momentum L is conserved and it can be measured by exploiting that conservation, precisely as the energy is usually measured in thermodynamics[4].

Similarly the mechanical angular momentum is observable (both I and ω are directly measurable). We disbar magnetic effects (as if the electrons were uncharged, or magnetic fields screened), and the spin angular momentum $(n_\uparrow - n_\downarrow)$ is assumed to be *unobservable.*

The thermodynamic fundamental equation is of the form

$$S = S(L, L_m, N) \tag{4.A4}$$

and the intensive parameters are defined by

$$\frac{1}{\tau} = \frac{\partial S}{\partial L}, \qquad -\frac{P_m}{\tau} = \frac{\partial S}{\partial L_m}, \qquad -\frac{\mu}{\tau} = \frac{\partial S}{\partial N} \tag{4.A5}$$

with

$$\delta S = \frac{1}{\tau}\,\delta L - \frac{P_m}{\tau}\,\delta L_m - \frac{\mu}{\tau}\,\delta N \tag{4.A6}$$

We can calculate the fundamental equation easily, as

$$S = k_B \ln \frac{N!}{n_\uparrow!\,n_\downarrow!} = k_B \ln \frac{N!}{\left(\dfrac{N+L-L_m}{2}\right)!\left(\dfrac{N-L+L_m}{2}\right)!} \tag{4.A7}$$

$$\simeq -Nk_B \ln\left[1-\left(\frac{L-L_m}{N}\right)^2\right] - \tfrac{1}{2}k_B(L-L_m)\ln\frac{N+L-L_m}{N-L+L_m} \tag{4.A8}$$

The various equations of state can be calculated directly, giving $\tau = \tau(L, L_m, N)$, etc. We find that $P_m = 1$, this trivial *equation of state* resulting from the simplicity of the model; specifically that the incoherent modes of the spins are independent of the coherent mode of mass rotation (rather than coupled together as the incoherent phonon modes are coupled to the volume mode in a real crystal). Inserting this equation of state we find from equation (4.A6) that

$$\delta S = \frac{\delta Q}{\tau}, \qquad \text{if} \qquad \delta N = 0 \tag{4.A9}$$

where

$$\delta Q = \delta L - \delta L_m \tag{4.A10}$$

Note that δQ is just the angular momentum in the incoherent spin modes. The equation 4.A9 for δS is the essential equation underlying considerations of reversibility and irreversibility and the second law. *The existence of a 'heat' δQ need have nothing to do with energy although it almost always does.*

References

1. J. B. Boyling. *Comm. Math. Phys.*, **10** (1968), 52
2. P. T. Landsberg. *Pure and Applied Chemistry*, **22** (1970), 215
3. L. Tisza. *Generalised Thermodynamics*, M.I.T. Press, Cambridge, Mass. (1966)
4. C. Truesdell. *Rational Thermodynamics*, McGraw-Hill, New York (1969)
5. E. P. Wigner. *Symmetries and Reflections*, Indiana Univ. Press, Bloomington, Ind. (1967)
6. A. Aharony and Y. Ne'eman. *Int. Jour. Theor. Phys.*, **3** (1970), 437
7. A. A. Grib, E. V. Damaskinskii and V. M. Maksimov. *Usp. Fiz. Nauk*, **102** (1970), 587 (English translation: *Sov. Phys. Uspekhi*, **13** (1971), 798

8. H. Wagner. *Zeit. für Physik*, **195** (1966), 273
9. P. W. Anderson. *Science*, **177** (1972), 393
10. R. V. Lange. *Phys. Rev.*, **146** (1966), 301
11. For a recent review see P. T. Landsberg and others in *A Critical Review of Thermodynamics*, ed. by E. B. Stuart, B. Gal-Or and A. J. Brainard, Mono, Baltimore (1970)
12. H. Callen and G. Horwitz. *Am. Jour. Phys.*, **39** (1971), 938
13. R. B. Woodward and R. Hoffmann. The conservation of orbital symmetry. *Verlag Chemie*, Wienheim and Academic Press, N.Y. (1970)
14. B. I. Halperin and P. C. Hohenberg. *Phys. Rev.*, **188** (1969), 898
15. P. C. Martin, O. Parodi and P. S. Pershan. *Phys. Rev.*, **A6** (1972), 2401
16. H. Callen. *Thermodynamics*, Wiley, New York (1960)
17. W. Pauli. *Sommerfeld Festschrift*, ed. by P. Debye, Hirzel, Leipzig (1928)
18. N. G. van Kampen. *Physica*, **20** (1954), 603
19. F. Coester. *Phys. Rev.*, **84** (1951), 1259
20. K. G. Wilson. *Phys. Rev.*, **B4** (1971), 3174; **4** (1971), 3184
21. L. D. Landau. *Physik Z. Sowjetunion*, **11** (1937). 545. See also ch. 14 of L. D. Landau and E. M. Lifshitz, *Statistical Physics*, Pergamon, London (1962)
22. E. Stanley. *Introduction to Phase Transitions and Critical Phenomena*, Oxford Univ. Press, New York and Oxford (1971)
23. A. Michelson (Technion, Haifa), private communication
24. V. L. Ginzburg and L. P. Landau. *J. Expt. Theor. Phys. (USSR)*, **20** (1950), 1064
25. E. Schrödinger. *Statistical Thermodynamics*, Cambridge (1936)
26. H. Weyl. *The Theory of Groups and Quantum Mechanics*, translated by H. P. Robertson, Methuen, London (1931) and Dover, New York (1950)
27. L. Onsager. *Phys. Rev.*, **37** (1931), 405; **38** (1931), 2265

Discussion

SCHLÖGL

I have two additional remarks to the, for me, very convincing scheme you have given.

It seems to me that a general distinction of time compared with space, and therefore of energy and temperature, is given in thermodynamics by the usual manner of asking for predictions from one time point to another.

As to second order phase transitions: they exist in nonlinear non-equilibrium thermodynamics as well. I have in mind an example given in Schlögl, *Z. Physik*, **253** (1972), 147. There the symmetry, broken below the critical point, is not space symmetry but time reversal symmetry.

CALLEN

As to the first point, I agree that thermodynamics of irreversible processes treats future and past asymmetrically. My remarks were restricted to thermostatics, in which future and past are symmetric.

TISZA

I thoroughly enjoyed Professor Callen's brilliant presentation. I am practically in complete agreement with all he said, but I wish to make two remarks to supplement his thesis

(1) Callen pointed out the lack of metric aspects of thermodynamics; however, I feel that this negative statement should be balanced by recognising the role of affine geometry (see L. Tisza, *Generalised Thermodynamics*, M.I.T. Press (1966), p. 105–6, 235–41).

(2) I fully agree with Callen's emphasis of the role of symmetry. However, Noether's theorem does not have such a dramatic impact when applied within classical mechanics. The importance of using quantum mechanics is a further manifestation of the harmony between this discipline and thermodynamics that I had pointed out in chapter 3.

Discussion

5. Microscopic Aspects of Entropy and the Statistical Foundations of Nonequilibrium Thermodynamics

I. Prigogine†

Abstract

The aim of this paper is to show how recent work in nonequilibrium statistical mechanics leads to a mechanical interpretation of the second law of thermodynamics.

First, we recall Boltzmann's definition of entropy and the difficulties associated with it (extension to dense systems, Loschmidt's paradox, etc.). On a simple model (McKean–Kac's model), we show that Boltzmann's definition is certainly not valid for all possible evolutions but that it is, nevertheless, possible to find out a Liapounoff function which is positive and can only decrease as a result of the time evolution. This leads to a microscopic definition of entropy for this model. The entropy defined in this way reduces to Boltzmann's entropy close to equilibrium.

We then give a short summary of the work in nonequilibrium statistical mechanics of the Brussels school and emphasise the fact that irreversibility appears as a symmetry breaking of the time reversal invariance which results from the appearance of dynamic operators which are *even* in the Liouville–von Neumann operator L. This symmetry breaking is a consequence of causality when applied to large systems formed by many interacting degrees of freedom. The introduction of nonunitary (called star unitary) transformation leads to a representation in which the time change of the distribution function is split into two parts, one odd and one even in the Liouville–von Neumann operators. The first corresponds to *reversible* changes, the second to *irreversible* ones. The correspondence with the second law is therefore complete. We may now introduce a Liapounoff function which leads to a general microscopic model of entropy. This definition is valid whatever the initial conditions. No additional probabilistic arguments are needed to derive the increase of entropy. On the contrary the probabilistic interpretation when valid is a consequence of dynamics. We also show that there is no Loschmidt paradox associated with our new definition of entropy, and that it reduces to Boltzmann's definition for systems close to equilibrium.

In the concluding section we stress the fact that our approach leads to a general expression for the entropy production independently of any assump-

† Université Libre de Bruxelles, Faculté des Sciences, Belgium, and Center for Statistical Mechanics and Thermodynamics, The University of Texas at Austin, USA.

tion of closeness to equilibrium. The perspectives opened by this new development which unifies dynamics and thermodynamics are briefly discussed.

5.1 Introduction

The classical work of Gibbs, Einstein and others has largely elucidated the foundations of equilibrium thermodynamics. However, in recent years much attention has been devoted to nonequilibrium thermodynamics. Here the situation was much less favourable. Even in 1949[1] the author had discussed the principles of nonequilibrium thermodynamics using Boltzmann's kinetic theory. However, Boltzmann's approach is valid only for dilute gases and even then under conditions corresponding to *molecular chaos.* It is only very recently that a general formulation of nonequilibrium statistical mechanics has been obtained[2–5] which leads in turn to a microscopic definition of entropy, that has a generality comparable to that of thermodynamic entropy postulated by the phenomenological formulation of the second law. I would like to summarise here some of those recent developments which, in my opinion, lead to the solution of the problem so clearly formulated by Boltzmann one hundred years ago, the *mechanical interpretation* of the second law of thermodynamics.

One of the basic concepts of thermodynamics is the concept of irreversible processes. According to Planck's definition an irreversible process is a process which once performed leaves the world in an altered state[6]: *By no experimental device, whatever the ingenuity of experimenter, should it be possible to restore the initial state.* The distinction between reversible and irreversible processes leads then to the formulation of the second principle (reference 6, p. 99). For isolated systems entropy can only increase

$$\frac{dS}{dt} \geqslant 0 \tag{5.1}$$

A typical irreversible process, from the point of view of the thermodynamics, is linear heat conduction. It is described by the Fourier equation

$$\frac{\partial T}{\partial t} = \kappa \frac{\partial^2 T}{\partial x^2} \tag{5.2}$$

The important point is that equation 5.2 is not time invariant. When the substitution

$$t \rightarrow -t \tag{5.3}$$

is made, one obtains the *anti-Fourier* equation

$$\frac{\partial T}{\partial t} = -\kappa \frac{\partial^2 T}{\partial x^2} \tag{5.4}$$

Both equations 5.2 and 5.4 have a physical meaning. Equation 5.2 corresponds to the situations in which we have an *initial* value problem and we want to calculate the temperature distribution in the future. The solutions of equation 5.2 are *retarded solutions*. On the contrary, in the case of equation 5.4 we have a *final value* problem as may arise as the result of a fluctuation in a system which was isolated for a long time. The uniform distribution corresponds then to the far distant past ($t \to -\infty$). The solution of equation 5.4 is an *advanced* solution.

We have now a pair of equations in each of which the direction of time plays a different role. We may say that the second law of thermodynamics, equation 5.1, summarises in a single inequality all laws such as Fourier's law, friction phenomena, etc., which are precisely described by phenomenological equations involving a *privileged* direction of time. This is the situation we associate with thermodynamic irreversibility.

What is the meaning of the second law? Is it limited to equilibrium or near equilibrium states? This question becomes specially urgent today as the recent development of *nonlinear* thermodynamics of irreversible processes has shown that fundamental aspects of nature—such as self organisation in nonequilibrium conditions—can be formulated in the frame of nonequilibrium thermodynamics[7].

To study this question we have to investigate the relation between the second law of thermodynamics and dynamics (classical or quantum). This is a very complicated problem. Thermodynamics is formulated in terms of *processes* while dynamics deals with *motion*. How to link these two descriptions of nature? It is well known that Boltzmann[8] has made a basic contribution to this problem. Why was Boltzmann so fascinated with the second law? What attracted him to this problem to an extent that he devoted his whole life to its discussion? We have a hint of his motivation in an article in his *Populäre Schriften*[9]. There he writes, 'if one would ask me which name we should give to this century, I would answer without hesitation that this is Darwin's century'. This is a most interesting statement. Boltzmann was obviously fascinated by the idea of evolution and specially by the *mechanical interpretation* of the process of evolution.

Even today—one hundred years after—Boltzmann's ideas are still so basic that we have to summarise them first before we can analyse the present situation of thermodynamics in respect to dynamics.

Boltzmann considered the case of dilute gases and, guided by intuitive arguments, proposed his famous kinetic equation for the velocity distribution function f,

$$\frac{\partial f}{\partial t} = \int d\Omega \int dv_1 \, \sigma(\Omega) \, |\boldsymbol{v}_1 - \boldsymbol{v}| \, (f' f_1' - f f_1) \tag{5.5}$$

He then introduced the $\mathscr{H}_B$ quantity

$$\mathscr{H}_B = \int \mathrm{d}\boldsymbol{v}\, f \ln f \tag{5.6}$$

and established the inequality

$$\frac{\mathrm{d}\mathscr{H}_B}{\mathrm{d}t} \leqslant 0 \tag{5.7}$$

This basic inequality led him to the identification of $\mathscr{H}_B$ with the thermodynamic entropy S

$$S = -k\mathscr{H}_B \tag{5.8}$$

In modern language $\mathscr{H}_B$ provides us with a *Liapounoff function* to which Boltzmann ascribed a basic thermodynamic meaning.

Therefore, we may summarise Boltzmann's scheme in the following way

Dynamics → *Stochastic Processes* (*Kinetic Equation*) → *Entropy*

We see why Boltzmann's investigations are so central. They link various levels of description which had been introduced independently in the history of science: *the dynamical description expressed through the laws of mechanics, the description in terms of probabilities and the thermodynamic description.*

Boltzmann's $\mathscr{H}$-theorem has led to a very strange situation, perhaps unique in the history of science. On the one hand, Boltzmann's kinetic equation has been applied successfully to a very large range of physical phenomena, such as transport processes in dilute gases, in plasmas, shock waves, hydrodynamics and chemical reactions. A good account may be found, for instance, in the textbook by Hirschfelder *et al*[10]. Molecular experiments, such as those performed by Alder and Wainwright[11], and more recently by Bellemans and Orban[12], completely verify Boltzmann's predictions. The quantity $\mathscr{H}_B$ indeed decreases in a fluctuating fashion and the system reaches thermodynamic equilibrium after a time corresponding to a few collisions per particle. The fluctuations decrease when the number of particles is increased. There is little doubt that in the thermodynamic limit (volume $V \to \infty$, number of particles $N \to \infty$, N/V = constant) we would observe for a dilute gas the monotonous approach to equilibrium predicted by Boltzmann.

On the other hand one has to recognise that Boltzmann's definition of entropy leads both to conceptual and practical difficulties. For dilute gases it applies only for certain initial conditions and in addition it has proved impossible until now to extend Boltzmann's ideas to more general situations such as dense gases or liquids. It is of course possible to use perturbational techniques for moderately dilute gases or slightly anharmonic solids, and verify then that (by definition) the entropy production remains positive as it is dominated by the Boltzmann type contribution. This, however, can hardly be considered as a nontrivial extension of Boltzmann's ideas.

In the first part of this chapter we shall discuss in some detail these difficulties. We shall see that Boltzmann's definition, equation 5.8, of entropy can be considered as valid *only* when the kinetic equation 5.5 applies. We shall indicate examples where this is not so. In such situations we have to introduce a more general definition of entropy which is such that the corresponding $\mathscr{H}$-theorem remains valid even when the kinetic equation is not.

We have to introduce, therefore, a sharp distinction between a *kinetic model* of entropy such as provided by Boltzmann's definition at least for dilute systems, and *dynamic models* of entropy which have to follow solely from the laws of dynamics when applied to systems formed by many interacting particles.

In the second part of this chapter we shall show how such a dynamical model of entropy may be constructed as the result of the recent development of nonequilibrium statistical mechanics[2–5]. As already mentioned this new definition of entropy has a generality comparable to the Gibbs entropy for equilibrium. It can only increase for *all initial value problems.* As it includes also all possible correlations it leads to a new and general definition of *order* in dynamic systems.

5.2 Velocity Inversion—Loschmidt's Paradox

Let us start with the formulation of the classical Loschmidt paradox[13,4]: 'Since the laws of mechanics are symmetrical with respect to the inversion of time,

$$t \to -t \tag{5.9}$$

to each process there belongs a corresponding time reversed process'. This seems to be in contradiction to the existence of irreversible processes. To discuss this paradox let us consider a velocity inversion experiment. Boltzmann's $\mathscr{H}$-quantity has been calculated on computer for two-dimensional hard spheres (hard disks), starting with disks on lattice sites with an isotropic velocity distributions[12]. The results are represented schematically in figure 5.1.

They conform to Boltzmann's predictions.

Now, if after 50 or 100 collisions, the velocities are inverted, a new ensemble is obtained. The evolution of the corresponding $\mathscr{H}_B$ is again followed in time. The results are again represented schematically in figure 5.2.

It is seen that, after the velocity inversion, Boltzmann's $\mathscr{H}$-quantity increases (instead of decreasing). The system deviates from equilibrium over a period of 50 to 60 collisions (corresponding to about 10^{-6} seconds in a dilute gas).

P. and T. Ehrenfest[14] made the remark that Boltzmann's equation could not be correct *both* before and after the inversion of velocities.

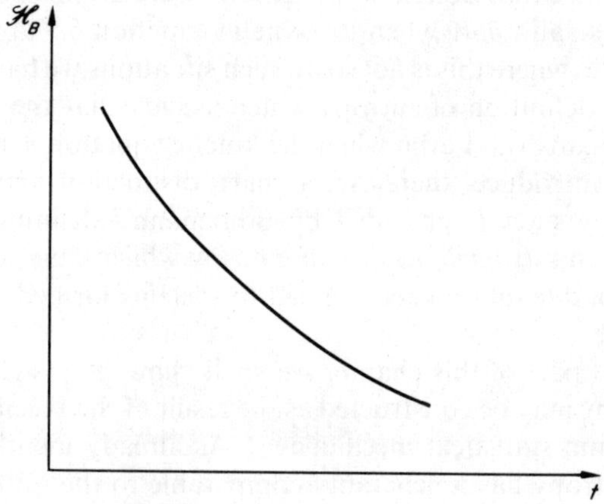

Figure 5.1

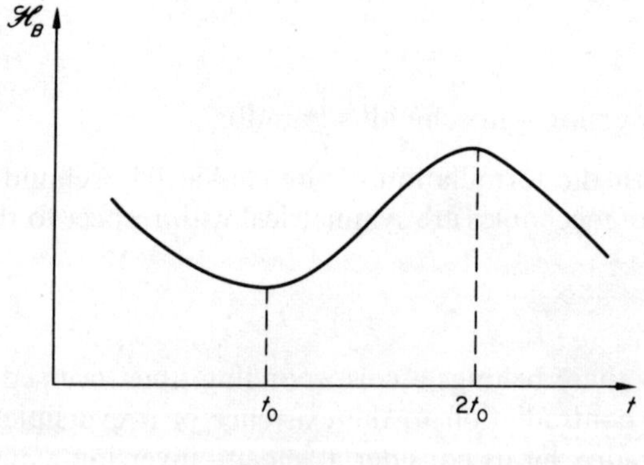

Figure 5.2

The question is now: what inference can we draw from the fact that there exist situations, for which the kinetic equation 5.5 is valid while, in other situations, this equation is not valid? Does this fact express a limitation of Boltzmann's statistical interpretation of entropy or a failure of the second law?

The physical situation is quite clear: velocity inversion creates, between particles, correlations which may be of macroscopic range. Particles which had collided at time t_1 have to collide again at time $2t_0 - t_1$. As a consequence, the anomalous correlations may be expected to disappear during the time period from t_0 to $2t_0$, after which the system shows again a *normal* behaviour.

Briefly speaking, entropy production can be understood in the interval 0 to t_0 as associated with the *maxwellianisation* of the velocity distribution, while, in the period t_0 to $2t_0$, it should be associated with the decay of anomalous correlations.

If it were really possible to use velocity inversion or similar experiments to destroy, during the time interval t_0 to $2t_0$, the *entropy* produced between 0 and t_0, there would exist, according to Planck's definition[6] which we have quoted at the beginning of this chapter, *no* irreversible process whatsoever and therefore *no* second law of thermodynamics!

Therefore, the conclusion we have to draw from the velocity inversion experiment is that Boltzmann's definition of entropy has to be restricted to situations where the kinetic equation 5.5 holds. Obviously velocity inversion does not destroy the validity of dynamics but still it destroys at least temporarily the validity of the kinetic equation 5.5. Therefore, Boltzmann's approach cannot be used to discuss in general the relation between dynamics and thermodynamics.

What is needed is a statistical expression of entropy which depends explicitly on the correlations as introduced by velocity inversion and which satisfies an $\mathscr{H}$-theorem both before and after velocity inversion. Before we show how this can be done let us consider a second example.

5.3 The MacKean–Kac Model†

In order to discuss further Boltzmann's approach to entropy it is useful to start from a master equation derived from a probabilistic model for binary collisions. Such probabilistic master equations have been studied a few years ago by Marc Kac[15,16]. More recently, Kac has discussed the master equation corresponding to an extremely simplified probabilistic model introduced by MacKean[17,18]. We shall use this model but we want to emphasise that all our conclusions apply as well to other models such as the Kac *caricature* of the Maxwell gas[15,16].

MacKean[17] considers *n particles* each capable of having only the *velocities* +1 and −1. When a particle with *velocity* $e_1 (= \pm 1)$ *collides* with a *particle*

† The results summarised in this section are due to Dr. F. Henin.

with velocity $e_2(=\pm 1)$ they emerge with velocities e_1^*, e_2^* respectively. With a probability 1/2 the final velocities are

$$e_1^* = e_1 \qquad e_2^* = e_1 e_2 \tag{5.10}$$

and with probability 1/2

$$e_1^* = e_1 e_2 \qquad e_2^* = e_2 \tag{5.11}$$

The various possibilities are represented by the following scheme

$$\begin{array}{ll} +1,\, +1 \begin{cases} +1,\, +1 \\ +1,\, +1 \end{cases} & -1,\, +1 \begin{cases} -1,\, -1 \\ -1,\, +1 \end{cases} \\ +1,\, -1 \begin{cases} +1,\, -1 \\ -1,\, -1 \end{cases} & -1,\, -1 \begin{cases} -1,\, +1 \\ +1,\, -1 \end{cases} \end{array} \tag{5.12}$$

This leads then to the master equation[17,18]

$$\frac{\partial \rho(e_1, e_2, \ldots, e_N, t)}{\partial t} = \frac{1}{N} \sum_{1 \leqslant i \leqslant j \leqslant N} \{\rho(e_1, \ldots, e_i, \ldots, e_i e_j, \ldots, e_N, t)$$
$$+ \rho(e_1, \ldots, e_i e_j, \ldots, e_j, \ldots, e_N, t) - 2\rho(e_1, e_2, \ldots, e_i, \ldots, e_j, \ldots, e_N, t)\} \tag{5.13}$$

This equation preserves the normalisation

$$\sum_{e_1 \quad e_N = \pm 1} \rho(e_1, \ldots, e_N, t) = 1 \tag{5.14}$$

There is however in this model an additional invariant. Indeed if both particles have velocities $+1$ before collision they also have velocities $+1$ after collision (see scheme 5.12). As a consequence the probability

$$\rho(+1, +1, \ldots, t) = \alpha \tag{5.15}$$

is invariant in time. The master equation 5.13 has an infinity of time-independent solutions corresponding to

$$\rho^0(+1, \ldots, +1) = \alpha$$
$$\rho^0(e_1 \ldots e_N) = \frac{1-\alpha}{2^N - 1} \qquad \{e\} \neq \{+1\} \tag{5.16}$$

If in addition we impose that the time independent solution be a factorised distribution

$$\rho^0(e_1 \ldots e_N) = \prod_{i=1}^{N} f^0(e_i) \tag{5.17}$$

we obtain a condition that α has to satisfy. As a result, the only numerical values of α compatible with equation 5.17 are[19]

$$\alpha = 1 \qquad \text{or} \qquad \alpha = \frac{1}{2^N} \tag{5.18}$$

The first case is without interest as all particles have then velocity $+1$ and this situation is propagated in time. On the contrary the second value, equation 5.18, leads at equilibrium to a distribution which plays here the role of the microcanical distribution. Indeed equation 5.16 gives then in the stationary state

$$\rho^0(\{e_i\}) = \frac{1}{2^N} \quad \text{for all values } \{e_i\} \tag{5.19}$$

All components of the distribution function ρ have then at equilibrium the same value. We shall therefore suppose that $\alpha \neq 1$.

After these preliminary considerations, let us now discuss the Boltzmann equation corresponding to the MacKean model. We first *suppose* that at each time t the distribution ρ is factorised as it is at equilibrium (see equation 5.17)

$$\rho(\{e_i\}, t) = \prod_{i=1}^{N} f(e_i, t) \tag{5.20}$$

with

$$f(+1, t) + f(-1, t) = 1 \tag{5.21}$$

If we replace ρ in equation 5.13 by equation 5.20 we obtain directly the Boltzmann equation

$$\frac{\mathrm{d}f(e)}{\mathrm{d}t} = f(e)f(+1) + f(-e)f(-1) - f(e) \tag{5.22}$$

or, (see equation 5.21) $\qquad (f(+1, t) \equiv f_+)$

$$\frac{\mathrm{d}f_+}{\mathrm{d}t} = 1 - 3f_+ + 2f_+^2 \tag{5.23}$$

One of the remarkable features of the MacKean model is that this nonlinear Boltzmann equation can be integrated directly.[17,18]. We obtain

$$f_+(t) = \frac{1}{2} + \frac{\Lambda}{2}\,\frac{e^{-t}}{1 - \Lambda(1 - e^{-t})}$$

$$\Lambda = 2f_+(t = 0) - 1 \tag{5.24}$$

For $t \to \infty$ this leads to the equilibrium value

$$f_+^0 = \frac{1}{2} \tag{5.25}$$

in agreement with equations 5.20 and 5.19. We can now introduce Boltzmann's $\mathscr{H}$-quantity, equation 5.6

$$\begin{aligned}\mathscr{H}_B &= f_+ \ln f_+ + f_- \ln f_- \\ &= f_+ \ln f_+ + (1-f_+)\ln(1-f_+)\end{aligned} \tag{5.26}$$

and verify that it can only decrease in time

$$\frac{\mathrm{d}\mathscr{H}_B}{\mathrm{d}t} = (1-f_+)(1-2f_+)\ln\frac{f_+}{1-f_+} \leqslant 0 \tag{5.27}$$

The necessary and sufficient condition for equilibrium is the extremum of $\mathscr{H}_B$ (note that we have discarded $\alpha = 1$, see equation 5.18, therefore $f_+ \neq 1$).

It is interesting to indicate the values of Boltzmann's $\mathscr{H}$-quantity, equation 5.26, as well as of the associated *entropy production*, equations 5.27, in the neighbourhood of equilibrium. We then write

$$f_+ = \tfrac{1}{2}(1+\varepsilon g) \qquad f_- = \tfrac{1}{2}(1-\varepsilon g) \tag{5.28}$$

Neglecting higher order terms in ε this leads to

$$\mathscr{H}_B = -\ln 2 + \tfrac{1}{2}(\varepsilon g)^2 + \ldots \tag{5.29}$$

$$\frac{\mathrm{d}\mathscr{H}_B}{\mathrm{d}t} = -(\varepsilon g)^2 + \ldots \tag{5.30}$$

Let us now discuss the evolution of the MacKean model without introducing *a-priori* the factorisation condition 5.20. We may describe the evolution of the system in terms of the moments

$$\langle e_1^{\alpha_1} e_2^{\alpha_2}, \ldots, e_N^{\alpha_N} \rangle \tag{5.31}$$

As

$$\begin{aligned} e_i^{\alpha_i} &= 1 \qquad \alpha_i \text{ even} \\ e_i^{\alpha_i} &= e_i \qquad \alpha_i \text{ odd}\end{aligned} \tag{5.32}$$

the only independent moments are then

$$x_p = \langle e_1 e_2 e_3, \ldots, e_p \rangle \tag{5.33}$$

Using the master equation 5.13 it is easy to establish the evolution equations for the moments x_p[19]. We obtain for $1 \leqslant p \leqslant N$

$$\frac{\mathrm{d}x_p}{\mathrm{d}t} = \frac{p(p-1)}{N} x_{p-1} - \frac{p(N-1)}{N} x_p + \frac{p(N-p)}{N} x_{p+1} \tag{5.34}$$

These equations replace, in this problem, the equations of the B.B.G.K.Y.

hierarchy. For $p \ll N$ we obtain

$$\frac{dx_p}{dt} = -p(x_p - x_{p+1}) + 0\left(\frac{1}{N}\right) \tag{5.35}$$

In the limit of a large system ($N \to \infty$) equations 5.35 have the factorised solution

$$x_p = \langle e_1 \rangle^p + 0\left(\frac{1}{N}\right) \tag{5.36}$$

with

$$\frac{d\langle e_1 \rangle}{dt} = -\langle e_1 \rangle(1 - \langle e_1 \rangle) \tag{5.37}$$

This is an alternative form of the Boltzmann equation 5.22 (note that $\langle e_1 \rangle = f_+ - f_-$). We verify therefore the Kac theorem of propagation of chaos[15,16]. If property 5.36 is valid at $t = 0$ it will remain valid for all times $t > 0$ for arbitrary fixed p in the limit of a large system. However, we may of course consider other situations than those described by equation 5.36. In fact, we can give at $t = 0$ arbitrary values to the moments $x_1, x_2, \ldots, x_N$ and then study through equation 5.34 their time evolution. For $t \to \infty$, we obtain the equilibrium solution:

$$x_1 = x_2 = \ldots = x_N \tag{5.38}$$

For factorised distributions this leads either to

$$x_p = 1 \qquad \text{or} \qquad x_p = 0 \tag{5.39}$$

according to the two values of α, given in equation 5.18, compatible with factorisation.

It is easy to impose initial values on $x_1 = e_1$ and x_2 such that as a consequence of equation 5.35 the time evolution of Boltzmann's $\mathscr{H}$-quantity has the wrong sign over a limited time period. (Examples are given in reference 19.) As in the velocity inversion example this is due to the neglect of correlations in the Boltzmann definition of $\mathscr{H}$-quantity.

However, it can be shown that correlations die out before the system has reached equilibrium[19]. As a consequence, Boltzmann's results are recovered asymptotically. This example as well as the velocity inversion paradox show, in a striking way, that the problem of approach to equilibrium and the problem of molecular chaos have to be sharply distinguished to avoid confusion.

Let us now construct a *Liapounoff* function which is positive and can decrease only as the result of the dynamical evolution as described by the master equation 5.13 or by the moment equations 5.34. As equations 5.34 are linear it is very natural to consider the quadratic functional

$$\sum_{\{e_i\}} \rho^2(e_1, \ldots, e_N, t) \tag{5.40}$$

We expand ρ in terms of the moments

$$\rho = \frac{1}{2^N} \sum_{\{\alpha_i = 1,2\}} \langle e_1^{\alpha_1}, \ldots, e_N^{\alpha_N} \rangle e_1^{\alpha_1}, \ldots, e_N^{\alpha_N} \tag{5.41}$$

This leads then to

$$\sum_{\{e_i\}} \rho^2 = \frac{1}{2^N} \sum_{p=0}^{N} \frac{N!}{p!(N-p)!} x_p^2 > 0 \tag{5.42}$$

and (see equation 5.34)

$$\frac{\mathrm{d}}{\mathrm{d}t} \sum_{\{e_i\}} \rho^2 = -(N-1) \sum_{p=0}^{N-2} \frac{(N-2)!}{p!(N-2-p)!} (x_{p+1} - x_{p+2})^2 \leqslant 0 \tag{5.43}$$

Obviously inequality 5.43 vanishes *only* when the equilibrium state 5.38 is reached.

The remarkable feature is now that it is easy to use the Liapounoff function 5.40 to define a generalised $\mathscr{H}$-quantity which both at equilibrium and near to equilibrium reduces to Boltzmann's $\mathscr{H}$-quantity. Indeed at microcanonical equilibrium only the term $p = 0$ in equation 5.42 gives a contribution and

$$\ln \sum_{\{e_i\}} \rho^2 = -N \ln 2 \tag{5.44}$$

Let us therefore define the generalised $\mathscr{H}$ through the relation ($\mathscr{H}_{\mathrm{eq}} = \ln (\sum \rho^2)_{\mathrm{eq}}$)

$$\mathscr{H} - \mathscr{H}_{\mathrm{eq}} = \tfrac{1}{2} \ln \frac{\sum_{\{e_i\}} \rho^2}{(\sum_{\{e_i\}} \rho^2)_{\mathrm{eq}}} \tag{5.45}$$

Then at equilibrium we recover Boltzmann's expression. Moreover, if we consider factorised distributions 5.36 and neglect higher orders in ε we obtain

$$\frac{\mathscr{H} - \mathscr{H}_{\mathrm{eq}}}{N} = -\ln 2 + \tfrac{1}{2} \ln (1 + \varepsilon^2 g^2) = -\ln 2 + \tfrac{1}{2}(\varepsilon g)^2 + \ldots \tag{5.46}$$

in agreement with equation 5.29.

We may consider equation 5.45 as the general *microscopic* expression for entropy for the MacKean model. It reduces to the Boltzmann expression near equilibrium but leads in addition to a positive entropy production for all possible dynamic evolutions of the system. Other functionals could be used here to provide us with a Liapounoff function and with a microscopic model of entropy. For example we could as well have used

$$\mathscr{H} = \sum_{\{e\}} \rho \ln \rho \tag{5.45a}$$

The choice of the functional we have to use can only be made on the basis of the dynamic theory which leads precisely to the expression 5.45 and not to 5.45*a*, except in the special cases corresponding to Markoff processes[20].

It should be emphasised, however, that the Boltzmann's $\mathscr{H}$-quantity (equation 5.26) on one side and equation 5.45 on the other correspond to completely different limiting procedures when the number of particles N increases. In Boltzmann's expression appears the one-particle distribution function f which may be defined as the limit

$$f(e_1) = \lim_{N \to \infty} \sum_{e_2, e_3, \ldots, e_N} \rho(e_1, e_2, \ldots, e_N, t) \tag{5.47}$$

Boltzmann's $\mathscr{H}$-theorem describes the approach of this reduced distribution function to equilibrium. We may say that it describes the approach to *canonical* equilibrium (the other particles forming the *heat bath*). On the contrary the generalised $\mathscr{H}$-quantity as defined through equation 5.45 refers to the system as a whole. What is involved here is the limit

$$\lim_{N \to \infty} \ln \frac{\sum_{\{e_i\}} \rho^2}{\left(\sum_{\{e_i\}} \rho^2\right)_{\text{eq}}} \tag{5.48}$$

The evolution of $\mathscr{H}$ now describes the approach to microcanonical equilibrium of the system as a *whole*.

There is no reason to expect that in general the entropy production associated with equation 5.45 can be expressed in terms of the kinetic equation 5.35 or equation 5.37 where the limit $N \to \infty$ has been performed *first*. What we have now to do is to solve the hierarchy for fixed values of N, replace in equation 5.42 and 5.43, and go to $N \to \infty$ at the end. In this simple case it can be shown[19] that these limits exist both for $\mathscr{H}/N$ and $1/N(\mathrm{d}\mathscr{H}/\mathrm{d}t)$. However, now the entropy production also contains quantities such as velocity correlations which cannot be calculated from the kinetic equation. It is only near equilibrium that the various $\mathscr{H}$-quantities lead to the same result. We have therefore to make a sharp distinction between the kinetic Boltzmann entropy, equation 5.26, and the *dynamic* entropy, equation 5.45.

After this discussion of a simplified model let us now go back to the general problem.

5.4 Irreversibility as Symmetry Breaking

Before we can discuss the statistical foundation of the second law we have first to discuss briefly how irreversibility appears in the dynamic description of classical of quantum systems. For obvious reasons we can present here only a short summary. A monograph dealing specifically with the dynamic theory of irreversible processes is in preparation.

Let us start from classical or quantum dynamics as expressed by Hamilton's equations of motion

$$\frac{\mathrm{d}q}{\mathrm{d}t} = \frac{\partial H}{\partial p} \qquad \frac{\mathrm{d}p}{\mathrm{d}t} = -\frac{\partial H}{\partial q} \tag{5.49}$$

or Schrödinger's equation

$$i\frac{\partial \psi}{\partial t} = H\psi \tag{5.50}$$

Both descriptions may be unified through the Liouville–von Neumann equation for the distribution function (or density matrix[21])

$$i\frac{\partial \rho}{\partial t} = L\rho \tag{5.51}$$

with

$$L\rho = \begin{matrix} -i\{H, \rho\} & \text{Poisson bracket} \\ [H, \rho]_- & \text{commutator} \end{matrix} \tag{5.52}$$

In both cases L is a hermitian operator (better superoperator, see references 2, 20, 22). Therefore

$$L = L^\dagger \tag{5.53}$$

A basic feature of equation 5.51 is its *Lt-invariance.* If we perform the operations

$$\begin{cases} L \to -L \\ t \to -t \end{cases} \tag{5.54}$$

the equation 5.51 remains invariant. Note that *if L is a possible Liouville operator so is $-L$.* On the other hand macroscopic equations involving thermodynamic quantities do not present such an invariance.

We have already seen that the time inversion (5.3) leads from the Fourier equation 5.2 to the anti-Fourier equation 5.4 (note that κ is positive and cannot be reversed). Similarly, the Boltzmann equation 5.5 has lost the Lt symmetry. Indeed if we perform a velocity inversion (which leads to $L \to -L$) together with a t inversion, Boltzmann's equation changes sign. This is due to the fact that the Boltzmann operator is even in the velocities (or equivalently in L).

How is then the Lt invariance, apparent on the Liouville equation (5.51), lost? As we shall see we can follow this process in detail and show that the symmetry breaking which indicates the appearance of irreversibility, is the consequence of causality when applied to large systems formed by many interacting degrees of freedom.

5.5 Causality and Irreversibility

Let us start with the Liouville equation 5.51. Its formal solution is

$$\rho(t) = \exp(-iLt)\rho(0) = \frac{1}{2\pi i}\int_C \mathrm{d}z \exp(-izt)\frac{1}{L-z}\rho(0) \tag{5.55}$$

In the case of the initial value problem the contour has to be traced in the *upper* half plane corresponding to the complex variable z[21], that is, for $\operatorname{Im} z > 0$; see figure 5.3*a*.

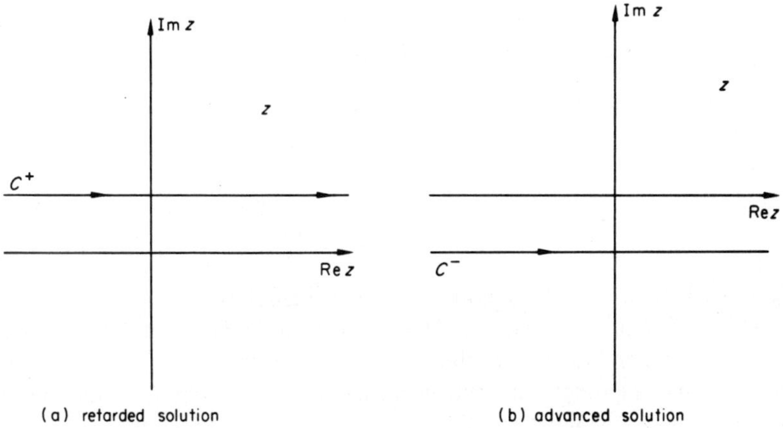

Figure 5.3

With this choice of the contour we calculate the retarded solution of the Liouville equation

$$\rho^r(t) = \frac{1}{2\pi i}\int_{C^+} \mathrm{d}z \exp(-izt)\frac{1}{L-z}\rho(0) \tag{5.56}$$

Similarly the *advanced* solution would be given by

$$\rho^a(t) = \frac{1}{2\pi i}\int_{C^-} \mathrm{d}z \exp(-izt)\frac{1}{L-z}\rho(0) \tag{5.57}$$

Both solutions satisfy the same differential equation. However causality leads to the two different integral representations 5.56 and 5.57. If the evaluation of the integrals 5.56 and 5.57 leads to a difference we may expect *thermodynamic behaviour*.

To proceed further let us remember that the concept of *collisions* plays a fundamental role in Boltzmann's kinetic equation. What we have to do therefore is first to introduce the idea of *processes* into the formulation of dynamics. For this purpose we define orthogonal hermitian projection operators P, Q such that

$$\mathrm{P}+\mathrm{Q}=1 \tag{5.58}$$

It is then easy to verify the identity for the resolvent $R(z) \equiv (L-z)^{-1}$ [23–25]:

$$R(z)=\{\mathrm{P}+\mathscr{C}(z)\}\frac{1}{\mathrm{P}L\mathrm{P}+\psi(z)-z}\{\mathrm{P}+\mathscr{D}(z)\}-\mathscr{P}(z) \tag{5.59}$$

with

$$\psi(z)=-\mathrm{P}L\mathrm{Q}\frac{1}{\mathrm{Q}L\mathrm{Q}-z}\mathrm{Q}L\mathrm{P} \tag{5.60}$$

$$\mathscr{D}(z)=-\mathrm{P}L\mathrm{Q}\frac{1}{\mathrm{Q}L\mathrm{Q}-z} \tag{5.61}$$

$$\mathscr{C}(z)=-\frac{1}{\mathrm{Q}L\mathrm{Q}-z}\mathrm{Q}L\mathrm{P} \tag{5.62}$$

$$\mathscr{P}(z)=-\frac{1}{\mathrm{Q}L\mathrm{Q}-z} \tag{5.63}$$

We have here the basic operators of our formulation of nonequilibrium statistical mechanics; the choice of the projection operators fixes the *language* in which we formulate our results. Generally P is chosen as projecting on to the diagonal elements in the representation in which some model-Hamiltonian $\mathscr{H}_0$ is diagonal

$$\langle m|\mathrm{P}\rho|n\rangle=\langle m|\rho|m\rangle\delta_{m,n} \tag{5.64}$$

For this reason $\mathrm{P}\rho$ is called the *vacuum of correlations*. Of special importance is the collision operator $\psi(z)$: reading equation 5.60 from right to left it corresponds to a transition from the vacuum of correlations, followed by a dynamical evolution in the correlation space, and finally followed by a return to the vacuum of correlations.

The operator $\psi(z)$ defines a *process* formed by a succession of interactions. As we shall see (equation 5.69) this process plays a role similar to that of collisions in the Boltzmann description. This is the reason we have called $\psi(z)$ the collision operator.

In the limit of large systems the sum over correlations involved in the collision operator is replaced by an integration (Cauchy integral, see[21]). In the retarded solution 5.56 $\psi(z)$ appears for z in the upper half plane. However when we perform the integration we shall pick singularities of $\psi(z)$ in the lower half plane where $\psi(z)$ is defined through analytic continuation. In the case of the advanced solution 5.57 the singularities obtained by analytic continuation lie on the contrary in the upper half plane. It is precisely the contribution of such singularities which leads to damping in the future for the retarded solution and in the past for the advanced solution.

When we introduce the formal decomposition 5.59 into equation 5.56 we derive directly the *master equation* for the density matrix ρ[21]. For the diagonal elements ρ_0 of ρ we obtain

$$i\frac{\partial \rho_0(t)}{\partial t} = \int_0^t \mathrm{d}\tau \mathscr{G}(t-\tau)\rho_0(\tau) + \mathscr{F}(t;\, \mathrm{Q}\rho(0)) \tag{5.65}$$

where

$$\mathscr{G}(t) = \frac{1}{2\pi i}\int_C \mathrm{d}z \exp(-izt)\psi(z) \tag{5.66}$$

and

$$\mathscr{F}(t;\, \mathrm{Q}\rho(0)) = \frac{1}{2\pi i}\int_C \mathrm{d}z \exp(-izt)\mathscr{D}(z)\mathrm{Q}\rho(0) \tag{5.67}$$

It should be emphasised that the master equation 5.65 is exact. No approximations have been introduced in its derivation from the Liouville equation.

Let us compare equation 5.65 to Boltzmann's kinetic equation 5.5. We see that there are two main differences. One is the *non-local* character of the collision operator in equation 5.65, as the time change at t depends on the previous history of the system (*non-markoffian* equation). The second one is the occurrence of the memory term $\mathscr{F}$ depending on the initial correlations. The master equation 5.65 has been applied successfully to many interesting problems†. It has also been shown that it describes correctly the evolution of a system both *before* and *after* velocity inversion[26,27]. Suppose that we start at $t = 0$ with no correlations. During the evolution from 0 to t_0 the diagonal elements evolve according to equation 5.65 (with $\mathscr{F} = 0$); correlations appear progressively as the result of the interactions. However, when we invert the velocities at $t = t_0$ we form a new ensemble. In the subsequent evolution from t_0 till $2t_0$ the memory term $\mathscr{F}$ plays an essential role as inversion of velocities leads to long range correlations. At time $2t_0$ we recover the original state at $t = 0$ with reversed velocities.

Let us now consider the limiting case in which equation 5.65 reduces to a local description. We proceed formally in the following way: we neglect the

† See the work of P. Résibois, M. De Leener and others in *Physica* and *Phys. Rev.* during the years 1966, 1969 and 1971.

memory term $\mathscr{F}$ and assume that

$$\int_0^t d\tau \mathscr{G}(\tau)\rho_0(t-\tau) \simeq \int_0^t d\tau \mathscr{G}(\tau)\rho_0(t) \simeq \left[\int_0^\infty d\tau \mathscr{G}(\tau)\right]\rho_0(t) \tag{5.68}$$

Then equation 5.65 takes the Boltzmannian *local* form

$$i\frac{\partial \rho_0}{\partial t} = \psi(0)\rho_0 \tag{5.69}$$

with

$$\psi(0) = \lim_{z\to +i\varepsilon}\left[-\mathrm{P}L\mathrm{Q}\frac{1}{\mathrm{Q}L\mathrm{Q}-z}\mathrm{Q}L\mathrm{P}\right] \tag{5.70}$$

(P has been chosen in such a way that PLP vanishes). We see that $\psi(0)$ plays indeed the role of Boltzmann's collision operator. It has a specially simple physical meaning in the case of scattering. The matrix elements (in momentum representation) $\langle p|\psi(0)|p'\rangle$ give then directly the scattering cross-section for the transition $p \to p'$[28].

Let us now indicate how this formulation leads to the breaking of the time invariance symmetry. In the limit of large systems, the sum over the intermediate states Q (the *correlations*) involves an integration. Therefore, a formal representation of equation 5.70 is given by[29]

$$-i\psi(0) = -\pi \mathrm{P}L\mathrm{Q}\delta(\mathrm{Q}L\mathrm{Q})\mathrm{Q}L\mathrm{P} + i\mathrm{P}L\mathrm{Q}\frac{1}{\mathrm{Q}L\mathrm{Q}}\mathrm{Q}L\mathrm{P} \tag{5.71}$$

where the second term is understood to be a principal part. If this formal expression is meaningful and each of the two terms exists, it follows by inspection that

(1) $-i\psi(0)$ is split into an even and an odd part in respect to L inversion

$$\psi(0) = \psi^{e}(0) + \psi^{o}(0) \tag{5.72}$$

(2) The even part is a negative operator

$$-i\psi^{e}(0) \leqslant 0 \tag{5.73}$$

(3) The even part $i\psi^{e}(0)$ is hermitian, while $i\psi^{o}(0)$ is antihermitian.

All these three properties are quite important. First of all if the even part $\psi^{e}(0)$ exists, the master equation 5.69 obviously loses its Lt invariance.

We indeed obtain after Lt inversion

$$i\frac{\partial \rho_0}{\partial t} = [-\psi^{e}(0) + \psi^{o}(0)]\rho_0$$

This is precisely what we would have found if in equation 5.55 we would have taken the contour below the real axis and constructed the *advanced* solutions. The situation is quite similar to that which we discussed in section 5.4 for the Fourier equation or the Boltzmann equation.

The inequality 5.73 shows that the even part may be considered as expressing a *damping* which occurs in the future in equation 5.56, and in the past in equation 5.57. For more details see[2].

We may even go further and show that inequality 5.73 contains, in a nutshell, the second law of thermodynamics, equation 5.1. We shall come back to this aspect in section 5.7.

Finally, the third property (hermicity of $i\psi^e(0)$) permits to give it at least in simple cases an interpretation as transition probabilities in the sense of a Markoff chain[2,30].

We see how deeply dynamics is altered when the collision operator $\psi(0)$ does not vanish. The appearance of an even part in L inversion leads to a radical change in the dynamic description of the system.

We have at present established the existence of $i\psi^e(0)$ for N body systems in the thermodynamic limit $N \to \infty$, $V \to \infty$, $N/V = \text{constant}$ using formal perturbation expansions. Also for simple field theoretical situations $i\psi^e(0)$ can be calculated rigorously without any perturbation expression[30,31]

We shall call *dynamic dissipative systems* systems such that

$$i\psi^e(0) \neq 0 \tag{5.74}$$

exists and is different from zero. Note that for quantum mechanical systems with discrete nondegenerate spectrum, ψ^e vanishes. In this case $(L-z)^{-1}$ has separate poles on the real axis and the two solutions 5.56 and 5.57 coincide.

As could be expected it is only in the limit of large systems that a system may become *dissipative.*

In summary, the remarkable feature of dissipative systems is that the equations of motion have two contributions one odd and the other even in L. This permits us to separate on the microscopic level *reversible* contributions from *irreversible* ones. The aim of the general theory summarised in the next section is to make this separation quite explicit without limiting us to the special case, equation 5.64, discussed until now.

5.6 Causal Dynamics

Transformation theory is an essential part of classical or quantum mechanics. The most important class of transformations in quantum mechanics are unitary transformations which lead to a representation in which the Hamiltonian is diagonal. Similarly, in classical mechanics we may often go to a cyclic Hamiltonian through a canonical transformation. Such transformations leave invariant the average value $\langle A \rangle$ of an observable A which is given in quantum mechanics as

$$\langle A \rangle = \operatorname{tr} \rho^{\dagger} A \tag{5.75}$$

The remarkable feature is that there exists a more general class of transformations $\Lambda(L)$ which still leaves equation 5.75 invariant, but separates neatly the even and the odd terms (in L) in the evolution equation. Such transformations are introduced through the relations

$$\rho^{\mathrm{p}} = \Lambda^{-1}(L)\rho \tag{5.76}$$

$$A^{\mathrm{p}} = \Lambda^{-1}(-L)A \tag{5.77}$$

Notice that in the second relation we have replaced L by $-L$. Indeed both in classical and quantum mechanics the evolution equation of A is[21]

$$i\frac{\mathrm{d}A}{\mathrm{d}t} = -LA \tag{5.78}$$

This equation differs from equation 5.51 by the sign of L. The invariance of equation 5.75 implies the condition

$$\Lambda(L)\Lambda^{\dagger}(-L) = \Lambda^{\dagger}(-L)\Lambda(L) = 1 \tag{5.79}$$

We have called such transformations *star-unitary transformations* as we have introduced the notion star to denote the *combined operations of taking the hermitian conjugate and reversing L*[2,22]

$$\Lambda^{*}(L) = \Lambda^{\dagger}(-L) \tag{5.80}$$

Except in the case where $\Lambda(L)$ does not depend on the sign of L, star unitary transformations are *non*unitary transformations. Still they preserve the average values of observables. They correspond therefore to equivalent (but not unitary equivalent) representations of dynamics.

Let us consider the equations of motion in the physical representation ρ^{p}. Using equations 5,51, 5.75 and 5.80 we obtain immediately for the retarded solution in the physical representation

$$i\frac{\partial \rho^{\mathrm{p}}}{\partial t} = \phi\rho^{\mathrm{p}} \tag{5.81}$$

with

$$\phi = \Lambda^{*}L\Lambda \tag{5.82}$$

$$\phi^{\mathrm{e}}(L) = \phi^{\mathrm{e}}(-L) \tag{5.83}$$

As we did for the collision operator in section 5.5, we may always decompose ϕ into an even part and an odd part with

$$\phi^{\mathrm{o}}(L) = -\phi^{\mathrm{o}}(-L) \tag{5.84}$$

Then equation 5.81 becomes

$$i\frac{\partial\rho^{\mathrm{p}}}{\partial t} = (\phi^{\mathrm{e}} + \phi^{\mathrm{o}})\rho^{\mathrm{p}} \tag{5.85}$$

The Lt symmetry of the Liouville equation is broken if and only if the even part ϕ^{e} may be defined and does not vanish.

We can make some general statements about the structure of ϕ. The hermiticity of L, equation 5.53, together with the star-unitarity of Λ (see equation 5.79) implies that ϕ has a basic invariance property

$$[i\phi(-L)]^{\dagger} = i\phi(L) \tag{5.86}$$

Introducing again the *star* notation, equation 5.80, we may say that $i\phi$ is a *star-hermitian operator*. Star-hermiticity may be realised in two ways

(1) Hermiticity together with positive parity in respect to L inversion.
(2) Antihermiticity together with negative parity in respect to L inversion.

In this terminology the collision operator $i\psi(0)$ as given in equation 5.70 is a star-hermitian operator. Each of its two parts corresponds to one of the two possible realisations of star-hermiticity.

There is one more basic property of $-i\psi(0)$ that we mentioned in section 5.5; it is the fact that its even part is a negative operator. This is also true for $-i\phi$.

Now the evolution of dynamic dissipative systems may be described in terms of a Liapounoff function. Let us consider the quadratic functional *in the physical representation* (we drop the superscript p)

$$\Omega = \operatorname{tr} \rho^{\dagger} \rho \tag{5.87}$$

It is easy to show, using equation 5.85, that

$$\frac{1}{2}\frac{\mathrm{d}\Omega}{\mathrm{d}t} = -\operatorname{tr} \rho^{\dagger}(i\phi^{\mathrm{e}})\rho \leqslant 0 \tag{5.88}$$

In the initial representation satisfying the Liouville equation Ω would be a constant. It is the fact that the two representations are linked through a *non*unitary transformation which makes the introduction of the Liapounoff function Ω possible.

We are therefore back to a situation quite similar to that which we studied in the case of the MacKean model in section 5.3 (see equations 5.42 and 5.43). The basic difference is that here we start from dynamics and we show that the symmetry breaking expressed by the appearance of operators even in L leads to a decrease of the quadratic functional Ω.

The fundamental new feature of the evolution equation 5.85, is that the dynamic evolution is now decomposed into two parts one of which may be, through equation 5.88, linked to irreversible processes decreasing the value of the Liapounoff function. The distinction between reversible and irreversible processes appears now explicitly in dynamics. Therefore, as we mentioned, the second law becomes in this way a theorem in dynamics valid for a well-defined class of dynamic systems that is essentially, the systems which satisfy the dissipativity condition 5.74.

5.7 Approach to Microcanonical Equilibrium—Statistical Model of Entropy

Let us come back to the Liapounoff function introduced in equation 5.87. Using the notation

$$\rho_{ij} \equiv \rho_{i-j}\left(\frac{i+j}{2}\right) \equiv \rho_\nu(N) \tag{5.89}$$

we may write Ω more explicitly

$$\Omega = \sum_{ij} \rho_{ij}^\dagger \rho_{ij} = \sum_N \rho_0^2(N) + \sum_{\nu N} |\rho_\nu(N)|^2 \tag{5.90}$$

Ω therefore includes both the diagonal elements ρ_0 and the off-diagonal elements ρ_ν (the *correlations*). The distribution function is assumed to be normalised

$$\operatorname{tr} \rho = \sum_N \rho_0(N) = 1 \tag{5.91}$$

It is obvious that the minimum of equation 5.90 subject to the constraint (5.91) is given by

$$\begin{cases} \rho_0(N) = \text{constant independent of } N \\ \rho_\nu(N) = 0 \end{cases} \tag{5.92}$$

We see that statistical equilibrium has then a very simple meaning. *All quantum states have the same probability and random phases.*

As in the MacKean model studied in section 5.3 we may now introduce the $\mathscr{H}$-quantity defined through

$$\mathscr{H} - \mathscr{H}_{\text{eq}} = \tfrac{1}{2} \ln \frac{\operatorname{tr} \rho^\dagger \rho}{(\operatorname{tr} \rho^\dagger \rho)_{\text{eq}}} \tag{5.93}$$

This corresponds then to the entropy given by

$$S = -k\mathscr{H} \tag{5.94}$$

The definition 5.93 satisfies all conditions known to us. Indeed

$$\mathcal{H} - \mathcal{H}_{\text{eq}} \geqslant 0$$

$$\frac{\mathrm{d}\mathcal{H}}{\mathrm{d}t} \leqslant 0 \tag{5.95}$$

also $\mathcal{H}$ is an additive function for independent systems.

Moreover the factor 1/2 in equation 5.93 ensures that, as in the MacKean model, this expression gives in the neighbourhood of equilibrium identical results to the Boltzmann expression[2, 19]. The term $(\operatorname{tr} \rho^{\dagger} \rho)_{\text{eq}}$ has a simple meaning, because at equilibrium by virtue of equation 5.92

$$(\operatorname{tr} \rho^{\dagger} \rho)_{\text{eq}} = \frac{1}{\nu} \tag{5.96}$$

where ν is the common value of $\rho_0(N)$. Because of the normalisation, equation 5.91, ν is equal to the number of accessible quantum states.

As already mentioned it is essential that we express ρ in the physical representation; if we do not, equation 5.94 would be a constant in time.

The remarks we presented when discussing the MacKean model are also valid here. The general $\mathcal{H}$-quantity describes the approach of the system to microcanonical equilibrium. It is a nonlinear functional of ρ and the limit to large systems has to be understood as in equation 5.48.

This $\mathcal{H}$-quantity can only decrease in time *whatever the initial* conditions. This is of course a basic difference from Boltzmann's definition, which even for dilute gases requires initial conditions compatible with the validity of the kinetic equations.

Finally, it is important that correlations are included in equation 5.94 as seen from equation 5.90. Let us emphasise that in agreement with equation 5.92 there are no *equilibrium* correlations in the causal formulation. Equilibrium correlations which would appear in other representations are here *included* in the diagonal elements. The correlations which are part of the entropy, equation 5.94, are therefore *nonequilibrium* correlations which ultimately die out. This separation between *natural* correlations included in the diagonal elements and transient correlations introduced by initial conditions, is of course very important.

Let us now illustrate these conclusions by showing that with our new statistical definition of entropy the Loschmidt paradox we have discussed in section 5.2 disappears.

5.8 Applications to Negative Time Evolution—The Resolution of Loschmidt's Paradox

Let us now come back to the velocity inversion experiment (see figure 5.2) and let us now represent $\mathcal{H}$, defined through equation 5.93, as a function of time. Suppose first we start at $t = 0$ with a state without correlations ($\rho_v = 0$) and isotropic velocity distribution. During time 0 to t_0, the diagonal elements tend to their equilibrium distribution. This gives rise to a decrease of $\mathscr{H}$. At time t_0 we reverse the velocities. This introduces *long range nonthermodynamical correlations* $\rho_v \neq 0$. As a consequence of this external action on the system, $\mathscr{H}$ increases. The system is ordered. During the time t_0 to $2t_0$ the abnormal correlations progressively die out. The details of the calculations are given elsewhere[2]. The time variation of $\mathscr{H}$ is represented schematically in figure 5.4. At time $2t_0$ the system is in the same state as at $t = 0$, but with reversed velocities. At $t = 0$ the system had an isotropic velocity distribution, so this is the same state.

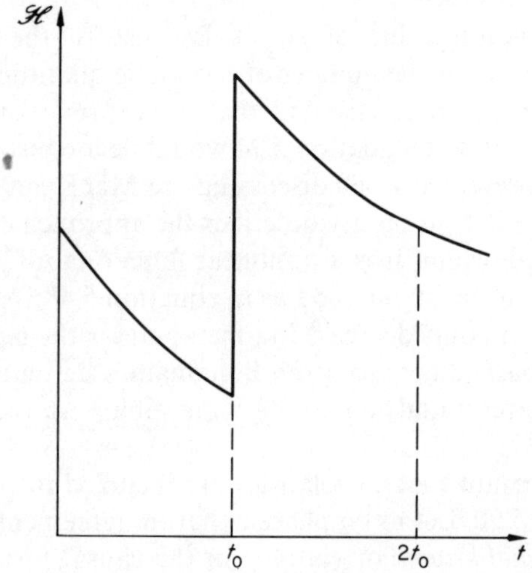

Figure 5.4 Time variation of $\mathscr{H}$ *as defined in equation 5.93.*

We have thermodynamic behaviour even when Boltzmann's model of entropy would predict *antithermodynamic* behaviour. We can now consider the entropy balance for the thermodynamic cycle over the time interval 0 to $2t_0$

$$\oint \mathrm{d}S = \oint \mathrm{d}_i S + \oint \mathrm{d}_e S = 0 \tag{5.97}$$

where $\mathrm{d}_i S$ is the entropy production and $\mathrm{d}_e S$ the entropy flow. As the entropy production is now positive everywhere in agreement with the second law, the entropy flow has to be negative. This corresponds to a flow of *information* received by the system.

The sign of the entropy flow can be directly calculated from equation 5.93 and we may verify that it is negative. These conclusions remain true even if we start with an arbitrary initial state (no more isotropic in the velocities, and which may include initial correlations). The cycle may then, for example, be represented by figure 5.5.

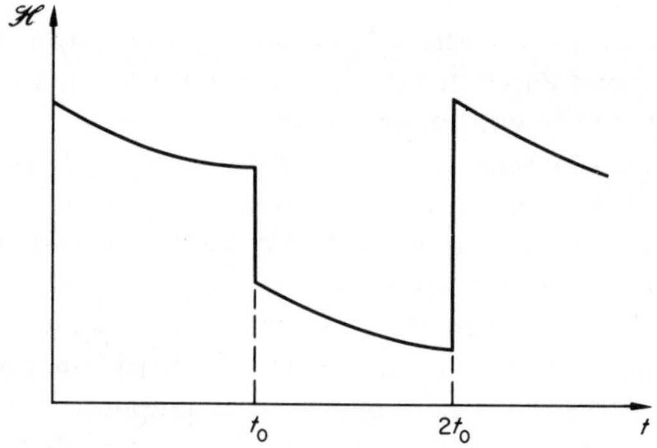

Figure 5.5

Velocity inversion at time t_0 brings the system *nearer* to thermodynamic equilibrium (by destroying partially the abnormal correlations which existed at time $t = 0$). We have to introduce a second velocity inversion at time $2t_0$ to bring back the system to the initial state. Whatever the initial conditions the total entropy flow for the complete cycle is again negative[2].

We can therefore calculate the thermodynamic prize for cycles involving *negative time evolution.* Of course the *prize of rejuvenation* is a functional of the initial state.

5.9 General Discussion

The result of our approach is a unified formulation of dynamics and thermodynamics. In the time evolution of the density ρ as described by equation 5.85 we may distinguish a *reversible* part given by ϕ^o and an *irreversible* one given by ϕ^e. It is this irreversible one which is responsible according to equation 5.88 for the time change of the Liapounoff function and therefore of the entropy.

It seems to us quite remarkable that the distinction of natural processes into two classes, the reversible and the irreversible ones, finds its transcription in the appearance of two classes of evolution operators. This distinction does not appear in the initial Hamiltonian formulation of dynamics as expressed by the Liouville equation 5.51, but becomes explicit through the nonunitary transformations 5.76 and 5.77.

In this way we obtain an explicit and general expression for entropy and entropy production. This appears to us to be an important result. Let us recall that the phenomenological formulation of the second law

$$dS = d_e S + d_i S \qquad d_i S \geqslant 0 \tag{5.98}$$

where $d_e S$ is the entropy flow and $d_i S$ the entropy production, is incomplete in the sense that classical thermodynamics does not provide us with a means to calculate explicitly the entropy production.

This has no serious consequence for equilibrium thermodynamics (thermostatics) where the mere *existence* of the positive entropy production is enough to drive the system to the equilibrium we want to study. But for non-equilibrium thermodynamics this has serious consequences.

We have to add supplementary assumptions to obtain a macroscopic expression for the entropy production. In our work on nonequilibrium thermodynamics we used the *local equilibrium* assumption[7] which leads then to the well-known bilinear expression for the entropy production

$$\frac{d_i S}{dt} = \sum_\rho J_\rho X_\rho \geqslant 0 \tag{5.99}$$

However, how do we extend the local equilibrium region? Or should one try to develop an entropy free thermodynamics? These questions are widely debated in the literature.

We can now investigate these questions on a more fundamental level.

(1) For equilibrium our definition (see equation 5.96)

$$\mathscr{H}_{\text{eq}} = \ln \operatorname{tr} \rho^+ \rho = -\lg v \tag{5.100}$$

gives the usual statistical interpretation. The entropy measures the number of accessible quantum states.

(2) For nonequilibrium in the local equilibrium range it gives the usual formula 5.99[32].

(3) For arbitrary states far from equilibrium the entropy (and the entropy production) depends on the complete specification of the density ρ. No macroscopic expression of the entropy can be expected to hold then. However, if the time dependence of the density function ρ may be absorbed in terms of macroscopic parameters $\{\alpha(t)\}$ then

$$\tilde{\rho}(q, p, t) = \tilde{\rho}(\{\alpha(t)\}, p, q) \tag{5.101}$$

and we have

$$S = S(\{\alpha(t)\}) \qquad \text{and} \qquad \frac{d_i S}{dt} = P(\{\alpha(t)\}) \tag{5.102}$$

The question is therefore: when can one find selfreproducing forms of the distribution function in which the time evolution is *parametrised* in a set of quantities $\alpha(t)$. We have studied an example in a recent publication[19] but much work remains to be done as this is the basic condition for the existence of a *macroscopic* formulation (in terms of the $\{\alpha(t)\}$) of the second law of thermodynamics.

Obviously we can go much further than the local equilibrium condition, as we should be able to introduce in the $\{\alpha(t)\}$ functions which may vanish at equilibrium.

(4) In special situations such as dilute gases there may be various *models*, of entropy such as equations 5.6 and 5.93.

At equilibrium and near equilibrium they are all equivalent. Further away from equilibrium it seems reasonable to consider equation 5.93 as the natural microscopic model for entropy, as it is the only expression which has a validity independently of any assumption about the physical nature of the mechanism involved in the interactions. The only condition used in its derivation is the dissipativity condition which introduces the difference between reversible and irreversible processes. On the contrary the Boltzmann definition, equation 5.6, does not extend to more general situations and can therefore not be used as a model for a law such as the second law of thermodynamics, whose most conspicuous characteristic is precisely its remarkable generality.

We have emphasised until now the importance of our formulation for thermodynamics. Inversely, however there are fundamental problems of dynamics which may be investigated from this new point of view. The transformation to the causal formulation of dynamics, which we have discussed briefly in section 5.6, is a generalisation of unitary transformations to which it reduces for nondissipative systems. This transformation makes explicit the part of the interaction which leads to a redefinition of dynamic variables (such as the introduction of appropriate action-angle variables) and the part which leads to irreversible processes and increases the entropy of the system. We are here at the heart of some of the most fascinating problems of modern physics, as it is in this way that we may hope to obtain a description of nature in which we may speak both of well-defined excitations (or *elementary particles*) and of interactions between these excitations. To separate these two parts, to speak meaningfully of *entities* and their *interactions* we need precisely the distinction between reversible and irreversible processes[33]. It is certainly very gratifying to find that basic aspects of nature can be understood only by using concepts originating in both dynamics and thermodynamics.

Acknowledgments

The ideas summarised in this report are the outcome of the work by the members of our group in Brussels and Austin. The specific aspects considered here have been developed and discussed in papers written in collaboration with Professors C. George, A. Grecos, F. Henin, G. Nicolis and L. Rosenfeld.

This research is being supported by the Fonds de la Recherche Collective (Belgium) and the R. Welch Foundation (Houston, Texas, USA).

References

1. I. Prigogine. *Physica*, **15** (1949), 272
2. I. Prigogine, C. George, F. Henin and L. Rosenfeld. *Chemica Scripta*, **4** (1973), 5
3. I. Prigogine. *The Development of the Physicist's Conception of Nature in the Twentieth Century*, ed. by J. Mehra, Reidel, Dordrecht-Holland (1973), p. 697, 561
4. I. Prigogine. Proceedings of the International Symposium *100 Years Boltzmann Equation*, ed. by E. G. D. Cohen and W. Thirring, *Acta Physica Austriaca*, Suppl. X, Springer Verlag (1973), p. 401
5. I. Prigogine. Irreversibility as a symmetry breaking process. *Nature* (1973), **246**, 67–71
6. M. Planck. *Vorlesungen über Thermodynamik*, Berlin and Leipzig, Walter de Gruyter (1930), p. 83
7. P. Glansdorff and I. Prigogine. *Structure, Stability and Fluctuations*, Wiley-Interscience (1971)
8. L. Boltzmann. Weitere studien über das wärmegleichgewicht unter gasmolekülen. *Wien Ber.*, **66** (1872), 275. See *Wissenschaftliche Abhandlungen*, Verlag von Johann Ambrosius Barth, Leipzig, **1** (1909)
9. L. Boltzmann. Der zweite hauptsatz der mechanische wärmetheorie. In *Populäre Schriften*, Verlag von Johan Ambrosius Barth, Leipzig (1919), p. 25
10. J. O. Hirschfelder, C. F. Curtiss and R. B. Bird. *The Molecular Theory of Gases and Liquids*, Wiley, New York (1959)
11. B. J. Alder and T. E. Wainwright. *J. Chem. Phys.*, **33** (1960), 1434
12. A. Bellemans and J. Orban. *Phys. Lett.*, **24A** (1967), 620
13. J. Loschmidt. *Wien Ber.*, **73** (1876), 139
14. P. and T. Ehrenfest. Begriffliche grundlagender statistischen auffasung der mechanik. *Encycl. Math. Wissenschafter*, **4** (1911), 4
15. M. Kac. Foundations of kinetic theory. Proc. Third Berkeley Symp. on *Math. Stat. and Prob.*, vol. III (1956), 171
16. M. Kac. *Probability and Related Topics in Physical Sciences*, Interscience, New York (1959)
17. H. P. MacKean Jr. *J. of Comb. Theory*, **2** (1967), 358
18. M. Kac. Some probabilistic aspects of the Boltzmann equation. Proc. of the International Symposium *100 Years Boltzmann Equation, Acta Physica Austriaca*, Supp. X, Springer Verlag (1973), 379
19. F. Henin and I. Prigogine, *P.N.A.S.*, to appear 1974; F. Henin, *Physica*, to appear 1974; F. Henin, *Ac. Roy. Belg., Bull. Cl. Sc.* to appear 1974
20. C. George, I. Prigogine and L. Rosenfeld. *Koningl. Dansk. Vid. Mat-fys. Medd.*, **38** (1972), 12
21. I. Prigogine, *Non Equilibrium Statistical Mechanics*, Wiley-Interscience, New York (1962)

22. C. George, *Physica*, **65** (1973), 277
23. M. Baus. *Acad. Roy. Belg. Bull. Cl. Sc.*, **53** (1967), 1291, 1332, 1352
24. L. Lanz and L. A. Lugiato. *Physica*, **44** (1969), 532
25. A. Grecos. *Physica*, **51** (1970), 50
26. I. Prigogine and P. Résibois. *Atti del Simposio Lagrangiano*, Academia delle Scienze, Torino (1964)
27. R. Balescu. *Physica*, **36** (1967), 433
28. F. Mayné and I. Prigogine. *Physica*, **63** (1973), 1
29. M. Baus. Thesis, Free University of Brussels (1968)
30. M. de Haan and F. Henin. *Physica*, **67** (1973), 197
31. G. Stey. *Physica*, **68** (1973), 273
32. G. Nicolis, J. Wallenborn and M. G. Velarde. *Physica*, **43** (1969), 263
33. I. Prigogine, C. George, A. Grecos. *P.N.A.S.*, to appear 1974
34. A. Grecos and I. Prigogine. *Physica*, **59** (1972), 77
35. A. Grecos and I. Prigogine. *P.N.A.S.*, **69** (1972), 1629

Discussion

PORTELA

I suppose that some restrictions have to be made regarding the distributions to which the formalism is applicable, because the image space used is a manifold with all the topological properties of such a space, and the Stieltjes–Laplace transform is not able to *regularise* all types of distributions.

As the cartesian product $H \times H$ does not inherit the properties of H, some sort of declarations should be made to render this product a *space*.

Distributions of microstructures are conceptually associated with a certain space–time dimension. If the paraleltrope is too small, distributions of microstructures are not significant, if too big, the variance of distribution is too big!

PRIGOGINE

I agree completely with the first remark. It is essential to consider initial distributions leaving some regularity properties. This problem is of great importance for the definition of the invariants of motion (see Grecos and Prigogine[34,35]). We can only prove the approach to equilibrium if specific restrictions on smoothness and regularity are made. I do not feel competent to comment on purely mathematical aspects but these questions are studied in various recent papers in which the mathematical structure of our approach has been analysed, (see Kummer, *Physica*, **65** (1973), 469; Shimizu, *Prog. Th. Phys.*, **47** (1972), 1181; Bongaarts, Fannes and Verbeure preprint; Alberti, Cotta-Ramusion and Ramella, preprint).

MÜLLER

We have heard from Professor Prigogine some remarks about the possibility or impossibility of writing the entropy as a function of a few macroscopic variables in a materially dependent manner. I realise the problem here, but I do not understand why entropy is singled out—from other constitutive quantities—as the object of these doubts. After all, according to the kinetic theory the heat flux and the stress are also not related to only a few derivatives of the macroscopic thermodynamic fields of density, velocity and temperature; and in fact, were it not for approximations such as the Burnett equation, we would not have any relation between the stress (say) and the macroscopic fields.

In the case of a monatomic dilute gas can you write down the new entropy function defined by you in terms of Boltzmann's distribution function, and how does it look?

PRIGOGINE

I believe that the two questions are discussed in my paper. I have indeed emphasised there that the quantity which plays the role of the *dynamic Liapounoff function* and which can be related to entropy, is obtained by a quite different limiting procedure than the reduced distribution functions. In other words, the heat flow is a linear functional of reduced distribution functions while the entropy is a nonlinear functional of the complete distribution function. Concerning the second question it is only near equilibrium that the new entropy function can always be expressed in terms of the Boltzmann velocity distribution functions. Whenever this is possible (in the near equilibrium linearised case) the dynamic entropy, as I defined it, coincides for a monoatomic gas with the Boltzmann entropy. For more details consult reference 19.

DOMINGOS

The outstanding lecture by Professor Prigogine is an essential contribution to this symposium because we are trying to make the bridge between microscopic and macroscopic continuum thermodynamics, and only a very small number of people are able to comprehend the whole subject. Professor Prigogine is one such person. Because most of us have a fundamental background in continuum mechanics and macroscopic thermodynamics, I am afraid that such a complete exposition on microscopic aspects will cause us to miss the answer to an essential question, which is: from a microscopic point of view, can we consider in continuum systems far from equilibrium the existence of a unique entropy?

PRIGOGINE

This question is discussed in section 5.9 of my paper (in the printed text this section has been enlarged).

GERMAIN

From my study of the local properties of shock waves in magnetofluid dynamics, I would say that the second law of thermodynamics gives us a quite general necessary condition of stability, but *that it may be not sufficient.* The stability requirement for a given problem is a very important question, and I agree completely with Professor Prigogine that the study of stability of steady states solution, bifurcation and study of the structure of the solutions, which do not belong to the thermodynamic branch, are among the most crucial problems of today. But they go beyond a purely thermodynamical problem. What is marvellous in the second law is its generality. But it may not be sufficient.

Does Professor Prigogine agree with this statement?

PRIGOGINE

I would say that the second law provides us with a necessary and sufficient condition of stability for *isolated systems*. A dissipative isolated system with broken *Lt* symmetry will reach, in time, the equilibrium state whatever the initial conditions (under some trivial restrictions such as regularity and so on...).

However, for nonisolated systems, the situation is quite different. There the stability of a steady state involves both thermodynamic and kinetic considerations.

6. Statistical Inequalities and Thermodynamics of Open Systems

F. Schlögl†

Abstract

A relative measure K for a probability distribution p with respect to a reference distribution p' turns out to be very useful in statistical thermodynamics of open systems. p' can describe the influence of the environment. With this notion the stability conditions of thermostatics are obtained directly. The Glansdorff–Prigogine stability criterion for steady nonequilibrium states, with the inclusion of final perturbations and Meixner's passivity conditions, can be deduced in statistical theory. K is connected with the probability of fluctuations in a stable steady state. That gives rise to relations between dynamics of small fluctuations and their correlations. With an adequate measure K for density matrices essentially all the results can be achieved by quantum theory. Heat capacity is related to another general statistical measure for probability distributions, and can be generalised to nonequilibrium states, especially to nonequilibrium phase transitions.

6.1 Introduction

Physical laws of the temporal evolution of a physical system in the normal case connect results of observations already made, with results of future observations. In classical physics of an isolated system these connections are sharp predictions if the initial observations are complete and fix a pure state. In quantum physics an initial maximal measurement does not allow sharp predictions for all kinds of future measurement, however, there always exists a certain kind of measurement for which the predictions are sharp. We say pure states are transformed in pure states by the temporal evolution of the system. For a certain kind of measurement, knowledge about the future result can decrease; it increases, however, for other measurements. Altogether no knowledge is lost.

Quantum dynamics in the formulation of the Schrödinger–von Neumann equation, or S-matrix, is not invariant with respect to time reversal. The correct time-inverted dynamics, however, also have physical meaning. They give an answer to a question into the past. If the result of a maximal

† RWTH Aachen, Institut für Theoretische Physik, Aachen, Germany.

measurement at a certain time is known, the time-inverted dynamics give the probabilities of results of an earlier made measurement (preparation) the kind of which is known, the results of which however are unknown (for instance not registrated). The direction of time which is distinguished by quantum dynamics is the direction of question (into future or past)[1].

Statistical physics is concerned with the situation that the initial observations are not complete. This is the normal case when a macroscopic system is described by macroscopic variables. The connections to future measurements become stochastic laws which can give only the probabilities of future results. In general, these laws are connected with a decreasing knowledge about the future results. For an isolated system, entropy is an adequate measure of the ignorance connected with the probabilities. Increase of entropy means irreversibility. Laws which describe the increase of entropy on a macroscopic level are not invariant with respect to time reversal. Time reversal leads to different laws. Here what was said for quantum dynamics is valid. The time reverted laws are not meaningless, but belong to the questions into the past, for instance in cosmology. If the momentary state is known only incompletely, the probabilities of earlier unknown states will be connected with increasing uncertainty, the farther back we look.

Isolated systems are an idealisation which can successfully be used in thermostatics but becomes more and more complicated in nonequilibrium thermodynamics, the more processes are included far away from equilibrium. Therefore, it seems reasonable to start with open systems and ask for the adequate measure of knowledge, or let me say of *quality of predictions*, connected with probabilities.

It is well known that entropy in thermostatics is connected with the bit-number

$$b_i = -\ln p_i \tag{6.1}$$

which is necessary to fix a pure state i if its probability is p_i. Entropy is the mean-value of this bit-number

$$S = \langle b \rangle = -\sum_i p_i \ln p_i \tag{6.2}$$

$-\langle b \rangle$ is called the *Shannon information measure*[2].

Here the pure states are described as denumerable. This is done only for simplicity. It is not, however, a serious restriction. The considerations can be done also without it. Denumerable states in classical physics can be realised by dividing the phase space into cells of equal phase volume.

For open systems yet another measure of knowledge seems to be adequate which compares two probability distributions p, p^0. This becomes plausible because the state of the environment brings some knowledge about the state of the system itself. For instance, if in thermostatics p^0 is the complete equilibrium, uniquely fixed by the environment, and p is a frozen equilibrium fixed by additional dates of the system itself, the question arises of how to measure the additional knowledge about the system itself.

Such a measure is given by the mean value of $b^0 - b$

$$K(p, p^0) = \langle b^0 - b \rangle = \sum_i p_i \ln \frac{p_i}{p_i^0} \tag{6.3}$$

This quantity is called *Kullback information measure* or *information gain*[3,4,5,6]. It has the following features

(1) Positive definiteness

$$K(p, p^0) \geqslant 0 \tag{6.4}$$

$$K(p, p^0) = 0 \quad \text{only for} \quad p \equiv p^0 \tag{6.5}$$

The proof is given by the inequality for positive x

$$\ln x \geqslant 1 - \frac{1}{x} \tag{6.6}$$

(2) Convexity: for infinitesimal variations δp_i the second order variation of K is positive

$$\delta^2 K = \tfrac{1}{2} \sum_i \frac{(\delta p_i)^2}{p_i} \geqslant 0 \tag{6.7}$$

(3) Monotony: in an adequate chosen space of independent parameters ξ which give a one to one mapping of all possible probability distributions p, over the same microstates

$$K(p, p^0) = L(\xi) \tag{6.8}$$

is a monotonous function. That means any surface in ξ-space on which L has constant values encloses only points and all points with smaller values L and no points with higher values L.

(4) If p, p' are subject to the same Pauli–Master equation

$$\dot{p}'_j = \sum_i l_{ji} p_i \tag{6.9}$$

(l_{ji} independent of p), then K never increases. As a rule it decreases.

The proof is possible generally for two Markov chains of first order and, with $t_2 > t_1$, is valid with the same transition matrix r

$$p_j(t_2) = \sum_i r_{ji} p_i(t_1) \tag{6.10}$$

$$p'_j(t_2) = \sum_i r_{ji} p'_i(t_1) \tag{6.11}$$

As r_{ji} is non-negative and

$$\sum_j r_{ji} = 1 \tag{6.12}$$

we get

$$K(p, p')_{t_1} - K(p, p')_{t_2} = \sum_{ij} r_{ji} p_i(t_1) \ln \frac{p_i(t_1)}{p_i'(t_1)} \frac{p_j'(t_2)}{p_j(t_2)} \tag{6.13}$$

With relation 6.6, we show that this expression is non-negative.

The statement (4) is given only as one of the illustrations of the role of the measure K in statistical physics. It is a generalisation of Boltzmann's $\mathscr{H}$-theorem but will not be used in the following analysis.

The special case that p^0 is equipartition over the microstates (for instance microcanonical distribution of an isolated system) leads back from K to entropy S. In this special case, K is the difference between S^0 and S.

The properties of the measure K allow very general and direct proofs of fundamental thermodynamical principles in the framework of a statistical theory of open systems. They give moreover the possibility of a revealing interpretation.

6.2 Thermostatics of Open Systems

In thermostatics certain macroscopic variables M^ν are in statistical theory mean values of observables M_i^ν which are defined in the microstates i

$$M^\nu \equiv \langle M^\nu \rangle = \sum_i M_i^\nu p_i \tag{6.14}$$

Let me call, in the following, such thermodynamic variables *direct variables*. A macroscopic thermostatic state can be described always by a set of such direct variables. To it corresponds a generalised *canonical distribution*

$$p_i = \exp(\phi - \lambda_\nu M_i^\nu) \tag{6.15}$$

It is the solution of the variational problem[7] to maximise entropy with fixed mean values M^ν. (Here and in the following we adopt the summation convention over equal sub and superscripts as ν in a product.) λ_ν are the intensive parameters conjugate to M^ν.

The more M^ν are given, the more the state p is a frozen equilibrium in comparison to a complete equilibrium p^0 in fixed environment.

$$K(p, p^0) = S^0 - S - \lambda_\nu^0 (M^{0\nu} - M^\nu) \geqslant 0 \tag{6.16}$$

gives very directly the equilibrium condition and stability conditions of thermostatics[8]. For instance, in the special form

$$S^0 - S - \frac{1}{T^0}(U^0 - U) - \frac{p^0}{T^0}(V^0 - V) \geqslant 0 \tag{6.17}$$

If p, p^0 are arbitrary thermostatic states, equation 6.16 gives the principle of Le Chatelier and Braun.

In macroscopic thermostatics such inequalities are deduced by including the environment, so that we get an isolated system. It should be stated that such procedures are not necessary in the deduction given here. K is attached only to the states of the system itself.

We can write the change of entropy

$$\Delta S \equiv S^0 - S = \Delta_I S + \Delta_E S \tag{6.18}$$

of the system during a process $p \to p^0$ where $\Delta_I S$ is the entropy produced in the interior of the system and $\Delta_E S$ the entropy exchanged with the environment. Then

$$K(p, p^0) = \Delta_I S \geqslant 0 \tag{6.19}$$

gives the positiveness of the produced entropy.

6.3 Entropy Production

If the environment remains unchanged and p^0 is the complete equilibrium with the environment and $p(t)$ is the changing state of the system

$$K(p(0), p^0) - K(p(t), p^0)$$

is the entropy produced in the interior of the system during the time t.

$$P = -\frac{\mathrm{d}}{\mathrm{d}t} K(p, p^0) \tag{6.20}$$

therefore is entropy production in the interior[8,9].

All changes of the probability distributions in the following are measured on a long time scale on which macroscopic changes can be observed. The restriction to systems for which a well-defined separation of a long time scale behaviour from microscopic time behaviour exists, is an essential condition for the following.

The central problem is to define the adequate probability distribution, $p(t)$, which corresponds to changing macroscopic variables $M^\nu(t)$. In several cases the generalised canonical distribution

$$p_i(t) = \exp\left[\phi(t) - \lambda_\nu(t) M_i^\nu\right] \tag{6.21}$$

constructed in any time t to the $M^{\nu}(t)$ will be an able approximation. We shall call it in the following the *accompagning canonical distribution* or *accompagning canonical ensemble*. It is, however, not the best adequate distribution because it neglects knowledge which comes from earlier states. The approximation tends to become worse, as memory effects play a greater role. It is good for slow processes without relaxations.

If we describe p by the accompagning ensemble, we get

$$P = (\lambda_{\nu} - \lambda_{\nu}^{0})\dot{M}^{\nu} = X_{\nu} I^{\nu} \tag{6.22}$$

This is a well-known form[10,11] where I^{ν} are the *rate fluxes* $\dot{M}^{\nu}$, and X_{ν} are the *forces* $\lambda_{\nu} - \lambda_{\nu}^{0}$. We can also justify this result, however, for so-called Mori–distributions[12] for hydrodynamical systems without relaxations. That shall be done in the more general framework of the following section.

6.4 Stability Criterion for Steady States

Nonequilibrium thermodynamics far away from equilibrium is called *nonlinear thermodynamics*, because transport equations become nonlinear in the deviations of equilibrium. It is a young field and brings very exciting new phenomena, namely the building up of dissipative structures[13]. These are special steady states.

Important questions in this field are, whether a steady state is stable against perturbations or fluctuations, and where the limits of stability are if perturbations become larger.

A simple example is a type of chemical reaction in an homogeneous reactor where all concentrations of reacting species are fixed by feeding and only one has variable concentration $n(t)$ and $\dot{n}$ is a nonmonotonous function of n of the type given in figure 6.1. There exist three steady states 1, 2, 3 but only 1, 2 are stable against small perturbations. 3 is unstable.

Such systems can show interesting dissipative structures if the variable concentration n is not homogeneous in the reactor, but can change in space by diffusion[14]. For such a system it was shown by theoretical analysis that the two steady states can behave like two coexistent phases, and separate in different spacial domains with minimal surface. The behaviour is very similar to that of droplets and bubbles, and the analogy to phase transitions of thermostatics goes in far more details. This kind of building up of domains as dissipative structures is a typical phenomenon of nonlinear thermodynamics. For nonequilibrium phase-transitions already other examples are known, such as laser-transition, Gunn-effect, parametric oscillator, and hydrodynamical instabilities[15–24].

It would be of great importance to find general principles in this new field of nonlinear thermodynamics but only a few are known. A central one is

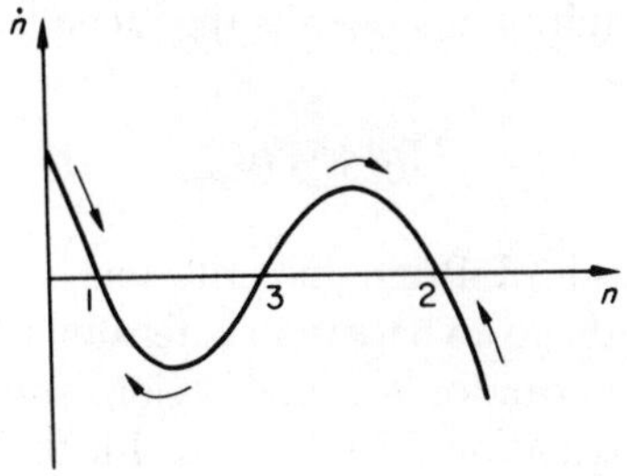

Figure 6.1

the stability criterion of Glansdorff and Prigogine[24] as a macroscopic principle.

It is possible to give a very general foundation of this criterion in statistical theory[25]. It is a criterion to be applied to given dynamics. In a statistical theory these dynamics give $p(t)$. If p^0 is a steady state, we seek stability regions round this state. As $K(p, p^0)$ is monotonous in an adequate parameter space ξ in which all possible p are represented in a one to one mapping, we can say

Any region round the steady state, given by

$$K \leqslant C$$

is a stability region if in it everywhere, at all time

$$\dot{K} \leqslant 0$$

K is used as a Liapounoff-function. So far, this criterion is applicable to any stochastic dynamics.

It can be formulated as a thermodynamic criterion under the very general conditions that there exists a theory in which the distribution p corresponds uniquely to the macroscopic state and the direct variables M^{ν} become additive for independent systems. Then with the statistical entropy of p

$$S = -\langle \ln p \rangle \tag{6.23}$$

and final deviations

$$\delta M^{\nu} = M^{\nu} - M^{0\nu} \tag{6.24}$$

the following is valid

$$K(p, p^0) = -\delta S + \left(\frac{\partial}{\partial M^{\nu}}(\delta S)\right)^0 \delta M^{\nu} = -\delta_{\mathrm{NL}} S \tag{6.25}$$

We call $\delta_{\mathrm{NL}} S$ the nonlinear part of the entropy variation. It is essential that M^{ν} are direct!

If the δM^ν become infinitesimal, $\delta_{NL}\dot{S}$ is the second variation $\delta^2\dot{S}$ of $\dot{S}$ and the criterion reduces to

$$\delta^2\dot{S} \geqslant 0 \tag{6.26}$$

This is the general Glansdorff–Prigogine criterion.

The form of the criterion given here is an extension to final deviations from the steady state, and is a criterion for final regions round the steady state.

Here S is defined by equation 6.23. If we call it thermodynamic entropy, the following is essential. So long as p is the accompagning canonical ensemble, S is connected with the M^ν as in thermostatics (Gibbs' equation). As was shown by H. K. Janssen[26] the same is true if p is the Mori-distribution for hydrodynamical systems without macroscopic relaxations. The Mori-distribution is constructed out of an accompagning canonical distribution $p^a(t)$ with the Liouville-operator L

$$p(t) = \exp(-iL\tau)p^a(t-\tau) \tag{6.27}$$

where τ is a time between long and short time scale. τ has to be long enough so that all irreversible fluxes are built up which are interrupted in p^a. On the other hand, τ has to be small compared with the times of macroscopic changes of the M^ν[12]. The shortness of time τ is also connected with the approximate description of the open system by an isolated one with an L. These conditions are fulfilled only for certain systems which are called hydrodynamical. The Mori-construction gives

$$p(t) = p^a(t)\exp\int_0^\tau \mathrm{d}s\, \lambda_\nu(t)\dot{M}^\nu(-s) \tag{6.28}$$

where
$$M^\nu(t) = \exp(-iLt)M^\nu \tag{6.29}$$

is a phase space function. Equivalent distributions were given also by McLennan[27] and Zubarev[28] by different arguments.

Macroscopic relaxations occur if internal degrees of freedom, which are relevant for a description without relaxations, are unknown and therefore not included in p^a. Then the conditions for the Mori-construction are not fulfilled[29] if the construction starts with p^a.

Glansdorff and Prigogine[24] have given still more special forms of the criterion for systems with localisable macroscopic variables and for moving material

$$\delta^2\,\dot{z} \geqslant 0 \tag{6.30}$$

$$z = s - \frac{1}{T^0}\tfrac{1}{2}v^2 \tag{6.31}$$

s is local entropy density, T^0 local temperature of the steady state, and v local velocity of the material.

This form of the criterion has been deduced by H. K. Janssen[26] as well, by the use of Mori-distribution. This deduction does not use the existence of local equilibria and shows that such an assumption is not necessary to justify the macroscopic criterion. A further result is the extension of the criterion to final deviations from the steady state.

In linear thermodynamics the Glansdorff–Prigogine criterion is always fulfilled and becomes the principle of minimal entropy production[30,31]. In linear thermodynamics the steady state is distinguished from other transport states by minimal value of P. Thus this principle as well finds a statistical foundation by these deductions without the assumption of the existence of local equilibria.

One additional remark: If we vary p, we get

$$\begin{aligned}\delta K(p, p^0) &\equiv K(p+\delta p, p^0) - K(p, p^0)\\ &= K(p+\delta p, p) - \sum_i \delta p_i \ln \frac{p_i}{p_i^0}\end{aligned} \tag{6.32}$$

Therefore, under the conditions formulated before equation 6.23 the non-linear part

$$\delta_{\mathrm{NL}} K(p, p^0) \doteq K(p+\delta p, p) = -\delta_{\mathrm{NL}} S \tag{6.33}$$

is non-negative and K becomes not only monotonous but moreover convex in the space of the M^ν. It is thus a convenient Liapounoff function in macroscopic theory.

6.5 Passivity

The comparison of two generalised canonical distributions p, p^0 changing with time gives

$$\dot{K}(p, p^0) = \int_{-\infty}^{t} dt\left[(\lambda_\nu^0 - \lambda_\nu)\dot{M}^\nu - \dot{\lambda}_\nu^0 (M^{0\nu} - M^\nu)\right] \geqslant 0 \tag{6.34}$$

if they were equal at time $-\infty$.

At first we assume that p^0 is the initial value of p at time $-\infty$, then λ_ν^0 are constant and we get

$$\int_{-\infty}^{t} dt'(\lambda_\nu^0 - \lambda_\nu(t'))\dot{M}^\nu(t') \geqslant 0 \tag{6.35}$$

This is a fundamental inequality which was given by J. Meixner[32] by macroscopic thermodynamic arguments, as a condition for passivity for a fluid medium without relaxations. The statistical deduction given here is very direct. It holds, however, only if the description of p as accompagning canonical ensemble is allowed.

J. Meixner [33,34] has given yet another inequality for fluid systems with relaxations

$$\int_{-\infty}^{t} dt'(\lambda_\alpha^0(t') - \lambda_\alpha(t'))\dot{M}^\alpha(t') \geq 0 \tag{6.36}$$

Here two kinds of local intensity parameters occur, dynamical λ and thermostatic λ^0. To understand this in statistical theory, Bausch[29] pointed out that we have to distinguish the observed macroscopic observables M^α from unobserved internal variables M^ξ. The whole set would allow macroscopic dynamics without retardation. Elimination of the internal variables brings relaxation. The λ^0 belong to the accompagning ensemble of the M^α alone. λ belongs to the whole set M. That means p is a frozen equilibrium compared with the unfrozen p^0. As all M^α are equal for the two ensembles, λ_ξ^0 vanish, and for the entropy S_I of the internal degrees of freedom is valid

$$\dot{S}_I = \lambda_\xi \dot{M}^\xi \tag{6.37}$$

we get from relation 6.34

$$\int_{-\infty}^{t} dt'(\lambda_\alpha^0(t') - \lambda_\alpha(t))\dot{M}^\alpha(t') \geq S_I(t) - S_I(-\infty) \tag{6.38}$$

If now the internal degrees of freedom change adiabatically, we get inequality 6.36.

Bausch[29] has given a statistical deduction by the use of Mori-distributions, and thus without the problematic use of the accompagning canonical ensemble. Moreover, he could precisely formulate the conditions for the validity of the inequality in local form without the assumption of the existence of local equilibria.

6.6 Probability of Fluctuations in a Steady State

If p^0 is a given distribution, describing for instance a steady state, then to another p corresponds a fluctuation. The probability of such a fluctuation can be expressed[35] by the probability of relative frequencies p_i in a large number N of observations. Then the p_i are interpreted as random variables. If N becomes large enough, the probability which can be gained by combinatorics becomes

$$w(p_1, p_2 \ldots) \sim \exp[-NK(p, p^0)] \tag{6.39}$$

Therefore the probability of a fluctuation p in state p^0 is

$$w(p) \sim \exp[-K(p, p^0)] \tag{6.40}$$

If we apply this formula to a microcanonical ensemble p^0, we get the well-known Einstein formula for fluctuations in a thermal equilibrium. If we apply it to a generalised canonical ensemble, we get a formula for a general class of thermostatic states given by Greene and Callen[36]

$$w \sim \exp(-\delta S + \lambda_\nu \delta M^\nu) \tag{6.41}$$

We can apply formula 6.40 also to a nonequilibrium stable steady state p^0.

Einstein's formula gives a connection of regression coefficients of deviations from equilibrium with autocorrelations of fluctuations. Equation 6.40 gives a similar connection for dynamics of small deviations from a stable nonequilibrium state [37,35]

$$\alpha^\mu = \delta M^\mu = M^\mu - M^{0\mu} \tag{6.42}$$

For small α we can assume linear equations of motion

$$\dot{\alpha}^\mu = L^{\mu\nu} X_\nu \tag{6.43}$$

with *forces* which are linear functions of the α's:

$$X_\nu = -\frac{\partial K}{\partial \alpha^\nu} = \frac{\partial}{\partial \alpha^\nu} \delta^2 S \tag{6.44}$$

For fluctuations α formula 6.40 gives

$$X_\nu = \frac{\partial}{\partial \alpha^\nu} \ln w \tag{6.45}$$

With the fluctuation regression hypothesis, that dynamics equation 6.43 is independent of the kind of formation of the α, this leads to

$$L^{\mu\nu} = -\langle \dot{\alpha}^\mu \alpha^\nu \rangle \tag{6.46}$$

where now the correlation-function on the right-hand side is a mean value in the nonequilibrium stable steady state, which can be far away from equilibrium.

6.7 Quantum Mechanics

In the previous sections all considerations were restricted to classical systems. The extension of most of the results to quantum systems, however, is possible. This is the case because a measure $K(\rho, \rho^0)$ for two density operators ρ, ρ^0 of the same system analogous to $K(p, p^0)$ of two probability distributions can be given[38].

To a given density operator

$$\rho = \sum_i |i > p_i < i| \tag{6.47}$$

is attached a Hermitian operator *bit-number*

$$b = -\ln \rho = -\sum_i |i > \ln p_i < i| \tag{6.48}$$

It is simultaneously diagonal with ρ and has the bit-numbers of the p_i as eigenvalues. The expectation value of b in ρ is defined as the statistical entropy of ρ

$$S = \langle b \rangle = -\mathrm{tr}\,(\rho \ln \rho) \tag{6.49}$$

The expectation value of the difference of bit-numbers of ρ and ρ^0 in ρ is

$$K(\rho, \rho^0) = \mathrm{tr}\,[\rho(\ln \rho - \ln \rho^0)] \tag{6.50}$$

It is the adequate measure for *gain of information* connected with the step from ρ^0 to ρ.

It can be shown that this measure has the following features

(1) Positive definiteness

$$K(\rho, \rho^0) \geqslant 0 \tag{6.51}$$

$$K(\rho, \rho^0) = 0 \quad \text{only for} \quad \rho = \rho^0 \tag{6.52}$$

(2) Convexity

$$\delta^2 K = \tfrac{1}{2} \sum_i \frac{(\delta p_i)^2}{p_i} \geqslant 0 \tag{6.53}$$

(3) Monotony: the definition here is more complicated. But all changes of ρ, ρ^0 which in principle can change the entropy can be parametrised by independent parameters ξ such that K is monotonous in ξ-space.

(4) With direct variables M^ν which become additive for independent systems the following is true

$$K(\rho, \rho^0) = -\delta S + \left(\frac{\partial}{\partial M^\nu} \delta S \right)^0 \delta M^\nu = -\delta_{\mathrm{NL}} S \tag{6.54}$$

in analogy to equation 6.25. δM^ν is the difference between the expectation values M^ν and $M^{0\nu}$ in the state ρ and ρ^0 respectively.

For generalised canonical thermostatic states

$$\rho = \exp\,[\phi - \lambda_\nu M^\nu] \tag{6.55}$$

where M^ν are observables (which may be noncommutable) the expectation values of which determine the state in macrophysics, we get

$$K(\rho, \rho^0) = S^0 - S - \lambda_\nu^0(\langle M^\nu\rangle^0 - \langle M^\nu\rangle) \geqslant 0 \tag{6.56}$$

in analogy to inequality 6.16.

The Glansdorff–Prigogine criterion in the generalised form holds in the same form as in classical physics.

A steady state ρ^0 has a stability region

$$\delta_{NL} S \geqslant C \tag{6.57}$$

if everywhere in it at all times is valid

$$\delta_{NL} \dot{S} \geqslant 0 \tag{6.58}$$

It can again be shown that the probability of a fluctuation ρ in a state ρ^0 is

$$w \sim \exp[-K(\rho, \rho^0)] \tag{6.59}$$

6.8 Fluctuations of Bit-numbers

The decision to measure the uncertainty which is connected with a probability p_i, by the bit-number b_i, brings also a remarkable interpretation of the quantity *heat capacity.*

For a given distribution the fluctuations of the bit-number in the different microstates i are

$$\Delta b_i = b_i - \langle b\rangle = b_i - S \tag{6.60}$$

The quadratic mean value may be called

$$Q = \langle(\Delta b)^2\rangle = \langle b^2\rangle - \langle b\rangle^2 \tag{6.61}$$

Its value for a generalised canonical distribution, equation 6.15, is

$$b_i = \lambda_\mu M_i^\mu - \phi \tag{6.62}$$

$$\Delta b_i = \lambda_\mu \Delta M_i^\mu \tag{6.63}$$

$$Q = \lambda_\mu \lambda_\nu \langle \Delta M^\mu \Delta M^\nu\rangle \tag{6.64}$$

Thus Q is connected with the correlations of the ΔM . It can also be written

$$Q = -\lambda_\mu \lambda_\nu \frac{\partial M^\mu}{\partial \lambda_\nu} \tag{6.65}$$

With
$$M^{\nu} = \frac{\partial \phi}{\partial \lambda_{\nu}} \tag{6.66}$$

$$\lambda_{\mu} \frac{\partial M^{\mu}}{\partial \lambda_{\nu}} = \frac{\partial}{\partial \lambda_{\nu}} (\lambda_{\mu} M^{\mu} - \phi) = \frac{\partial S}{\partial \lambda_{\nu}} \tag{6.67}$$

this gives
$$Q = -\lambda_{\nu} \frac{\partial S}{\partial \lambda_{\nu}} \tag{6.68}$$

When M^0 is chosen as internal energy, then

$$\lambda_0 = \beta = T^{-1} \tag{6.69}$$

with temperature T. It is now common to write

$$\lambda_{\nu} = \beta \alpha_{\nu} \tag{6.70}$$

and to choose β, α_{ν} as independent intensity variables. For instance, if M^1, M^2, M^3 are volume, magnetisation, particle number, then λ_1, $-\lambda_2$, $-\lambda_3$ are respectively pressure, magnetic field, and chemical potential. The change from the independent variables λ to the β, α gives

$$\beta \left(\frac{\partial S}{\partial \beta} \right)_{\alpha} = \beta \left(\frac{\partial \lambda_{\nu}}{\partial \beta} \right)_{\alpha} \frac{\partial S}{\partial \lambda_{\nu}} = \lambda_{\nu} \frac{\partial S}{\partial \lambda_{\nu}} \tag{6.71}$$

Thus
$$Q = T \left(\frac{\partial S}{\partial T} \right)_{\alpha} = C_{\alpha} \tag{6.72}$$

When the system does not exchange material with another system, then C_{α} is the heat capacity for fixed intensity parameters α_{ν} which occur in the generalised canonical distribution. In systems which can change its material composition, for instance its particle number, C_{α} is a generalised heat capacity.

By relation 6.72 the specific heat is distinguished from the other *susceptibilities*

$$X_{\nu} = -\frac{\partial M^{\nu}}{\partial \alpha_{\nu}} \tag{6.73}$$

This connection between heat capacity and Q for generalised canonical ensembles leads to a question in the field of dissipative structures. There analogies to phase transitions are found. In thermostatics, a phase transition in general is connected with a characteristic dramatic behaviour of specific heat. If now a process in nonlinear thermodynamics which shows the phenomenon of the nonequilibrium phase transition, can be described by a stochastic theory, then Q can be formed for the probabilities in this theory. The question arises: does Q behave dramatically at the phase transition? So far as we could study adequate models, this seems to be the case.

References

1. J. Rayski. Refined interpretation of quantum mechanics. Talk on *Symposium on Mathematical Physics*, University Torun, Poland, December 1972
2. C. Shannon and W. Weaver. *The mathematica! theorie of communication*, Urbana, Univ. of Illinois Press (1949)
3. S. Kullback. *Annals of Math. Statistics*, **22** (1951), 79
4. S. Kullback. *Information Theory and Statistics*, Wiley, New York (1951)
5. A. Rényi. *Wahrscheinlichkeitsrechnung*, VEB Deutscher Verlag der Wissenschaften, Berlin (1966)
6. A. Hobson and B. K. Cheng. *Journal of Statistical Physics*, **7** (1973), 301
7. E. T. Jaynes. *Phys. Rev.*, **106** (1957), 620
8. F. Schlögl. *Z. Physik*, **191** (1966), 81
9. F. Schlögl. *Z. Physik*, **198** (1967), 559
10. S. R. de Groot. *Thermodynamics of Irreversible Processes*, North-Holland Publ. Co., Amsterdam (1951)
11. J. Meixner and H. G. Reik. *Handbuch der Physik*, III, 2, Springer, Berlin-Göttingen-Heidelberg (1959)
12. H. Mori. *Phys. Rev.*, **115** (1959), 298
13. P. Glansdorff and I. Prigogine. *Structure, Stabilité et Fluctuations*, Masson, Paris (1971)
14. F. Schlögl. *Z. Physik*, **253** (1972), 147
15. R. Graham and H. Haken. *Z. Physik*, **237** (1970), 31
16. H. Haken. In *Festkörperprobleme X*, ed. by O. Madelung, Braunschweig, Vieweg (1970)
17. V. de Giorgio and M. O. Scully. *Phys. Rev.*, **A2** (1970), 1170
18. S. Grossmann and P. H. Richter. *Z. Physik*, **242** (1971), 458
19. V. Dohm. *Solid State Commun.*, **11** (1972), 1273
20. V. Dohm. Dissertation, Aachen (1973)
21. E. Pytte and H. Thomas. *Phys. Rev.*, **179** (1969), 431
22. J. W. F. Woo and Landauer. *I.E.E.E. J. Qu. El.*, **7** (1971), 435
23. R. Landauer and J. W. F. Woo. IBM Research (1972)
24. P. Glansdorff and I. Prigogine. *Physica*, **46** (1970), 344
25. F. Schlögl. *Z. Physik*, **248** (1971), 446
26. H. K. Janssen. *Z. Physik*, **253** (1972), 176
27. J. A. McLennan. *Advances in Chemical Physics*, ed. by J. Prigogine, Interscience, New York (1963)
28. D. N. Zubarev. *Soviet Phys. Doklady*, **10** (1965), 526
29. R. Bausch. *Z. Physik*, **244** (1971), 190
30. I. Prigogine. *Étude Thermodynamique des Phénomènes Irreversibles*, Desoer, Liege (1947)
31. P. Mazur. *Bull. Acad. Roy. Belgique Cl. Sc.*, **38** (1952), 182
32. J. Meixner. ARPA-SD 86 Report E25, Division of Engineering, Brown University, Providence, R.I. (1965)
33. J. Meixner. *Z. Physik*, **219** (1969), 79
34. J. Meixner. *Arch. Rat. Mech. Anal.*, **33** (1969), 33
35. F. Schlögl, *Z. Physik*, **244** (1971), 199
36. R. F. Greene and H. B. Callen. *Phys. Rev.*, **83** (1951), 1231
37. F. Schlögl. *Physics Letters*, **36A** (1971), 193
38. F. Schlögl. *Z. Physik*, **249** (1971), 1

7. Entropy and Entropy Production

J. Meixner†

Abstract

The limitations of a thermodynamic theory of a continuum by the atomic structure of matter are briefly discussed. They imply that any thermodynamic theory is of an approximate nature. Main emphasis is laid on the concept of a nonequilibrium entropy. It is shown that to an isothermal electrical network one can apply thermodynamic reasoning. When it is considered as a black box, that is, characterised by its impedance only, one can assign to the same *state* an infinite number of different entropy values. Thus one is led to doubt the existence of a unique nonequilibrium entropy in continuous matter, if one adopts here again the black box point of view, that is, if constitutive equations are used which relate the external variables only. Network models which also model the temperature by a voltage at one pair of terminals confirm the conjecture.

7.1 Introduction

The purpose of this lecture is to discuss the concepts of entropy and entropy production in a thermodynamic material which is not in an equilibrium state.

Thermodynamics is a branch of physics, and one needs at first a wealth of experimental results before the basic concepts can be developed and before it can be put into an abstract mathematical form. This process has successfully been carried through for the special case of thermostatics, and the concept of an equilibrium entropy was developed more than a hundred years ago by Clausius and has found many important applications. Since Carathéodory's fundamental contribution there has been much endeavour to derive this abstract mathematical form of thermostatics from a set of axioms or postulates. While, as I think, this has not contributed much to an extension of the scope of thermostatics, it has certainly contributed to a better understanding of the mathematical structure of thermostatics.

In nonequilibrium thermodynamics, or briefly, in thermodynamics the situation is somewhat different. The main point is that the question whether in nonequilibrium states a well-defined entropy with the expected properties exists, has not received enough attention by many protagonists. So the entropy is introduced by Truesdell[1] as a primitive, undefined variable,

† RWTH Aachen, Institut für Theoretische Physik Aachen, W. Germany.

described only by such properties as are laid down for it. In our opinion such an attitude cannot be assumed, in a mathematical abstraction of a branch of physics, before the concept of a nonequilibrium entropy has been clearly and definitely developed, either from experimental results or by theoretical arguments derived from molecular theories. And, herewith, we are, in fact at a loss. When looking into Clausius' work, we find that he introduces a nonequilibrium entropy without any motivation, probably in the expectation that the thermostatic entropy concept can be extended to nonequilibrium situations just as is the case with other concepts which have been developed and defined for static cases only. The existence of a nonequilibrium entropy is considered to be proved at least for a special system which is described by the Boltzmann equation of the kinetic gas theory. As a consequence, one can derive from it the famous $\mathscr{H}$-theorem which gives even an explicit expression for the nonequilibrium entropy. But there is a gap in this deduction because, as to my knowledge, it has not been proved that there is only one $\mathscr{H}$-theorem. Furthermore, in the generalisations of the Boltzmann theory by Bogoliubov, Born and Green, Kirkwood, Yvon, it is not even known whether an $\mathscr{H}$-theorem exists at all.

The question whether a nonequilibrium entropy exists at all or under certain conditions only, will be our main concern. It can be answered to a great extent by analysing the most perspicuous thermodynamic system, which is an electrical network with a finite number of concentrated capacitances, resistances and inductances. The results can be carried over to thermodynamic materials with linear constitutive equations, because they can be mapped on to linear electrical networks; thus definite conclusions on the existence or nonexistence of a nonequilibrium entropy in the case of nonlinear constitutive equations, are possible.

7.2 Electrical Networks as Thermodynamic Systems

Electrical networks serve as models of thermodynamic systems, but they are also thermodynamic systems in their own right. The only shortcoming is that restriction to isothermal conditions is necessary in order that simplicity of the arguments and of the properties is not lost. But the study of electrical networks from a thermodynamic point of view gives a better understanding of thermodynamics and an analysis of some of its concepts.

We restrict attention to electrical networks which are built up from a finite number of capacitances, resistances and inductances. Apart from some degenerate cases, the network can be decomposed in n independent loops. The total voltages generated in these loops are $u_k(t)$; the respective currents are $i_k(t)$; their time integrals are $q_k(t)$ and are assumed to be zero at $t = -\infty$. Thus the process starts from an *empty* network at $t = -\infty$. The network equations for the individual loops are

$$u_k = \Gamma_{km} q_m + R_{km} \dot{q}_m + L_{km} \ddot{q}_m \tag{7.1}$$

the summation convention being adopted. The matrices Γ_{km}, R_{km}, L_{km} are symmetric and non-negative definite. The stored electromagnetic energy is

$$W = = W_e + W_m \tag{7.2}$$

$$W_e = \tfrac{1}{2} q_k \Gamma_{km} q_m \tag{7.3}$$

$$W_m = \tfrac{1}{2} \dot{q}_k L_{km} \dot{q}_m \tag{7.4}$$

The dissipated power is

$$P = \dot{q}_k R_{km} \dot{q}_m \tag{7.5}$$

From the network equations 7.1 one obtains

$$\int_{-\infty}^{t} u_k(s) i_k(s)\,\mathrm{d}s = W_e(t) + W_m(t) + \int_{-\infty}^{t} P(s)\,\mathrm{d}s \geqslant 0 \tag{7.6}$$

If the voltages are constant after a finite time in such a manner that the currents go to zero asymptotically, then the above inequality reduces to a special case of Clausius' first inequality if $W_e(t)$ is interpreted as the free energy of the network. Therefore, we name $W(t)$ in equations 7.2 to 7.4, the free energy of the network at time t. It is well defined if the $u_k(s)$ are given in $-\infty < s < t$, by integration of the equations 7.1 with the initial conditions $q_k(-\infty) = 0$, $\dot{q}_k(-\infty) = 0$.

According to the black box concept of an electrical network, one has a network with unknown internal composition which is accessible only through j pairs of terminals, across which voltages $u_a(t)$ are applied which produce currents $i_a(t)$ through the terminals ($a = 1, 2, \ldots, j$). We prepare this point of view by setting, in equation 7.1, $u_k = 0$ ($k = j+1, \ldots, n$). We also introduce a compact notation by defining two voltage vectors

$$\boldsymbol{u}_1 = u_1, u_2, \ldots, u_j, \qquad \boldsymbol{u}_2 = u_{j+1}, u_{j+2}, \ldots, u_n$$

and the corresponding charge vectors $\boldsymbol{q}_1$, $\boldsymbol{q}_2$ and current vectors $\boldsymbol{i}_1$, $\boldsymbol{i}_2$. We also assume that the matrix L_{km} has a nonvanishing determinant (this is not a very essential assumption). Then we can express the currents as linear functions of the magnetic fluxes which are defined by $L_{km} i_m = \phi_k$. They are combined in two flux vectors $\boldsymbol{\phi}_1$, $\boldsymbol{\phi}_2$. We also understand that the free energy W is now expressed as a function of the charge and the flux vectors. Then it is easily verified that the following equations are equivalent to the network equations

$$u_1 - \partial W/\partial q_1 = R_{11}\dot{q}_1 + R_{12}\dot{q}_2 + \dot{\phi}_1 \tag{7.7a}$$
$$-\partial W/\partial q_2 = R_{21}\dot{q}_1 + R_{22}\dot{q}_2 + \dot{\phi}_2 \tag{7.7b}$$
$$-\partial W/\partial \phi_1 = -\dot{q}_1 \tag{7.7c}$$
$$-\partial W/\partial \phi_2 = \qquad -\dot{q}_2 \tag{7.7d}$$

These are the equations of a linear thermodynamic formalism[2,3]. The variables u_1, q_1 are external variables and the q_2 are even, the ϕ_1, ϕ_2 odd internal variables. This is the simplest example in which odd internal variables occur and it also indicates that odd internal variables may describe inertial effects. The R matrix in equation 7.7 is symmetric, while the coefficients of $\dot{\phi}_k$ and $\dot{q}_k$ $(k = 1, 2)$ are of equal magnitude but opposite in sign. Consequently we can consider the symmetry properties in the right members of equation 7.7 as Onsager–Casimir reciprocal relations (OCRR), although derived from network properties which can be very directly established. This result corroborates the interpretation of the equations 7.7 as a thermodynamic formalism and gives a very simple example of the OCRR.

We introduce now the

Definition: *The state of a system at time t is given by a set of data referring to times* $t \leqslant t_0$ *which determines the properties of the system at time* t_0 *and also the future development of the system under given external action in* $t \geqslant t_0$.

It is clear that the state of the electrical network at time t_0 is completely specified by the values of the external variables q_1 and of the internal variables q_2, ϕ_1, ϕ_2 at time t_0, because, if $u^1(t)$ is given for $t \geqslant t_0$, the linear differential equations 7.7 have a unique solution in $t \geqslant t_0$, with these initial values of q_k, ϕ_k $(k = 1, 2)$ at time t_0. It is also obvious that the free energy of the system and the dissipated power at any time t are uniquely determined by the values of the q_k, ϕ_k at time t. For the evaluation of the energy dissipation one needs the time derivative of q_1, q_2. But it can be expressed in terms of ϕ_1, ϕ_2 by equations 7.7*c* and *d*.

By familiar techniques the variables q_2, ϕ_1, ϕ_2 can be eliminated from the equations 7.7. What results is a functional relation between $u_1(t)$ and $q_1(t)$ of the after-effect type. It is, read in one direction or the other, a vector-valued linear passive system[4,5]. If, for instance, $u_1(t)$ is given in $-\infty < t \leqslant t_0$, we can evaluate $q_1(t)$, $\dot{q}_1(t)$ in $t \leqslant t_0$ and, by integration of the equations 7.7, obtain the values of the internal variables at time t_0. They, in turn, determine the free energy of the network and the dissipated power.

The functional relation between $u_1(t)$ and $q_1(t)$ experiences its simplest expression when restriction is made to processes which start at $t = 0$ and have two continuous derivatives in $-\infty < t < \infty$, if it is written in Laplace transforms

$$f(p) := \int_0^\infty \exp(-pt) f(t)\, dt \qquad \mathrm{Re}\, p > 0 \tag{7.8}$$

Then we have

$$\boldsymbol{u}_1(p) = \boldsymbol{Z}(p)\boldsymbol{i}_1(p) \qquad \boldsymbol{i}_1(p) = \boldsymbol{Y}(p)\boldsymbol{u}_1(p) \tag{7.9}$$

with the impedance matrix $\boldsymbol{Z}(p)$ and the admittance $\boldsymbol{Y}(p)$ being positive matrix functions due to the inequality 7.6. $\boldsymbol{Z}(p)$ is a positive matrix function of p if it is holomorphic in $\mathrm{Re}\, p > 0$ and $\mathrm{Re}\, \tilde{\boldsymbol{x}}\boldsymbol{Z}(p)\boldsymbol{x} \geqslant 0$ in $\mathrm{Re}\, p \geqslant 0$ for all complex vectors $\boldsymbol{x}$; the tilde denotes transposition of a vector or a matrix. The matrix $\boldsymbol{Y}(p) = \boldsymbol{Z}(p)^{-1}$ is assumed to exist. The matrix $\boldsymbol{Z}(p)$ is symmetric. This is a consequence of the symmetry of the matrices occurring in equation 7.1. It would not hold if the network would contain gyrators as well.

The impedance matrix of an electrical network can be evaluated if we know its structure in detail, but it can be measured by appropriate actions at the terminals alone, even when the internal structure is not known, that is, even if we adopt now the black box point of view. We have only to observe the reaction $\boldsymbol{i}_1(t)$ to one or more appropriate stimuli $\boldsymbol{u}_1(t)$ and to relate their Laplace transforms by an equation of the type 7.7*a*.

The impedance matrix, or its reciprocal matrix, the admittance matrix, is all that counts when we have to use the network in some experimental device. If only this knowledge is available then the following questions can be posed:

(1) How can the state of the network be specified?

(2) What is the free energy and the dissipated power within the network?

At first, the second question will be answered. It is well known that the impedance matrix does not determine the structure of the network except for trivial cases. If at least one resistance is contained in a network then there exists an infinite number of networks with the same impedance matrix. For the same stimulus function $\boldsymbol{u}_1(t)$ they differ in the time dependence of the free energy and of the dissipated power.

Consequently, from the black box point of view it is not possible to assign a unique free energy and a unique dissipated power to the network at all times when there is no equilibrium. Although the left member in equation 7.6 is, for a given process, well-determined, its value will be distributed in different ways over the three parts of the middle member according to the considered network realisation of the given impedance matrix.

The answer to the first question can no longer be that the state at time t be specified by the values of $\boldsymbol{q}_1(t)$ and of the internal variables at time t, because the internal structure of the network to a given impedance matrix is unknown and so are the internal variables to be used.

There are, however, other specifications of the state available which are in accordance with the general definition. For instance

(1) The state of the network at time t is specified by the values $\boldsymbol{u}_1(s)$ at all previous times $s \leqslant t$. The after-effect representation of the linear functional relation $\boldsymbol{u}_1(t) \rightarrow \boldsymbol{i}_1(t)$ then permits the evaluation of $\boldsymbol{i}_1(s)$ for $s > t$ if the subsequent action $\boldsymbol{u}_1(s)$ in $s \geqslant t$ is known.

(2) The state of the network at time t is specified by the values $\boldsymbol{i}_1(s)$ at all previous times $s = t$. Then $\boldsymbol{u}_1(s)$ in $s \leqslant t$ can be evaluated from the after-effect representation of the linear functional relation $\boldsymbol{i}_1(t) \rightarrow \boldsymbol{u}_1(t)$, and the subsequent action $\boldsymbol{i}_1(s)$ in $s \geqslant t$ yields a unique continuation of the response $\boldsymbol{u}_1(s)$ into $s \geqslant t$.

It is customary to write the mentioned functional relations in the forms

$$\boldsymbol{i}_1(t) = \mathfrak{I}\{\boldsymbol{u}_1(s), -\infty < s \leqslant t\} \tag{7.10a}$$

$$\boldsymbol{u}_1(t) = \mathfrak{U}\{\boldsymbol{i}_1(s), -\infty < s \leqslant t\} \tag{7.10b}$$

the first of which is to express that $\boldsymbol{i}_1(t)$ depends on all values of $\boldsymbol{u}_1$ in the interval $-\infty < s \leqslant t$, or on the history of $\boldsymbol{u}_1$ with respect to time t. An explicit expression for the first functional is

$$\boldsymbol{i}_1(t) = \boldsymbol{A}\dot{\boldsymbol{u}}_1(t) + \int_{-\infty}^{t} \boldsymbol{P}(t-s)\boldsymbol{u}_1(s)\,\mathrm{d}s + \int_{-\infty}^{t} [\boldsymbol{P}(0) - \boldsymbol{P}(t-s)]\,\ddot{\boldsymbol{u}}_1(s)\,\mathrm{d}s \tag{7.11}$$

where $\boldsymbol{A}$ is a non-negative definite symmetric matrix and $\boldsymbol{P}(t)$ is a real symmetric matrix-valued positive definite function in the sense of Bochner[6]. The symmetry of $\boldsymbol{P}(t)$ is a consequence of the symmetry of $\boldsymbol{Z}(p)$. A similar representation holds for the second functional in equation 7.10.

With respect to the after-effect representation, equation 7.11, it is often said that the network at time t has a memory for its past treatment $\boldsymbol{u}_1(s)$ in $-\infty < s \leqslant t$. Of course, this formulation is misleading. There may be families of histories with an infinite number of specimens which lead to the same state at time t and it may be possible to parametrise these families. Such parameters can be used to define a possible set of internal variables. In such cases, the knowledge of $\boldsymbol{u}_1(s)$ in $-\infty < s \leqslant t$ gives redundant information on the state at time t[7].

We speak of the network equations 7.1 or 7.8 as the highest level of description, and of the network equations 7.9 or 7.10 or 7.11 as the lowest level of description, meaning that it relates only the external variables. One can also study intermediate levels of description, but we shall not discuss this subject further.

It is important to note that, whatever the network realisation of an impedance matrix is, the difference $W_e(t) - W_m(t)$ is the same; in other words it can be expressed by the stimulus $\boldsymbol{u}_1(t)$ and the impedance matrix $\boldsymbol{Z}(p)$[8]. This has the following consequence: if one network realisation of $\boldsymbol{Z}(p)$ contains only resistances and capacitances (inductances), then all other network realisations with the same kinds of elements have the same values $W_e(t)$, while $W_m(t) = 0$ ($W_m(t)$ while $W_e(t) = 0$) and the same dissipated power $\boldsymbol{P}(t)$ under the same stimulus $\boldsymbol{u}_1(t)$. In such cases this $W_e(t)(W_m(t))$ can be considered as a preferred free energy function, although there are other network realisations with three kinds of elements and different free energy under the same stimulus. The above mentioned network realisations are usually named *RL*, *RC* and *RCL* networks.

If the impedance matrix is such that there is no realisation as an *RC* or an *RL*-network, then we see two ways of defining a distinguished, although not unique, free energy function $W_{1,2}(t)$. The first definition is

$$W_1(t) = \inf\{W_e(t) + W_m(t)\} \tag{7.12}$$

with the infimum being taken over all network realisations of the given impedance matrix. An explicit expression of $W_1(t)$ has not yet been found. But in case there exists one realisation of $\boldsymbol{Z}(p)$ as an *RC* or an *RL*-network, then this infimum is given by $W_e(t)(W_m(t))$ of this network[8].

A second way of defining a distinguished free energy $W_2(t)$ derives from the concept of the lost energy at time t. The energy delivered to the network by a stimulus $\boldsymbol{u}_1(s)$ in $-\infty < s \leqslant t$ is given by the left member of equation 7.6. We consider now all continuations of this stimulus into $t \geqslant s$ and determine

$$W_2(t) = -\inf \int_t^{\infty} \boldsymbol{u}_1(s)\boldsymbol{i}_1(s)\,\mathrm{d}s \tag{7.13}$$

where the infimum is taken over all these continuations. The functions $\boldsymbol{u}_1(s)$ $(-\infty < s < \infty)$ are assumed to be in C_2 which is no essential restriction. This $W_2(t)$ is the maximal energy which can be recovered from the energy delivered to the network in $-\infty < s \leqslant t$. It cannot be greater than the stored energy at time t.

The idea of the recoverable energy has been enunciated for the first time by König and Tobergte[9] (see also reference 10); a special case which corresponds to *RC*-networks has been treated by Breuer and Onat,[11], while for the general case of an arbitrary positive matrix-valued function $\boldsymbol{Z}(p)$ an explicit formula for $W_2(t)$ has been derived by Tobergte[12].

Even for impedance functions which can be realised by *RC*-networks, there is no simple relation between $W_1(t)$ and $W_2(t)$. This gives rise to doubt as to whether deeper physical significance can be attributed to $W_2(t)$. But it is possible to derive from $W_2(t)$, by a simple mathematical procedure, all free energy functions[13] which occur in the various network realisations of the impedance matrix.

In concluding we can state that from the black box point of view a free energy and a power dissipation during a process cannot be defined, unless one is satisfied with an infinite number of different free energies for the same state. If this is so in one thermodynamic system, we must expect the same situation to occur with the free energy and hence also with the entropy and entropy production in all thermodynamic systems. In other words, from the black box point of view, a thermodynamic system has in a given non-equilibrium state either no defined entropy at all or an infinity of different entropy values, even if for some reference equilibrium state the entropy is given a definite value. Therefore, we must conclude that nonequilibrium entropy is not a primitive quantity and cannot uniquely be defined.

7.3 The Entropy of Thermodynamic Materials

For a material in equilibrium it is, in many cases, quite easy to specify the state of a material element. For a gas it is enough to know, for instance, the temperature and the density and the concentrations of the components. Then the internal energy, the pressure, the chemical potentials, and also the index of refraction have definite values. The situation is more complicated in materials which are plastically deformed and in ferromagnetic materials. But such cases will be excluded from consideration.

The state of a material element in a process at time t can be specified by the external action which it has endured from an equilibrium state (at $t = -\infty$) through the process up to time t. This corresponds to the definition of the state of an electrical network from the black box point of view. If only mechanical and thermal external actions occur, then we can specify the state, for instance, by the histories of the surface motion and the heat flow through the surface elements. If the material element is sufficiently small and the process field is sufficiently smooth over the dimension of the material element, then the specification of its state at time t can be reduced to the knowledge of the histories of the specific internal energy u, the deformation gradient $\boldsymbol{F}$ and the heat flux $\boldsymbol{q}$ at the position of the material element. The values of other parameters at time t, like temperature T, stress tensor $\boldsymbol{\sigma}$, temperature gradient ∇T are functionals of these histories with respect to time t.

Although this sounds quite simple, we are confronted with the fact that material elements cannot be made infinitely small. It is necessary for a thermodynamic theory that they themselves can be considered as continuous and so they must be so small that the process field is smooth over their dimension, and they also must be large on the atomic scale.

These restrictions on the size of the material elements place restrictions on the permitted process fields in any thermodynamic theory of continuous matter. They also exclude infinitely fast changes in the external actions, and they indicate that any thermodynamic theory of processes is of an approximate nature with the approximation being the better the smoother the processes are.

Practically, it is often impossible to consult the history of the external action on a material in order to know its state at time t. Also from a theoretical point of view one would like a specification of the state at time t in terms of the values of a set of variables, all of them being taken at the same time t. Of course, the state at time t would be completely specified if the positions and velocities of all atoms in the material element were known. But quite apart from the impossibility of acquiring such knowledge, it would not help in a thermodynamic theory which approximates matter by a continuum and is not interested in the motion of the individual atoms.

What we need is a set of variables of a character which is meaningful in a continuum theory, describes the molecular processes which occur under external action on the material, and replaces the information on the state which is lost when the knowledge of the history of the external action is thrown away.

In chemical thermodynamics such variables have been introduced long ago. They are called internal variables and may be concentrations of components in reacting mixtures, population numbers of molecular levels, concentrations of *impurities* on various sites in a crystal lattice, etc.

In any one particular case it is usualiy difficult to recognise and identify all the pertinent internal variables. Nevertheless a formal introduction is all one needs for a formal development of the theory. An important point is, of course, that we dispose of a *complete* set of internal variables, or all internal variables which are related to molecular processes (chemical reactions, etc.) which are slow as compared to an atomic time scale. Also with such a set of internal variables we can describe only such phenomena whose process fields are sufficiently smooth.

We discuss now, for simplicity of presentation, exclusively mechanical and thermal external action; also we leave diffusion out of consideration. Then we have as state variables u, $\boldsymbol{F}$, $\boldsymbol{q}$ and the internal variables ξ_α, all of them taken at the same time t.

This specification of the state is at the basis of the classical thermodynamics of processes (named TIP for short) to which references are found in [2,14].

We define the class of materials to which TIP applies by the following postulates

(1) In equilibrium the internal variables are no longer independent parameters of state, but reduce to functions of u and $\boldsymbol{F}$.

(2) The internal changes can be, at any values of the ξ_α within a certain domain, inhibited by appropriate anticatalysts. Such a state is called a frozen equilibrium state, and it is assumed that it has a well-defined specific entropy $s_f(u, \boldsymbol{F}, \xi_\alpha)$. This can be substantiated by statistical mechanics.

(3) In a nonequilibrium state there exists a specific entropy which is equal to the specific entropy of the frozen equilibrium state with the same values of u, $\boldsymbol{F}$, ξ_α.

(4) The entropy $s_f(u, \boldsymbol{F}, \xi_\alpha)$ satisfies a balance equation

$$\rho\, \mathrm{d}s_f/\mathrm{d}t + \nabla\cdot(\boldsymbol{q}/T) = \sigma \geqslant 0 \tag{7.14}$$

where σ is the rate of entropy production per unit time which is never negative.

(5) The constitutive equations are of differential type and of complexity one.

The assumption of the existence of the nonequilibrium entropy is, of course, objectionable. But if we were to assume at this stage that no entropy exists, how could we justify that an entropy exists if the state is specified by the histories of the external action without the knowledge of the relevant internal variables? After all, if we have a complete set of internal variables, the state of a material element in the process field is very close to the state of the corresponding frozen equilibrium and so we can at least try out the given postulates.

The postulated type of constitutive equations is, at first sight, very special. More complicated constitutive equations can be constructed by elimination of one or more internal variables, and it is quite useful to do this in aged systems.

The specific entropy $s_f(u_1, \boldsymbol{F}, \xi_\alpha)$ permits a frozen state temperature T_f and stress tensor $\boldsymbol{\sigma}_f$ as well as the affinities A_α to be defined in the entropy language by

$$\mathrm{d}s_f = \frac{1}{T_f}\mathrm{d}u - \frac{1}{\rho T_f}\mathrm{Tr}\,\boldsymbol{\sigma}_f\,\mathrm{d}\boldsymbol{F}\boldsymbol{F}^{-1} + A_\alpha\,\mathrm{d}\xi_\alpha \tag{7.15}$$

By virtue of the balance equation for the internal energy we obtain from equations 7.14 and 7.15 the balance equation

$$\frac{\rho\,\mathrm{d}s_f}{\mathrm{d}t} + \nabla\cdot\left(\frac{\boldsymbol{q}}{T}\right) = \left(\frac{1}{T_f} - \frac{1}{T}\right)\rho\dot{u} + \mathrm{Tr}\left(\frac{\boldsymbol{\sigma}}{T} - \frac{\boldsymbol{\sigma}_f}{T_f}\right)\dot{\boldsymbol{F}}\boldsymbol{F}^{-1} + \boldsymbol{q}\cdot\nabla\left(\frac{1}{T}\right) + \rho A_\alpha\dot{\xi}_\alpha \tag{7.16}$$

The right member is the non-negative entropy production rate per unit volume. Its first term has been overlooked in the earlier presentations of TIP. But why should the temperature T of the nonequilibrium state not differ from the temperature T_f of the corresponding frozen equilibrium state if it is generally accepted that this may be the case for the stress tensors $\boldsymbol{\sigma}_f$ and $\boldsymbol{\sigma}$?

The constitutive equations of differential type and of complexity one are written in the form

$$-\frac{1}{T}+\frac{\partial s_f}{\partial u_f} = \boldsymbol{\Phi}_T \tag{7.17a}$$

$$\boldsymbol{F}^{-1}\frac{\boldsymbol{\sigma}}{T}+\frac{\partial s_f}{\partial \boldsymbol{F}} = \boldsymbol{\Phi}_\sigma \tag{7.17b}$$

$$\nabla\frac{1}{T} = \boldsymbol{\Phi}_\nabla \tag{7.17c}$$

$$\frac{\partial s_f}{\partial \xi_\alpha} = \boldsymbol{\Phi}_{A\alpha} \tag{7.17d}$$

with the $\boldsymbol{\Phi}$-functions depending on the state variables u, $\boldsymbol{F}$, ξ_α and the first order rates $\dot{u}$, $\dot{\boldsymbol{F}}$, $\dot{\xi}_\alpha$, $\boldsymbol{q}$. They have, for all permissible processes the property

$$\boldsymbol{\Phi}_T\rho\dot{u}+\mathrm{Tr}\,\boldsymbol{\Phi}_\sigma\dot{\boldsymbol{F}}+\boldsymbol{\Phi}_\nabla\cdot\boldsymbol{q}+\Phi_{A\alpha}\rho\dot{\xi}_\alpha \geqslant 0$$

which gives a restriction on these $\boldsymbol{\Phi}$-functions. They must, moreover, vanish in an equilibrium state with $A_\alpha = 0$.

The equations 7.17 constitute a thermodynamic formalism. In particular, if the state of the material element stays at all times close to an equilibrium reference state, then the right members can be approximated by linear functions of $\dot{u}$, $\dot{\boldsymbol{F}}$, $\boldsymbol{q}$, $\dot{\xi}_\alpha$ with coefficients that depend on the reference state only. The similarity of equations 7.17 and 7.7 is then quite obvious and also complete if we apply to these linearised equations the OCRR.

The equations 7.17 are differential equations of first order for the unknowns T, $\boldsymbol{\sigma}$, $\nabla(1/T)$, ξ_α if the functions of time u, $\boldsymbol{F}$, q are given. Assuming that the state at $t = -\infty$ was an equilibrium state, the integration of these equations yields the unknowns as functionals of the histories of u, $\boldsymbol{F}$, $\boldsymbol{q}$. If we now discard the internal variables, then we have constitutive equations which give the effect of the history of the external variables u, $\boldsymbol{F}$, q on the external variables T, $\boldsymbol{\sigma}$, $\nabla(1/T)$, that is, a state specification and constitutive equations on the lowest level of description. Also the entropy s_f as well as the rate of entropy production can be expressed as functionals of these histories. And so we have proved the existence of a unique entropy on this level of description. Have we?

Yes, under the provision that besides the constitutive equations which relate the external variables we know the internal variables and how they depend on the histories of u, $\boldsymbol{F}$, $\boldsymbol{q}$ and we should also know how the entropy of the frozen equilibrium depends on u, $\boldsymbol{F}$, ξ_α.

If we do not have this additional knowledge, we are in the same position as with an electrical network when it is considered as a black box. There may be materials which have the same responses of the dependent external variables to all actions of the independent external variables (in a certain domain), and which differ in the internal structure and in the molecular mechanisms which contribute to the entropy production. Thus we should expect, in analogy to the situation which we have discussed in the example of electrical networks, that on this lowest level of description we cannot assign a unique entropy to a given state, but rather an infinite number of different entropy values.

One might object to the applicability of the results for the network example to continuous thermodynamic materials, because we have restricted ourselves to isothermal networks and ignored the exchange of heat between the black box and its surroundings which is certainly something which can be measured.

Before we refute this objection we shall give arguments which lead to the fundamental inequality. The process in the material element is given by the functions $u(t)$, $\boldsymbol{F}(t)$, $\boldsymbol{q}(t)$. At each time t there exists an accompanying static specific entropy $s_{st}(u(t), \boldsymbol{F}(t))$ which is the value of the specific entropy if the material element were in equilibrium with the values $u(t)$ and $\boldsymbol{F}(t)$. Obviously, the inequality

$$s_{st}(u(t), \boldsymbol{F}(t)) \geqslant s_f(u(t), \boldsymbol{F}(t), \xi_\alpha(t)) \tag{7.18}$$

holds because the entropy value in the left member refers to a state in which all ξ_α assume their equilibrium values $\xi_\alpha = \xi_\alpha(u, \boldsymbol{F})$. From $s_{st}(u, \boldsymbol{F})$ we also define an accompanying static temperature and stress as functions of u, $\boldsymbol{F}$ by

$$\mathrm{d}s_{st} = \frac{1}{T_{st}}\mathrm{d}u - \frac{1}{\rho T_{st}}\operatorname{Tr}\boldsymbol{\sigma}_{st}\,\mathrm{d}\boldsymbol{F}\,\boldsymbol{F}^{-1} \tag{7.19}$$

Because the right member of equation 7.16 is non-negative we obtain from equations 7.16 and 7.18

$$\int_{-\infty}^{\tau}\left[\dot{s}_{st} + \frac{1}{\rho}\nabla\cdot\left(\frac{\boldsymbol{q}}{T}\right)\right]\mathrm{d}t \geqslant \int_{-\infty}^{\tau}\left[\dot{s}_f + \frac{1}{\rho}\nabla\cdot\left(\frac{\boldsymbol{q}}{T}\right)\right]\mathrm{d}t = 0 \tag{7.20}$$

By replacing s_{st} from equation 7.19 and applying the energy balance law the inequality, valid for all τ

$$\int_{-\infty}^{\tau}\left[\left(\frac{1}{T_{st}}-\frac{1}{T}\right)\dot{u}+\left(\nabla\frac{1}{T}\right)\cdot\frac{1}{\rho}\boldsymbol{q}+\frac{1}{\rho}\mathrm{Tr}\left(\frac{\boldsymbol{\sigma}}{T}-\frac{\boldsymbol{\sigma}_{st}}{T_{st}}\right)\dot{\boldsymbol{F}}\boldsymbol{F}^{-1}\right]\mathrm{d}t\geqslant 0 \quad (7.21)$$

is obtained. This is the so-called fundamental inequality which has also been motivated on the basis of the Clausius inequality[15,16]. It expresses the restriction which the second law imposes on the constitutive equations.

The constitutive equation can be so chosen that

$$\frac{1}{T_{st}}-\frac{1}{T} \qquad \nabla\frac{1}{T} \qquad \frac{\boldsymbol{\sigma}}{T}-\frac{\boldsymbol{\sigma}_{st}}{T_{st}} \quad \text{at time } t \quad (7.22)$$

are functionals of the histories with respect to time t of the variables

$$u \qquad \boldsymbol{q} \qquad \boldsymbol{F} \quad (7.23)$$

If the state of the material element always stays close to an equilibrium reference state $u = u^+$, $q = 0$, $\boldsymbol{F} = \boldsymbol{F}^+$, $\rho = \rho^+$ then we can instead introduce the histories of

$$\dot{u} \qquad \frac{\boldsymbol{q}}{\rho} \qquad \frac{1}{\rho} \qquad \frac{\dot{\boldsymbol{F}}(\boldsymbol{F}^+)^{-1}}{\rho\rho^+} \quad (7.24)$$

and in addition the fixed parameters u^+, $\boldsymbol{F}^+$, ρ^+. Then the functionals which represent the quantities in 7.22 in terms of the histories of the quantities in 7.24 constitute a linear passive system with a certain admittance matrix $\boldsymbol{Y}(p)$, because the integral in inequality 7.21 expresses a passivity property which is analogous to equation 7.6.

We consider now the special case where $\boldsymbol{Y}(p)$ is rational. Then the functional relation between 7.22 and 7.24 can be modelled by an infinite number of equivalent networks. The point is now that $1/T_{st}-1/T$, the three components of $\nabla(1/T)$, etc., correspond to voltages across pairs of terminals while u, $\boldsymbol{q}/\rho^+$, etc., correspond to currents through the respective terminals. To each network model we can introduce a set of internal variables which can be normalised to zero in the reference state. From the stored energy W of this model network we define an entropy

$$s = s_{st}(u, \boldsymbol{F}) - W \quad (7.25)$$

Then it can be proved that this entropy satisfies a Clausius–Duhem inequality

$$\rho\dot{s}+\nabla\cdot\left(\frac{\boldsymbol{q}}{T}\right)\geqslant 0$$

But it is obvious that we can introduce in this way an infinite number of entropies for the same state by considering the various network models with the same admittance but different values of W for the same state of the network. For a special case, a model of linear heat conduction, the calculations can be easily performed with the help of the equations given in section 8 of [17]. The general proof will be given elsewhere.

Here the network models only serve to construct a thermodynamic formalism with internal variables. It is of no relevance that these networks are also considered under *isothermal* conditions. They are not treated as thermodynamic systems but as real models in which the temperature is modelled by the voltage at one pair of terminals.

References

1. C. Truesdell. *Rational Thermodynamics*, McGraw-Hill, New York (1969)
2. J. Meixner and H. G. Reik. Thermodynamik der irreversiblen prozesse. *Encyclopedia of Physics*, III/2, section 23B, ed. by S. Flügge, Springer-Verlag, Berlin (1959), 413–523
3. J. Meixner. Thermodynamic theory of relaxation phenomena. *Non-Equilibrium Thermodynamics, Variational Techniques, and Stability*, ed. by R. J. Donnelly, R. Herman and I. Prigogine, Univ. of Chicago Press (1966), 73–89
4. H. König and J. Meixner. Lineare systeme und lineare transformationen. *Mathematische Nachrichten*, **19** (1958), 265–322
5. J. Meixner. On the theory of linear passive systems, *Arch. Rat. Mech. Anal.*, **17** (1964), 278–96
6. S. Bochner. *Vorlesungen über Fourier'sche Integrale*, Leipzig (1932)
7. J. Meixner. Non-linear continuum theories. *Mathematics and Physics and their Applications*, Centro Internazionale Matematico Estivo. Edizioni Cremonese, Roma (1970)
8. J. Meixner. Impedanz und Lagrange-funktion linearer passiver systeme. *Zeitschrift für Physik*, **156** (1959), 200–10
9. H. König and J. Tobergte. *Journal für Reine und Angewandte Mathematik*, **212** (1963), 104–8
10. J. Meixner. *Zeitschrift für Naturforschung*, **16a** (1961), 721–6
11. S. Breuer and E. T. Onat. *Jour. App. Mech. Phys.* (Z.A.M.P.), **15** (1964), 12–21
12. J. Tobergte. *Invariante Teilräume und die Verlorene Energie Linearer Passiver Transformationen*, Dissertation, Köln (1965)
13. W. Kern. *Zur Vieldeutigkeit der Gleichgewichtsentropie in Kontinuierlichen Medien*, Dissertation, Aachen (1972)
14. S. R. de Groot and P. Mazur. *Non-Equilibrium Thermodynamics*, Amsterdam (1962)
15. J. Meixner. Thermodynamik der vorgänge in einfachen fluiden medien und die charakterisierung der thermodynamik irreversibler prozesse. *Zeitschrift für Physik*, **219** (1969), 79–104
16. J. Meixner. Processes in simple thermodynamic materials. *Arch. Rat. Mech. Anal.*, **33** (1969), 33–53
17. J. Meixner. On the linear theory of heat conduction. *Arch. Rat. Mech. Anal.*, **39** (1970), 108–30

8. Entropy and Entropy Production: Discussion Paper

J. Kestin†

8.1 Introduction

I conceive my role to be that of a trigger for what, I hope, will turn out to be a lively discussion.

I begin by making an observation. Even a superficial reading of the scientific literature on thermodynamics of the last decade reveals the existence of two divergent trends or schools. The one, tracing its roots to the work of S. R. de Groot, J. Meixner, and I. Prigogine reigns, almost unchallenged, in the work of fluid dynamicists. The other stems from contemporary attempts to unify the sciences of thermodynamics and continuum mechanics with the possible inclusion of fluid mechanics into a coherent, logical and rigorous formalism. The two schools diverged so much that they even developed mutually inconsistent terminologies, leading to quite serious semantic differences and to difficulties in communication. Sometimes differences in terminology hide an essential unity of thought, but they also often point to genuine differences in fundamental concepts. One such difficulty was identified by Professor Meixner in his introduction when he spoke about entropy for the first time.

8.2 Entropy in Thermodynamics

I sometimes sense that even the concept of entropy in an equilibrium state differs from presentation to presentation, and feel it necessary to state it here at the cost of sounding trite and trivial. The entropy difference between two states of unconstrained or constrained (frozen) equilibrium is given by Clausius' integral‡

$$S_2 - S_1 = \int_{R^1}^{2} \frac{dQ^0}{T} \tag{8.1}$$

taken along an arbitrary *reversible* path R. If no such path can be indicated for some system, the entropy difference $S_2 - S_1$ cannot be evaluated for it, and the statement of the second law in the form that

$$S_2 > S_1 \tag{8.2}$$

† Brown University, Providence, R.I., USA.

‡ The superscript 0 emphasises that the quantity is measured along a reversible process.

for adiabatic processes is devoid of physical meaning in this particular case. Whenever we use equation 8.2, we imply that at least one reversible way of reaching state 2 from state 1 (and, hence, any two mutually accessible states) can be found for any system under consideration. The path R is assumed to exist in a space of

$$r = 1+m+n$$

dimensions, where r is the number of independent thermodynamic properties of the system. One such space can be represented by the variables which appear in

$$\mathrm{d}Q^0 = T\,\mathrm{d}S = \mathrm{d}U + A_\alpha\,\mathrm{d}\xi_\alpha + P_\beta\,\mathrm{d}a_\beta \quad \text{(sums)} \tag{8.3}$$

with

$$\mathrm{d}W^0 = A_\alpha\,\mathrm{d}\xi_\alpha + P_\beta\,\mathrm{d}a_\beta \tag{8.4}$$

denoting the *work* of a reversible process. Here P_β are the n external forces acting on the external deformation variables a_β, and A_α are the m affinities (or generalised forces) acting on the internal deformation variables, ξ_α. Naturally, the integrating denominator

$$T = T(U, \boldsymbol{a}, \boldsymbol{\xi}) \tag{8.5}$$

is a function of the independent variables, equation 8.3. The numbers m and n, and the nature of the ξ_α's and a_β's must be discovered by experiments.

8.3 The Concept of State

The previous reiteration reminds us that the *concept of state* is essential in thermodynamics as well as in thermostatics. Our concept of state colours what we think about entropy and, more generally, about the proper form to be given to the second law.

Professor Meixner says

(1) The state of a system at time t_0 is given by a set of data referring to time $t \leqslant t_0$ which determines the properties of the system at time t_0, and also the future development of the system under given external action in $t \geqslant t_0$.

(2) With respect to the after-effect representation, equation 7.11, it is often said that the network at time t has a memory for its past treatment $\boldsymbol{u}_1(s)$ in $-\infty < s \leqslant t$. Of course, this formulation is misleading. There may be families of histories with an infinite number of specimens which lead to the same state at time t, and it may be possible to parametrise these families. Such parameters can be used to define a possible set of internal variables. In such cases the knowledge of $\boldsymbol{u}_1(s)$ in $-\infty < s \leqslant t$ gives redundant information on the state at time t.

(3) The state of a material element in a process at time t can be specified by the external action which it has endured from an equilibrium state (at $t = -\infty$) through the process up to time t. This corresponds to the definition of the state of an electrical network from the black box point of view.

(4) Practically, it is often impossible to consult the history of the external action on a material in order to know its state at time t. Also, from a theoretical point of view, one would like a specification of the state at time t in terms of the values of a set of variables, all of them being taken at the same time t.

As far as I am concerned, only statement (4) is acceptable as a definition of state. In other words, the concept of state refers to a set of variables which one imagines are measured over the system *instantaneously*. The words *history, set of data referring to times* $t \leqslant t_0$; *time-dependent properties*, as well as *functionals of functions of time* conjure up in my mind the concept of a *process*. I believe it essential to keep the two apart, and will revert to the point later.

8.4 Incomplete Versus Complete Information

In the four preceding statements, Professor Meixner seems to pose two problems. First, what is the form of the second law when we have a complete description of the state, inclusive of internal and global deformation parameters. The second question asks what we should do if a complete description (*black box point of view*) is not available. I believe that thermodynamics, in all its clarity, can be developed only in the first case. The second case poses a legitimate question which, however, may or may not lead to a satisfactory answer, depending on how much information we choose to withhold from ourselves in a particular situation. This is, in essence, the problem of thermodynamically consistent *properties* (parameters of state) here extended to a search for thermodynamically consistent *processes.* Personally, I prefer to work hard to get inside the box in order to discover the ξ_α's, because then all questions of the second kind can be answered by mathematical manipulation alone.

8.5 The Second Law in Thermodynamics

Curiously enough, once we accept that an entropy can be assigned to every point in the continuum at every instant of time, all schools agree that the generalised thermodynamic statement of the second part of the second law (excluding diffusion, etc.) must be of the form

$$\rho \frac{\mathrm{d}s}{\mathrm{d}t} + \frac{\partial(q_i/T)}{\partial x_i} = \sigma \tag{8.6}$$

where

$$\sigma \geqslant 0 \tag{8.7}$$

is the rate of entropy production per unit volume. Although open to different interpretations, equations 8.6 and 8.7 seem to be accepted by all concerned, as already stated, except that they are sometimes written

$$\int_V \left[\rho \dot{s} + \frac{\partial(q_i/T)}{\partial x_i}\right] \delta V > 0 \tag{8.6a}$$

and called the Clausius–Duhem inequality.

8.6 Entropy Production

It is clear that stopping at this point will prevent us from *solving our problem.* By this I mean the formulation of a closed set of partial differential equations whose solution, in the form of a set of functions of time and space-coordinates (as well as of functionals of the prescribed actions at the boundary of the system), constitutes the mathematical description of the *process* of interest. In order to achieve this, we need an explicit form for the entropy production, σ.

8.7 Classical Formalism (TIP)

The differences in interpretation once again turn on what we conceive to be the state of the system. In the classical de Groot–Meixner–Prigogine formalism (called TIP in Professor Meixner's lecture) the Gibbs equation 8.3 is retained as a consequence of our acceptance of the *principle of local state*[1]. Then, the entropy production, σ, emerges in the form of a sum of products of fluxes, J_γ and generalised forces F_γ, so that

$$\sigma = J_\gamma F_\gamma \quad \text{(sum)} \tag{8.8}$$

The entropy-production equation itself does not constitute one of the field equations, but identifies the fluxes and forces and indicates that they depend on each other satisfying homogeneous, *linear* or *nonlinear*, relations which also include the local state variables. These relations are variously referred to as *phenomenological assumptions* or *rate equations.*

Let me emphasise that even linear force–flux relations seldom lead to linear field equations. The adoption of linear relations does not linearise the problem.

In the TIP formalism it is recognised that equation 8.4 must be modified, because the work of an irreversible process cannot help but differ from that of a reversible process. This means that

$$\mathrm{d}Q \neq \mathrm{d}Q^0 \qquad \text{and} \qquad \mathrm{d}W \neq \mathrm{d}W^0$$

with

$$\mathrm{d}W = P'_\beta \,\mathrm{d}a_\beta$$

if only forces on the boundary of the whole system are applied during the irreversible process. During a reversible process, the internal forces A_α must also be balanced. Thus,

$$\mathrm{d}U = \mathrm{d}Q^0 - \mathrm{d}W^0 = \mathrm{d}Q - \mathrm{d}W$$

with

$$\mathrm{d}S = \frac{\mathrm{d}Q^0}{T} = \frac{\mathrm{d}Q}{T} + \frac{\mathrm{d}W^0 - \mathrm{d}W}{T}$$

for a small element in the continuum.

Assuming that the boundary of the system is displaced in a velocity field, v_i, and that the P_β and P'_β add up to tensors σ_{ij} and σ'_{ij}, we can easily show that

$$\rho\frac{\mathrm{d}u}{\mathrm{d}t} + \frac{\partial q_i}{\partial x_i} - \sigma_{ij}\frac{\partial v_i}{\partial x_j} = 0 \tag{8.9}$$

is the energy equation, and that

$$\sigma = q_i\frac{\partial T^{-1}}{\partial x_i} - \frac{\sigma_{ij} - \sigma'_{ij}}{T}\frac{\partial v_i}{\partial x_j} + \frac{A_\alpha \dot{\xi}_\alpha}{T} \tag{8.10}$$

is the entropy production.

Since the internal forces A_α which act on the internal displacements ξ_α are not now balanced from the outside, the work rate $A_\alpha \dot{\xi}_\alpha$ is dissipated and contributes the last term in equation 8.10.

8.8 Proposed Modification

Professor Meixner proposes a modification to this formalism, and I would like to ask for a more detailed physical motivation for it. As far as I can see, his proposal to make a distinction between T and T_f in Gibbs' equation 8.3 parallels the distinction made between P_β and P'_β (or σ_{ij} and σ'_{ij}), and is justified by a feeling for symmetry (...'why should the temperature T of the nonequilibrium state not differ from the temperature T_f of the corresponding frozen equilibrium state, if it is generally accepted that this may be the case for the stress tensors σ_f and σ?').

It seems to me that this question should be settled by reference to experiment. However, before we pursue this matter in this vein, I would like to pose two questions

(1) Why, for the same reasons, is it not necessary to make a similar distinction with respect to the affinities A_α in equation 7.15?

(2) Why is it necessary to retain $\nabla \cdot (\boldsymbol{q}/T)$ rather than replace it with $\nabla \cdot (\boldsymbol{q}/T_f)$ in equation 7.14?

Returning to the problem of experimental evidence, I wish to quote the case of the Navier–Stokes equations. These are known to represent Newtonian laminar flows (I disregard turbulent flows to avoid a potentially distracting controversy) as well as we can measure them with our finest instruments. They are, of course, derived, on the assumption that $T \equiv T_f$.

Secondly, if we accept Professor Meixner's equation 7.16, we might come to the following conclusion. Consider a quantity of liquid mercury (thermal conductivity asymptotically infinite) confined in a spherical rigid vessel, so that only the term

$$\sigma = \left(\frac{1}{T_f} - \frac{1}{T}\right)\rho\dot{u} \tag{8.11}$$

remains significant. At very slow rates of heating ($\dot{u} \to 0$) the relation $T(u)$ would have to be different from that at very high heating rates $\dot{u} \neq 0$. Thus, adding the same amount of energy at two disparate rates would result in two different final temperatures. Clearly, this cannot be true generally, as in the example with mercury.

It is interesting to observe that a temperature difference, $T - T_f$, can arise spontaneously in a composite system and physically parallel the appearance of a non-zero bulk viscosity in a relaxing fluid. Imagine a gas which can store energy in an internal degree of freedom with a long relaxation time. Under such conditions, a very slow addition of heat at constant volume would maintain a uniform temperature (assuming a very large thermal conductivity). If the same amount were added sufficiently fast, the two co-existing systems, the set of degrees of freedom with short relaxation time and the internal degree of freedom, would develop different temperatures for short times. Ultimately, the temperatures would equalise with an entropy production given by equation 8.11.

A similar process would occur in the composite system shown in figure 8.1. The system consists of two subsystems, A and B, separated by a partition which allows a slow transfer of heat between them. At very low rates $\dot{Q} \approx 0$, the two subsystems would have equal temperatures, but at very high rates $\dot{Q} \neq 0$ the temperatures would first differ, ultimately relaxing to a common magnitude with an entropy production once more given by equation 8.11.

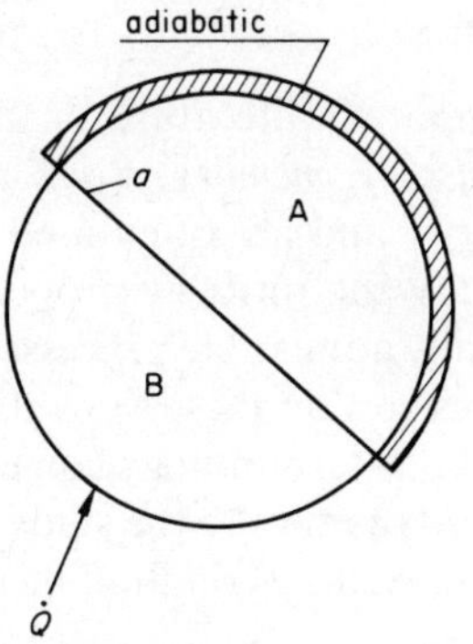

Figure 8.1

However, in either example $\dot{Q} \neq \dot{u}$, because $\dot{u}$ represents the rate of *internal* heat transfer.

8.9 Solving the Problem

Reverting to the TIP formalism, we can say that the problem of determining all future states ($t \geqslant t_0$) of a system is solved by the applications of

(1) The set of general conservation laws.

(2) The fundamental (equilibrium) equation of state, say of the form $U = U(S, \boldsymbol{a}, \xi)$ in the absence of diffusion.

(3) The set of rate equations for the forces and fluxes identified through an explicit expression for the entropy production.

(4) The set of properties at $t = t_0$ which determine the initial state.

(5) The set of functions which describe the imposed actions at the boundary for all $t > t_0$.

The result, a set of functions of position and time, describes the *process.* As already stated, these functions will also, generally speaking, contain functionals of the functions (5).

Naturally, once we have succeeded in describing the process mathematically for $t \geqslant t_0$, we can determine any future state, say at t_1, because a process is a continuous succession of states. However, a theory which assumes that the state at t_1 is determined by the whole *history* in an interval $t_0 \leqslant t \leqslant t_1$, or by a *memory*, seems to me incapable of solving problems of practical interest.

The set of empirical statements (2) and (3) can be referred to as the *constitutive laws* of the material under consideration.

8.10 Questions of Semantics

As I examine the contemporary literature on the subject, I gain the impression that the terms *history*, *memory*, *stress–strain law*, and *constitutive equation* (*or law*), lack clarity and are often used to characterise, separately or in combination, not only the intrinsic properties of materials, but also classes of thermodynamically admissible processes which can occur in them.

I would welcome a discussion on these semantic difficulties. In particular, I would like to ask why did this terminology come into existence when efforts were made to apply thermodynamics to the study of solid continua, and why is it almost totally absent in writings on fluid mechanics?

8.11 The Boltzmann Equation

As a last point, I would like to make a connection to Professor Prigogine's lecture, chapter 5.

We all seem to agree that the Boltzmann equation faithfully represents the thermodynamics of low-density (strictly speaking only monatomic) gases. In its first two Chapman–Enskog approximations, as shown by I. Prigogine[2], this equation reproduces the classical TIP formalism exactly. Furthermore, in this very special case there is no distinction between T and T_f or between the traces of σ and σ_f (vanishing bulk viscosity). Would it be of interest to re-discuss the concepts of *state* and *process* in terms of this, presumably exact, mathematical description of what is, admittedly, a very special system?

8.12 Summary

To conclude this discussion, I should like briefly to summarise the points raised:

(1) What are the reasons for the existence of several distinct formalisms? Are the differences purely semantic or do they imply genuine conceptual differences which can be expected to lead to contradictory predictions of experimental results?

(2) What is the meaning of the terms: *state*, *process*, *history*, *memory*, *constitutive law*, *stress–strain relation*, *phenomenological law*, *rate equation*, *after-effects*, *time-dependent properties*?

(3) Why is it necessary to introduce functionals other than in the solution to the problem?

(4) Why is the classical formalism (TIP), based on the acceptance of the principle of local state, inadequate?

(5) What is the physical motivation for Professor Meixner's fundamental

inequality? Can we think of systems in which the distinction between T and T_f is essential?

(6) Is the search for classes of thermodynamically admissible processes fruitful?

(7) What can we infer from a re-study of Boltzmann's equation that can throw light on the preceding questions?

References

1. J. Kestin. *A Course in Thermodynamics*, Blaisdell, vol. I (1966, repr. 1974; vol. II (1968)
2. I. Prigogine. Le domaine de validité de la thermodynamique des phenomenes irreversibles. *Physica*, **15** (1949), 272

Discussion

MÜLLER

As Professor Meixner has explained, different temperatures may well be defined on the grounds of statistical considerations. However, I believe that the real question is which one of these temperatures is put into the entropy inequality, if indeed temperature is put into that inequality at all. I should prefer a treatment which remains noncommittal about that, as I have explained in chapter 2.

I wish to comment about Professor Kestin's remark that the inequality

$$\rho \frac{\mathrm{d}s}{\mathrm{d}t} + \frac{\partial (q_i/T)}{\partial x_i} \geqslant 0$$

is generally accepted, where T is the absolute temperature.

It seems to me that Professor Meixner does not accept this inequality, because apart from the fact that he proposes to assume the time integral over the left-hand side as non-negative, he does not consider T as the absolute temperature but as a constitutive theory.

Secondly, as I have described in my talk I reject the above inequality on the grounds that the kinetic theory of gases contradicts the idea that the entropy flux is equal to the heat flux divided by absolute temperature.

KESTIN

Dr. Müller's statements are correct. However, I wish to emphasise that I said *generally* in its weaker meaning, referring to the two main schools. I did not wish to imply that absolutely everybody uses the inequality cited by Dr. Müller.

RIVLIN

I would like to turn now to the discussion of the use of functionals and internal variables as a specification of the *condition* of a material at some point s, say, of an irreversible process. I advisedly use the word *condition* rather than *state* in order to avoid any confusion with the concept of state as used in the thermodynamics of reversible processes, although the object of these specifications are similar in the two cases. It is to give enough information about the material at the point s of the process to enable us to predict what will be the subsequent behaviour of the system as the process continues. This may be done, either by specifying the values at the point s of the external variables, and a sufficient number of internal variables to describe the condition of the material at the point s, or by describing what we have done to the material in the interval between some fixed point s_1 on the path, at which the condition is known, and the point s, that is, by specifying the histories of the external variables.

It is perfectly true, as Professor Kestin has pointed out, that this second description of the condition of the material may be redundant in the sense that many different histories may correspond to a single set of values of the internal variables. In other words, while the internal variables must necessarily be single-valued functionals of the histories of the external variables describing the process, these histories do not necessarily have single-valued dependence on the values of the external and internal variables at the point s. This fact does not, it seems to me, vitiate the usefulness of the functional description.

To see that the functional approach can indeed be useful, we have only to consider the case of isothermal linear viscoelasticity theory. For simplicity we can restrict ourselves to a consideration of time-dependent simple shear. In this case the theory leads to the result that the shearing stress σ at time t is a linear functional of the history of the amount of shear $\kappa(\tau)$ at times τ in the interval $-\infty < \tau \leqslant t$.

This functional relation can be given the representation

$$\sigma = \mu\kappa + \int_{-\infty}^{t} f(t-\tau)\kappa(\tau)\,\mathrm{d}\tau \tag{8.12}$$

where μ is a constant. From measurements of σ corresponding to certain histories $\kappa(\tau)$, we can actually determine μ and the kernel $f(t-\tau)$. Using these results, we can then determine the values of σ for other histories of the amount of shear. Since calculations of this type are made every day in order to predict the response of structures of linear viscoelastic material to applied forces, it is difficult to see why we should discard formalisms of the functional type.

KESTIN

I do not advocate 'discarding formalisms of the functional type'. It is clear that, generally speaking a solution of a set of field equations (in fluid mechanics, heat transfer or solid mechanics) will contain *functionals* of the functions of time which characterise the externally imposed boundary conditions, and of the functions of space which characterise the externally imposed initial conditions. What I meant to say was that expressions like equation 8.12 describe a process and not a state. Introducing the vague word *condition* does not make the discussion more precise. It is clear that the state (employing the word in its precise meaning) of a system at any instant t can be given in many ways

(1) If a set of $r+r'$ variables is given.

(2) If the set of r variables is given together with r' equations of state.

(3) If the process between times t_0 and t is given together with the state at t_0. In the latter case, as a rule, expressions with functionals and *histories* will make their appearance. I never intended to object to that.

NEMAT-NASSER

I wish to address a question to Professor Kestin, who expresses the second law in the form of Gibbs' equation involving unspecified hidden coordinates and their conjugate forces. Viewed from a purely macroscopic point, a physical law stated in terms of unspecified *hidden* quantities, may indeed be unsatisfactory to many. I wonder whether Professor Kestin would like to comment on this.

In view of the fact that I commented on the use of hidden variables, I want to point out that in setting up constitutive relations, the use of hidden variables and a direct functional representation while not always identical, are pretty much the same. If the hidden variables are, for example, defined by certain differential equations, one may in principle solve these equations, and eliminating the hidden variables, arrive at a functional representation. Of course, not all *implicit* representation by hidden variables may have an easily accessible, mathematically tractable functional counterpart, nor does the converse necessarily apply, but their basic relationship is quite obvious.

Moreover, I want to stress that it is not at all difficult to know more or less precisely how these variables can be identified in a thermodynamic set-up. To begin with, one must limit one's scope to a well-defined problem. Thermodynamics cannot solve all the physical problems at one stroke, providing specific quantitative results. Suppose, for example, one wants to deal with the stress–strain relations in metals, or a limited problem of that kind. It appears to me that there are at least two ways that one may approach hidden variables.

(1) Guided by some experimental results and good sense, one can write down a sufficient number of internal variables of a certain kind, say, scalars or second-order tensors, and proceed *ad hoc*; by using a procedure that I shall submit to you in my lecture, one can arrive at the final stress–strain relations which will involve certain macroscopically determinable parameters. These parameters are then fixed by means of a given input–output experimental setup. The problem here is one of optimisation. The material representing a black box, the question is: what are the minimum number of parameters which provide the maximum information of the kind sought, under the given input–output setup.

(2) One may try to construct for a given problem some kind of micro-

scopic model, and then, based on this, identify suitable hidden variables. If, for example, the inelastic behaviour is caused solely by the migration of voids in a crystal, the void density may be used as an internal variable. In this case, the calculation of unique entropy at nonequilibrium states is clearly possible. All one needs is to establish an equilibrium path (experimentally, for example) in the space of deformation, temperature, and the void density. For a given void density one can then easily calculate, as I shall explain in my lecture, chapter 14, the entropy at other nonequilibrium states. Of course, it takes an intelligent man to construct a meaningful microscopic model of this kind.

Finally, I would like to comment on the two temperatures which occur in Professor Meixner's fundamental inequality. In metal plasticity, for example, which involves clearly nonequilibrium processes, the particle density is very large compared with the density of dislocations and impurities which give rise to the plasticity. In such a case I should think that the usual thermostatic empirical temperature will be quite adequate, while other complicated nonequilibrium phenomena are definitely involved.

KESTIN

We seem to be plagued by semantic problems. It is clear that in any concrete problem the *hidden* variables must be specified. I expressed this thought when I said 'I believe that thermodynamics, in all its clarity, can be developed only in the first case'. *First case* here refers to the preceding sentence which suggests that, generally speaking, we must think of 'a complete description of the state, inclusive of internal and global deformation parameters'.

Perhaps some people take the work *hidden* in *hidden variables* too literally. Were the internal deformation variables to remain truly hidden, we could make no progress. This, however, is not a question of taste or satisfaction. If a system can perform internal work (as defined in my remarks), an appropriate set of internal deformation variables must be identified and introduced into Gibbs' equation, that is, into the combined expression of the first and second laws for reversible processes.

Having said the above, we must not let ourselves be stopped if, as we have often done in the past, we explore the general behaviour of a system capable of performing internal work, with a *provisionally* unspecified *number* of internal deformation parameters.

Concerning Professor Nemat-Nasser's other comments, I once again wish to advocate the use of the terms

state, process, equation of state, rate equation

as they appear in the thermodynamics of irreversible processes. If these terms are used consistently, many apparent contradictions vanish.

Clearly, as recognised by Professor Nemat-Nasser, the number and nature of the appropriate internal variables in a particular case must follow from our understanding of the physics of the situation either directly (macroscopic experiments) or via properly constructed and proven microscopic models.

SCHLÖGL

I should like to make two remarks to the questions of Professor Kestin.

The first refers to the necessity for two temperatures in the Meixner-inequality. I remarked on the deduction of this inequality in chapter 6. The statistical theory gives clear conditions of its validity and shows the necessity for two temperatures if macroscopic after-effects occur.

The second remark refers to question (7) in section 8.12. Boltzmann's equation seems to me not to be a good starting point. However, the extension of it, called Boltzmann's–Waldmann–Snyder equation, introduces internal degrees of freedom and could be a better one.

KESTIN

I thank Professor Schlögl for his clarifications which I gratefully accept.

MEIXNER

This is an answer to question (5) raised by Professor Kestin in section 8.12.

The fundamental inequality is obtained from Clausius' original formulation of the second law

$$S(B) - S(A) \geqslant \int \frac{\mathrm{d}Q}{T}$$

where S is the system entropy, A and B are two consecutive equilibrium states, the $\mathrm{d}Q$ is the heat transferred to the system in the course of the process, and T is the temperature at which $\mathrm{d}Q$ is transferred.

Of course, the question arises of what the T means from a physical point of view. Our assertion is that it is the translational temperature which, in a process, may greatly depart from T_{st}. In order to corroborate this point of view we consider a very simple example. Take hydrogen gas, cool it down to its boiling point, wait until practically all molecules have assembled in the lowest rotational state, and then warm it up during a short time to room temperature. Then practically all molecules are in parastates. They remain in these states—for weeks if there are no catalysts, that is, long enough to do all sorts of thermostatic experiments, without an essential change of the internal state of the gas occurring. What we call the temperature of this gas is obviously equal to the translation temperature, and it is this temperature which should enter the above inequality. The accompanying static temperature in this state of the hydrogen gas is obtained when—in an imaginary or real experiment—we let, under fixed volume and constant internal energy, the gas come to equilibrium. Then orthostates will also become populated and so the total rotational energy will increase at the cost of the translational energy. Thus the gas cools down, and the final temperature is just T_{st}, or the accompanying static temperature of the original para-hydrogen gas. Incidentally, the difference of T and T_{st} in this example may amount to 30 K or more according to the value of T.

If this interpretation of T is used, then the entropy flow can be chosen as $\boldsymbol{q}/T$ only and not as $\boldsymbol{q}/T_{st}$ or something else. Consequently, only equation 7.16 of my lecture gives the correct entropy production.

LEE

My comments will reiterate and reinforce what has already been said, but will extend the ideas presented. Professor Kestin's suggestion of representing the state of a system with a few external and internal variables is fine when the internal structure of the system is known, and hence the appropriate internal variables are known, and when the system response permits representation in this form. The usual problem, particularly in dealing with solids, is to deduce a set of internal variables which will generate a satisfactory representation of the response of the material. In viscoelasticity and plasticity, for example, an embarrassing number of variables may be needed to represent the complicated material characteristics. This question is touched upon in my Discussion Paper, chapter 13.

With regard to plasticity, there is the additional difficulty that after plastic flow a state is reached which cannot be attained without plastic flow, and hence cannot be attained by a reversible path. Hence, the usual procedure in irreversible thermodynamics of considering a state to be reached by a reversible path in order to define thermodynamic variables there, is not available in this case. This difficulty was, of course, discussed by Bridgman, (*Rev. Mod. Phys.*, **22,** 56, 1950).

KESTIN

I agree with the opening comments and assert that a proper set of external and internal variables must be found for each individual system in order to link measurement with theory. Whether a *small* or *large* number of variables is needed depends on the amount of detail we demand from an analysis and cannot be answered by theory. For example, if a low-frequency process in a diatomic gas is considered, there is no need to take into account the internal variables at all. At high frequency, at least one *hidden* variable must be introduced. Often, the impression that 'an embarrassing number of' internal variables is needed is created when an essentially nonlinear system is modelled as a superposition of linear elements.

As far as Bridgman's objection is concerned, I would like to refer the speaker to: J. Kestin, Thermodynamics in Thermoplasticity (*Jablonna notes*, 1973), to be published by the Polish Academy of Sciences. It is argued there that a conceptual reversible path *can* be found in this case.

9. The Onsager Relations; Theoretical Basis

S. R. de Groot†

Abstract

The Onsager reciprocal relations between irreversible processes are derived from the time (motion) reversal invariance of the microscopic equations of motion within the framework of two models: first, the statistical theory of macroscopic quantities and linear regression laws, and second, the kinetic theory of gases.

Recently a relativistic version of the latter theory has been developed, in which also reciprocal relations have been derived.

9.1 Introduction

In this chapter, reciprocal relations between the transport coefficients which characterise irreversible processes are derived from the time reversal invariance for the individual particles of which the systems exist. Proofs are given in the framework of two types of theories: first, the statistical theory of macroscopic variables and linear regression laws[1–4] (section 9.2), and second, the kinetic theory of gases, both in their nonrelativistic[5] and relativistic[6–10] versions (sections 9.3 and 9.4). In both models certain assumptions of a statistical nature are already incorporated. The irreversibility of the phenomena studied, for instance, is already taken for granted from the beginning in both of the theories. Whereas in the first type of theory only relations between transport coefficients are obtained, in the second type they may also be calculated in terms of the microscopic properties of the constituent particles, both for systems in the nonrelativistic and the relativistic regime. The extremely relativistic case of neutrino gases[7], where all particles move with the speed of light, because they have no rest mass, attracted interest because of its relevance to astrophysical problems. In the latter example, one has to deal with the weak interaction, rather than the electromagnetic forces, which determined the preceding cases.

Onsager reciprocal relations are obtained for the interference processes between heat conduction and diffusion and also for those between relaxation phenomena and chemical or nuclear reactions[11–14]. The influence of the velocity parity of the macroscopic variables[2] (that is, whether these are even

† Instituut voor Theoretische Fysica, Amsterdam; also Centre de Recherches Mathématiques Université de Montréal. Québec, and Institut des Hautes Etudes Scientifiques Bures-sur-Yvette (Essonne), France.

or odd functions of the particle velocities), of the tensorial character[2–4,15–19] of the transport processes, and of external, in particular magnetic or Coriolis, fields, are also studied[2,8]. Moreover some general properties of invariance and the connection of the Onsager relations with related properties and extensions of the theory of irreversible processes are considered[20–37] (section 9.5).

It may be noted that if time reversal invariance (T-invariance) or equivalently (because of the validity of the CPT-theorem) CP-invariance is violated, one should in principle find deviations from the reciprocal relations. In practice these might be so small, that they could not be detected by means of present experimental techniques of measuring transport coefficients. In fact the deviations from T-invariance which have been suggested for electromagnetic interactions as well as for weak interactions are relatively small effects only[38].

9.2 Statistical Theory of Macroscopic Variables and Linear Regression Laws

9.2.1 Statistical theory of macroscopic variables

Let us write the set of n dynamical variables, which describe a system from a macroscopic point of view, as the n-component vector

$$\boldsymbol{\alpha} = \boldsymbol{\alpha}(\boldsymbol{r}^N, \boldsymbol{p}^N) \tag{9.1}$$

where $\boldsymbol{r}^N$ and $\boldsymbol{p}^N$ represent the coordinates and momenta of all particles of the system. (The number n is very much smaller than N, since the n quantities were supposed to give a macroscopic description of the system.) Since one is interested in certain averages, the probability of finding the system in a state $\boldsymbol{a} < \boldsymbol{\alpha} < \boldsymbol{a} + \mathrm{d}\boldsymbol{a}$ is needed. This quantity may be written as

$$f(\boldsymbol{a}, t)\,\mathrm{d}\boldsymbol{a} = \int_{(\boldsymbol{a},\, \boldsymbol{a}+\mathrm{d}\boldsymbol{a})} \rho(\boldsymbol{r}^N, \boldsymbol{p}^N, t)\,\mathrm{d}\boldsymbol{r}^N\,\mathrm{d}\boldsymbol{p}^N \tag{9.2}$$

with $\rho(\boldsymbol{r}^N, \boldsymbol{p}^N, t)$ the microscopic distribution function, which multiplied by $\mathrm{d}\boldsymbol{r}^N\,\mathrm{d}\boldsymbol{p}^N$ gives the probability of the microscopic state ($\boldsymbol{r}^N$, $\boldsymbol{p}^N$; $\boldsymbol{r}^N + \mathrm{d}\boldsymbol{r}^N$, $\boldsymbol{p}^N + \mathrm{d}\boldsymbol{p}^N$). It is normalised such that the integral over all values of $\boldsymbol{r}^N$ and $\boldsymbol{p}^N$ yields unity

$$\int \rho(\boldsymbol{r}^N, \boldsymbol{p}^N, t)\,\mathrm{d}\boldsymbol{r}^N\,\mathrm{d}\boldsymbol{p}^N = 1 \tag{9.3}$$

Then, according to equation 9.2, the function $f(\boldsymbol{a}, t)$ is also normalised, if integrated over all values of $\boldsymbol{a}$

$$\int f(\boldsymbol{a}, t)\,\mathrm{d}\boldsymbol{a} = 1 \tag{9.4}$$

For convenience the average $\langle \boldsymbol{a} \rangle$ of $\boldsymbol{\alpha}$ will conventionally be normalised to zero

$$\langle \boldsymbol{a} \rangle \equiv \int \boldsymbol{a} f(\boldsymbol{a}, t)\,\mathrm{d}\boldsymbol{a} = 0 \tag{9.5}$$

A joint probability of finding the system in a state $(\boldsymbol{a}, \boldsymbol{a}+\mathrm{d}\boldsymbol{a})$ at a time t, and in a state $(\boldsymbol{a}', \boldsymbol{a}'+\mathrm{d}\boldsymbol{a}')$ at a time $t+\tau$ may be written as

$$f(\boldsymbol{a}, t; \boldsymbol{a}', t+\tau)\,\mathrm{d}\boldsymbol{a}\,\mathrm{d}\boldsymbol{a}' = \int_{\substack{(\boldsymbol{a},\, \boldsymbol{a}+\mathrm{d}\boldsymbol{a})\\(\boldsymbol{a}',\, \boldsymbol{a}'+\mathrm{d}\boldsymbol{a}')}} \rho(\boldsymbol{r}^N, \boldsymbol{p}^N, t) P(\boldsymbol{r}^N, \boldsymbol{p}^N | \boldsymbol{r}'^N, \boldsymbol{p}'^N; \tau)\,\mathrm{d}\boldsymbol{r}^N\,\mathrm{d}\boldsymbol{p}^N\,\mathrm{d}\boldsymbol{r}'^N\,\mathrm{d}\boldsymbol{p}'^N \tag{9.6}$$

where
$$P(\boldsymbol{r}^N, \boldsymbol{p}^N | \boldsymbol{r}'^N, \boldsymbol{p}'^N; \tau)\,\mathrm{d}\boldsymbol{r}^N\,\mathrm{d}\boldsymbol{p}^N\,\mathrm{d}\boldsymbol{r}'^N\,\mathrm{d}\boldsymbol{p}'^N \tag{9.7}$$

is the probability of finding the system in $(\boldsymbol{r}'^N, \boldsymbol{p}'^N; \boldsymbol{r}'^N+\mathrm{d}\boldsymbol{r}'^N, \boldsymbol{p}'^N+\mathrm{d}\boldsymbol{p}'^N)$ at time τ, when at time 0 it was at $(\boldsymbol{r}^N, \boldsymbol{p}^N; \boldsymbol{r}^N+\mathrm{d}\boldsymbol{r}^N, \boldsymbol{p}^N+\mathrm{d}\boldsymbol{p}^N)$. The conditional probability is now defined as the quotient of equation 9.6 and 9.2

$$P(\boldsymbol{a}, t | \boldsymbol{a}', t+\tau)\,\mathrm{d}\boldsymbol{a}' = \frac{f(\boldsymbol{a}, t; \boldsymbol{a}', t+\tau)\,\mathrm{d}\boldsymbol{a}\,\mathrm{d}\boldsymbol{a}'}{f(\boldsymbol{a}, t)\,\mathrm{d}\boldsymbol{a}} \tag{9.8}$$

If at a certain time t_0 the system is known to be in the state $(\boldsymbol{a}, \boldsymbol{a}+\mathrm{d}\boldsymbol{a})$, such that $\rho(\boldsymbol{r}^N, \boldsymbol{p}^N, t)$ is uniform in the cell $(\boldsymbol{a}, \boldsymbol{a}+\mathrm{d}\boldsymbol{a})$ and has there the value, say, ρ^c, then the conditional probability, equation 9.8, valid for an arbitrary, nonequilibrium, state, reduces to the conditional probability for the equilibrium state, as described by the microcanonical ensemble

$$\rho(\boldsymbol{r}^N, \boldsymbol{p}^N) = \rho^0 \text{ in } (E, E+\mathrm{d}E), \text{ zero elsewhere} \tag{9.9}$$

with ρ^0 a constant and $(E, E+\mathrm{d}E)$ the energy shell. In fact, since according to equation 9.2 and 9.6 the constant ρ^0 would drop out of expression 9.7, one may replace it by the constant ρ^c, which proves that indeed equation 9.8 becomes equal to the equilibrium conditional probability (which is independent of t)

$$P(\boldsymbol{a} | \boldsymbol{a}', \tau)\,\mathrm{d}\boldsymbol{a}' = \frac{f(\boldsymbol{a}; \boldsymbol{a}', \tau)\,\mathrm{d}\boldsymbol{a}'}{f(\boldsymbol{a})\,\mathrm{d}\boldsymbol{a}} \tag{9.10}$$

The probability $f(\boldsymbol{a})$ is supposed to fulfil a *central limit theorem*, which means that it has the Gaussian form

$$f(\boldsymbol{a}) = \{|\boldsymbol{g}|/(2\pi k)^n\}^{\frac{1}{2}} \exp(-\tfrac{1}{2}k^{-1}\boldsymbol{g}{:}\boldsymbol{a}\boldsymbol{a}) \tag{9.11}$$

where $\boldsymbol{g}$ is a tensor, the double dot a double contraction, and where the first factor is found from the normalisation, equation 9.4. As a consequence one has the correlation expression

$$\langle \boldsymbol{aa} \rangle \equiv \int \boldsymbol{aa} f(\boldsymbol{a})\, \mathrm{d}\boldsymbol{a} = k\boldsymbol{g}^{-1} \tag{9.12}$$

with $\boldsymbol{g}^{-1}$ the inverse matrix of $\boldsymbol{g}$.

9.2.2 Motion reversal invariance and microscopic reversibility

Time (motion) reversal invariance may be expressed by stating that the Hamiltonian is invariant under the transformation $\boldsymbol{p}^N \leftrightarrow -\boldsymbol{p}^N$ or, as a consequence, that

$$P(\boldsymbol{r}^N, \boldsymbol{p}^N | \boldsymbol{r}'^N, \boldsymbol{p}'^N; \tau) = P(\boldsymbol{r}'^N, -\boldsymbol{p}'^N | \boldsymbol{r}^N, -\boldsymbol{p}^N; \tau) \tag{9.13}$$

We then have the *theorem* that from the motion reversal invariance, equation 9.13, follows the property

$$f(\boldsymbol{a})P(\boldsymbol{a}|\boldsymbol{a}', \tau) = f(\boldsymbol{a}')P(\boldsymbol{a}'|\boldsymbol{a}, \tau) \tag{9.14}$$

which is usually referred to as *microscopic reversibility*.

Proof: From equations 9.6, 9.9 and 9.10 one obtains

$$f(\boldsymbol{a})P(\boldsymbol{a}|\boldsymbol{a}', \tau) = \rho^0 \int_{\substack{(\boldsymbol{a},\, \boldsymbol{a}+\mathrm{d}\boldsymbol{a}) \\ (\boldsymbol{a}',\, \boldsymbol{a}'+\mathrm{d}\boldsymbol{a}')}} P(\boldsymbol{r}^N, \boldsymbol{p}^N | \boldsymbol{r}'^N, \boldsymbol{p}'^N; \tau)\, \mathrm{d}\boldsymbol{r}^N \mathrm{d}\boldsymbol{p}^N \mathrm{d}\boldsymbol{r}'^N \mathrm{d}\boldsymbol{p}'^N \tag{9.15}$$

with the ranges $(\boldsymbol{a}, \boldsymbol{a}+\mathrm{d}\boldsymbol{a})$ and $(\boldsymbol{a}', \boldsymbol{a}'+\mathrm{d}\boldsymbol{a}')$ in the energy shell $(E, E+\mathrm{d}E)$. With equation 9.13, the change of variables $\boldsymbol{p}^N \rightarrow -\boldsymbol{p}^N$ and $\boldsymbol{p}'^N \rightarrow -\boldsymbol{p}'^N$, and the fact that we suppose the variables $\boldsymbol{\alpha}$ to be even functions of the momenta (*cf.* section 9.2.4 for other situations), so that the integrations domains remain the same, the right-hand side of equation 9.15 becomes the right-hand side of equation 9.14. Q.E.D.

9.2.3 Linear regression laws and Onsager reciprocal relations between transport coefficients

It is known empirically that after a time greater than the time between two collisions, but less than the macroscopic relaxation time[3,4,20], irreversible phenomena may be described by means of linear regression laws of the type

$$\frac{\mathrm{d}\bar{\boldsymbol{a}}^{a_0}(t)}{\mathrm{d}t} = -\boldsymbol{M} \cdot \bar{\boldsymbol{a}}^{a_0}(t) \tag{9.16}$$

with (conditional) averages defined as

$$\bar{\boldsymbol{a}}^{a_0}(t) \equiv \int \boldsymbol{a} P(\boldsymbol{a}_0 | \boldsymbol{a}, t)\, \mathrm{d}\boldsymbol{a} \tag{9.17}$$

and the matrix of transport coefficients $\mathbf{M}$. Alternatively one may write them in another, habitual, form

$$\frac{\mathrm{d}\bar{\boldsymbol{a}}^{\boldsymbol{a}_0}(t)}{\mathrm{d}t} = \boldsymbol{L}\cdot\bar{\boldsymbol{X}}^{\boldsymbol{a}_0} \tag{9.18}$$

with the usual transport coefficients, defined as

$$\boldsymbol{L} \equiv \boldsymbol{M}\cdot\boldsymbol{g}^{-1} \tag{9.19}$$

and the *thermodynamic forces*, defined as

$$\boldsymbol{X} = -\boldsymbol{g}\cdot\boldsymbol{a} \tag{9.20}$$

Theorem: The property of microscopic reversibility, equation 9.14, has as a consequence the symmetry of the matrix 9.19

$$\boldsymbol{L} = \tilde{\boldsymbol{L}} \tag{9.21}$$

or, in other words, the validity of the *Onsager reciprocal relations* between the transport coefficients.

Proof: Equation 9.18 has the formal solution

$$\bar{\boldsymbol{a}}^{\boldsymbol{a}_0}(t) = \mathrm{e}^{-\boldsymbol{M}t}\cdot\boldsymbol{a}_0 \tag{9.22}$$

If one multiplies this relation (on the left) by $\boldsymbol{a}_0 f(\boldsymbol{a}_0)$, integrates over $\boldsymbol{a}_0$ and applies equation 9.17, the result is

$$\int \boldsymbol{a}_0\boldsymbol{a}\, f(\boldsymbol{a}_0)P(\boldsymbol{a}_0\,|\,\boldsymbol{a},t)\,\mathrm{d}\boldsymbol{a}_0\,\mathrm{d}\boldsymbol{a} = \int \boldsymbol{a}_0(\mathrm{e}^{-\boldsymbol{M}t}\cdot\boldsymbol{a}_0)f(\boldsymbol{a}_0)\,d\boldsymbol{a}_0 \tag{9.23}$$

Interchange $\boldsymbol{a}_0$ and $\boldsymbol{a}$ at the left-hand side, apply equations 9.14 and 9.17 with equation 9.22; apply equation 9.12 at both sides. Then one gets

$$\boldsymbol{g}^{-1}\cdot\mathrm{e}^{-\tilde{\boldsymbol{M}}t} = \mathrm{e}^{-\boldsymbol{M}t}\cdot\boldsymbol{g}^{-1} \tag{9.24}$$

Since this is valid for arbitrary times t, one concludes that

$$\boldsymbol{g}^{-1}\cdot\tilde{\boldsymbol{M}} = \boldsymbol{M}\cdot\boldsymbol{g}^{-1} \tag{9.25}$$

With the help of equation 9.19 it is seen that these are the Onsager reciprocal relations, equation 9.21. Q.E.D.

9.2.4 Generalisations

The quantities in equation 9.1 were supposed to be alpha-variables, that is, even functions of the particle velocities. If beta-variables, which are odd functions of the particle velocities, play a role, one gets three types of Onsager reciprocal relations, connecting alpha-variables with each other, alpha-variables with beta-variables and beta-variables with each other respectively. The ensuing Onsager reciprocal relations then become, according to the same type of reasoning[2], as given above:

$$\boldsymbol{L}_{\alpha\alpha} = \tilde{\boldsymbol{L}}_{\alpha\alpha}, \quad \boldsymbol{L}_{\alpha\beta} = -\tilde{\boldsymbol{L}}_{\beta\alpha}, \quad \boldsymbol{L}_{\beta\beta} = \tilde{\boldsymbol{L}}_{\beta\beta} \tag{9.26}$$

respectively.

If an external magnetic field is present, one must not only reverse the velocities of the particles but also the magnetic field $\boldsymbol{B}$, if one wants to have the particles retrace their former paths, as is a consequence of the Lorentz force, which contains the vector product of the particle velocity and the magnetic field. This has as a consequence that the Onsager reciprocal relations, equation 9.21, have to be replaced by

$$\boldsymbol{L}(\boldsymbol{B}) = \tilde{\boldsymbol{L}}(-\boldsymbol{B}) \tag{9.27}$$

(Similar modifications are needed in Coriolis fields where the force contains the vector product of the particle velocity and the angular velocity of the local rotation.) It is clear that if alpha and beta-variables occur in magnetic systems, one must modify equation 9.27 in the spirit of equation 9.26.

The laws 9.18 were written down as relations between scalars. However, many irreversible processes are described by vectorial laws (heat conduction, diffusion and cross-phenomena) or tensorial laws (viscous flow). In order to find the reciprocal relations, one first transforms all laws to scalar laws, either by means of appropriate Fourier transforms[2] or with the use of a delta-function formalism[3]. If macroscopically nonmeasurable effects are ignored the reciprocal relations retain the same form as before.

9.3 Kinetic Theory of Gases

9.3.1 The transport equation linearised

The kinetic theory of gases is based on the Boltzmann integro-differential equation

$$\frac{\partial f^i}{\partial t} + \boldsymbol{u}^i \cdot \frac{\partial f}{\partial \boldsymbol{r}} = \sum_j \int (f'^i f'^j W'^{ij} - f^i f^j W^{ij})\,\mathrm{d}\boldsymbol{u}^j\,\mathrm{d}\boldsymbol{u}'^i\,\mathrm{d}\boldsymbol{u}'^j \tag{9.28}$$

with the distribution function f^i of the species i defined in such a way that

$$f^i(\boldsymbol{r}, \boldsymbol{u}^i; t)\,\mathrm{d}\boldsymbol{r}\,\mathrm{d}\boldsymbol{u}^i \tag{9.29}$$

is the number of particles of species i in the interval $(\boldsymbol{r}, \boldsymbol{r}+\mathrm{d}\boldsymbol{r})$ and velocities in the interval $(\boldsymbol{u}^i, \boldsymbol{u}^i+\mathrm{d}\boldsymbol{u}^i)$ at time t. Furthermore one has the transition rates W^{ij} of collisions in which particles i, j with velocities $\boldsymbol{u}^i$ and $\boldsymbol{u}^j$ get velocities $\boldsymbol{u}'^i$ and $\boldsymbol{u}'^j$, and the transition rates W'^{ij} for the inverse collision

$$\left.\begin{aligned} W^{ij} &\equiv W^{ij}(\boldsymbol{u}^i, \boldsymbol{u}^j \,|\, \boldsymbol{u}'^i, \boldsymbol{u}'^j) \\ W'^{ij} &\equiv W^{ij}(\boldsymbol{u}'^i, \boldsymbol{u}'^j \,|\, \boldsymbol{u}^i, \boldsymbol{u}^j) \end{aligned}\right\} \tag{9.30}$$

The unitarity of the scattering matrix implies the property of *bilateral normalisation* of the transition rates

$$\int W^{ij}\,\mathrm{d}\boldsymbol{u}'^i\,\mathrm{d}\boldsymbol{u}'^j = \int W'^{ij}\,\mathrm{d}\boldsymbol{u}'^i\,\mathrm{d}\boldsymbol{u}'^j \tag{9.31}$$

The Boltzmann equation 9.28 is linearised by writing in the first place

$$f^i = f_0^i(1+\phi^i) \tag{9.32}$$

where f_0^i satisfies the *local equilibrium* condition

$$f_0^i f_0^j = f_0'^i f_0'^j \tag{9.33}$$

Then by retaining only f_0^i at the left-hand side, and only terms up to first order in ϕ^i at the right-hand side of equation 9.28 one obtains, with equation 9.31

$$\frac{\partial f_0^i}{\partial t} + \boldsymbol{u}^i \cdot \frac{\partial f_0^i}{\partial \boldsymbol{r}} = f_0^i \sum_j \int f_0^j(\phi'^i + \phi'^j - \phi^i - \phi^j) W'^{ij}\,\mathrm{d}\boldsymbol{u}^j\,\mathrm{d}\boldsymbol{u}'^i\,\mathrm{d}\boldsymbol{u}'^j \tag{9.34}$$

the *linearised Boltzmann equation.* If no (macroscopic) velocity gradients are present in the system, one has a solution

$$\phi^i = -\boldsymbol{A}^{iq} \cdot \frac{\nabla T}{T} - \sum_{j=1}^{n-1} \boldsymbol{B}^{ij} \cdot T\nabla \frac{\mu^j - \mu^n}{T} \tag{9.35}$$

with coefficients $\boldsymbol{A}^{iq}$ and $\boldsymbol{B}^{ij}$, which may be found from the equation 9.34. However, for the present purpose no further information on these coefficients is needed. Expression 9.35 contains the gradients of the temperature T and of the chemical potentials μ^i, that is, the *thermodynamic forces.*

9.3.2 Linear laws and transport coefficients

Substitution of the solution 9.35 into the general expressions for the heat flow $\boldsymbol{I}^q$ and the diffusion flows $\boldsymbol{I}^i$ yields linear laws between these thermodynamic fluxes and the thermodynamic forces, which are in the present case the gradients of the temperature and of the chemical potentials:

$$\boldsymbol{I}^q = -L^{qq} \frac{\nabla T}{T} - \sum_{j=1}^{n-1} L^{qj} T\nabla \frac{\mu^j - \mu^n}{T} \tag{9.36}$$

$$\boldsymbol{I}^i = -L^{iq} \frac{\nabla T}{T} - \sum_{j=1}^{n-1} L^{ij} T\nabla \frac{\mu^j - \mu^n}{T} \tag{9.37}$$

These linear laws contain as transport coefficients L^{qq}, which represents the heat conductivity, L^{qj} the Dufour coefficients, L^{iq} the thermal diffusion coefficients and L^{ij} the diffusion coefficients. The latter three, which are of interest here, may be written as

$$L^{qj} = \tfrac{1}{3}kT \sum_{k,m=1}^{n} (\boldsymbol{B}^{ki}, \boldsymbol{A}^{(km)q}) \tag{9.38}$$

$$L^{iq} = \tfrac{1}{3}kT \sum_{k,m=1}^{n} (\boldsymbol{A}^{kq}, \boldsymbol{B}^{(km)i}) \tag{9.39}$$

$$L^{ij} = \tfrac{1}{3}kT \sum_{k,m=1}^{n} (\boldsymbol{B}^{kj}, \boldsymbol{B}^{(km)i}) \tag{9.40}$$

with quantities, called the *collision brackets*, of the type

$$(\boldsymbol{A}^k, \boldsymbol{B}^{(km)}) \equiv$$
$$-\int f_0^k f_0^m \boldsymbol{A}^k \cdot (\boldsymbol{B}'^k + \boldsymbol{B}'^m - \boldsymbol{B}^k - \boldsymbol{B}^m) W^{km}(\boldsymbol{u}'^k, \boldsymbol{u}'^m \,|\, \boldsymbol{u}^k, \boldsymbol{u}^m)\, d\boldsymbol{u}^k\, d\boldsymbol{u}^m\, d\boldsymbol{u}'^k\, d\boldsymbol{u}'^m \tag{9.41}$$

(indices i or q, that appear at the symbols $\boldsymbol{A}$ and $\boldsymbol{B}$ in equations 9.38 to 9.40 have been omitted here for convenience).

9.3.3 Microscopic time reversal invariance and Onsager reciprocal relations between transport coefficients

The following *theorem* will first be proved: the property of microscopic motion (time) reversal invariance:

$$W^{km}(\boldsymbol{u}^k, \boldsymbol{u}^m \,|\, \boldsymbol{u}'^k, \boldsymbol{u}'^m) = W^{km}(-\boldsymbol{u}'^k, -\boldsymbol{u}'^m \,|\, -\boldsymbol{u}^k, -\boldsymbol{u}^m) \tag{9.42}$$

implies that for the collision brackets the symmetry relation

$$\sum_{k,m} (\boldsymbol{A}^k, \boldsymbol{B}^{(km)}) = \sum_{k,m} (\boldsymbol{B}^k, \boldsymbol{A}^{(km)}) \tag{9.43}$$

holds.

Proof: interchanging the accented and nonaccented quantities in equation 9.41 yields the expression

$$(\boldsymbol{A}^k, \boldsymbol{B}^{(km)}) =$$
$$\int f_0^k f_0^m \boldsymbol{A}'^k (\boldsymbol{B}'^k + \boldsymbol{B}'^m - \boldsymbol{B}^k - \boldsymbol{B}^m) W^{km}(\boldsymbol{u}^k, \boldsymbol{u}^m \,|\, \boldsymbol{u}'^k, \boldsymbol{u}'^m)\, d\boldsymbol{u}^k\, d\boldsymbol{u}^m\, d\boldsymbol{u}'^k\, d\boldsymbol{u}'^m \tag{9.44}$$

where equation 9.33 has been used. Subsequently all velocities, which are integration variables, may be interchanged by their opposites. Then the property of motion (time) reversal invariance, equation 9.42, is used and one takes half the sum of the result and of expression 9.41. Now one takes the sum over the indices k and m. In the result k and m may be interchanged. Again half the sum of the result and of the original expression is now taken.

In this way one obtains finally

$$\sum_{k,m}(A^k, B^{(km)}) = \tfrac{1}{4}\sum_{k,m}\int f_0^k f_0^m (A'^k + A'^m - A^k - A^m) \times (B'^k + B'^m - B^k - B^m) W^{km}\, \mathrm{d}u^k\, \mathrm{d}u^m\, \mathrm{d}u'^k\, \mathrm{d}u'^m \quad (9.45)$$

This expression shows the validity of the symmetry relation 9.43. Q.E.D.

If the symmetry relation 9.43, which expresses now the microscopic time (motion) reversal invariance, is employed in the expressions 9.38 to 9.40 for the transport coefficients, one finds the Onsager reciprocal relations

$$L^{qi} = L^{iq} \quad (9.46)$$

$$L^{ij} = L^{ji} \quad (9.47)$$

The first set connects the Dufour coefficients to the thermal diffusion coefficients, while the second set interrelates the various cross-diffusion coefficients of a mixture.

9.3.4 Generalisations

Just as in the theory of section 9.2 one may study systems in external magnetic or Coriolis fields. Then the reciprocal relations have to be modified in the same way, as explained there. Furthermore one may study the scalar linear laws, valid for relaxation phenomena and chemical or nuclear reactions. Their cross-phenomena also obey a number of Onsager reciprocal relations. The linear laws of viscous flow contain two viscosities (for isotropic systems): the shear viscosity and the volume viscosity. If the latter phenomenon is present at the same time as a relaxation process one obtains a minus sign in the reciprocal relations, as a result of the interplay of alpha and beta-variables, as shown by the second relation of 9.26. If the systems consist of spherical particles one may derive Onsager reciprocal relations from the so-called detailed balancing property, which itself follows from the spherical symmetry mentioned. Thus in this case the Onsager relations do not necessarily reflect time reversal invariance, although they might alternatively be derived from that property.

It might be noted in passing that space symmetries of the system are also reflected in the scheme of transport coefficients. For instance, for isotropic systems the *Curie principle* may be proved. It states that thermodynamic fluxes and thermodynamic forces of vectorial character are coupled by scalars, and that thermodynamic forces of different tensorial character do not couple. This situation was found to be present in the preceding sections, since throughout the systems were supposed to be isotropic. For crystals however different schemes have been set up.

In particle physics one employs usually the collision cross-section σ rather than the transition rate W. For the case of the collision of two particles with masses m_i and m_j one has the connection

$$W = m_i m_j (m_i + m_j)^2 \delta(E_i' + E_j' - E_i - E_j)\delta^{(3)}(m_i \boldsymbol{u}_i' + m_j \boldsymbol{u}_j' - m_i \boldsymbol{u}_i - m_j \boldsymbol{u}_j)\sigma \quad (9.48)$$

where E_i, etc. are the energies of the particles. Quantities without and with dashes refer to properties before and after the collision respectively. The delta-functions reflect the properties of energy and momentum conservation.

9.4 Relativistic Kinetic Theory

9.4.1 Massive particles

In recent years a relativistic kinetic theory has been created in which the properties of transport coefficients for relativistic systems have been derived. The basis of the theory is the relativistic version of the transport equation, which may be written as

$$p_\alpha^i \partial^\alpha f^i = \sum_j \int (f'^i f'^j W'^{ij} - f^i f^j W^{ij}) \frac{d^3 p^j}{p^{j0}} \frac{d^3 p'^i}{p'^{i0}} \frac{d^3 p'^j}{p'^{j0}} \quad (9.49)$$

This equation has covariant properties: in particular the distribution functions and the momentum volume elements $d^3 p/p^0$ are covariants. With the use of the (relativistic) bilateral normalisation property

$$\int W^{ij} \frac{d^3 p'^i}{p'^{i0}} \frac{d^3 p'^j}{p'^{j0}} = \int W'^{ij} \frac{d^3 p'^i}{p^{i0}} \frac{d^3 p'^j}{p'^{j0}} \quad (9.50)$$

one obtains, after linearisation, the equation

$$p_\alpha^i \partial^\alpha f_0^i = f_0^i \sum_j \int f_0^j (\phi'^i + \phi'^j - \phi^i - \phi^j) W'^{ij} \frac{d^3 p^j}{p^{j0}} \frac{d^3 p'^i}{p'^{i0}} \frac{d^3 p'^j}{p'^{j0}} \quad (9.51)$$

which is the relativistic counterpart of the linearised equation 9.34. The transition rates depend again only on the three-momenta, since the zero-component of the four-momentum is dependent upon the other three. With the starting points just quoted, reciprocal relations may be derived according to a similar scheme, as employed in the nonrelativistic theory[6–10,37].

If external magnetic fields are present, many more phenomena arise, a number of which are related by means of reciprocal relations[8]. The case of scalar phenomena, such as relaxation processes and chemical or nuclear reactions, also contains reciprocal relations[9–10].

Since in the relativistic theory one employs the collision cross-section in lieu of the transition rate, their connection is given here

$$W = P^2 \delta^{(4)}(p' + p_1' - p - p_1)\sigma \quad (9.52)$$

for the collision of two particles with four-momentum p^α and p_1^α which become p'^α and $p_1'^\alpha$ after the collision. (P is the total momentum of the particles.) For the inverse collision one has

$$W' = P^2\delta^{(4)}(p'+p_1'-p-p_1)\sigma' \tag{9.53}$$

Both formulae show energy–momentum conservation, expressed by the presence of the delta-function.

9.4.2 Neutrinos

The example of a neutrino gas is interesting, because it represents the extremely relativistic case[7]. In fact, since these particles possess no mass, they are always animated with the speed of light c. They suffer only the so-called weak interaction, whereas in all preceding examples one had to deal with electromagnetic interactions. As a Hamiltonian one uses a product of four neutrino field operators and the appropriate Dirac-matrices. The coupling constant of the weak interaction is called G. This Hamiltonian gives rise to a cross-section

$$\sigma = \frac{G^2E^2}{4\pi^2\hbar^4c^4} \tag{9.54}$$

where E is the total energy of the colliding neutrinos in their centre-of-momentum system. Ultimately one finds for the neutrino gas as transport coefficients: the heat conductivity

$$\lambda = \frac{3\pi}{80}\frac{\hbar^4c^5}{G^2}\frac{1}{kT^2} \tag{9.55}$$

and the shear viscosity

$$\eta = \frac{3\pi}{184}\frac{\hbar^4c^3}{G^2}\frac{1}{kT} \tag{9.56}$$

both in the first approximation of the first Enskog order. Their quotient satisfies the relation

$$\frac{\lambda}{\eta}\frac{T}{c^2} = \frac{23}{10} \tag{9.57}$$

in remarkably close analogy to the *Eucken relation* of nonrelativistic theory, which may be cast in the form

$$\frac{\lambda}{\eta}\frac{T}{\overline{v^2}} = \frac{5}{4} \tag{9.58}$$

One notices the mean square velocity $\overline{v^2}$, which for neutrinos is c^2, and a numerical constant of the same order of magnitude as the one which appears in 9.57.

There are two kinds of neutrinos, depending on whether they are connected with electrons or muons, called e-neutrinos and mu-neutrinos. Mixtures would show heat conduction, diffusion and their cross-effects. The calculation scheme employed shows that these cross-effects (thermal diffusion and the Dufour-effect) are connected by a reciprocal relation of the Onsager type. So even in this extreme example, in principle, a reciprocal relation would be valid as a consequence of time reversal invariance, which is usually thought to be satisfied also in weak interaction.

9.5 Related Subjects

In the preceding sections the main lines of the theoretical basis of the Onsager relations have been outlined. Several subjects in the field of transport phenomena are related to the theory of reciprocal processes.

One of these is the question of the transformation properties of the Onsager relations[21,22,3,23]. Another point concerns quantum-theoretical proofs of the reciprocal relations[24–28]. Finally, it should be noted that the reciprocal relations have been brought into connection with the fluctuation–dissipation theorem and related properties[29–35].

Acknowledgements

The author is indebted to Professors T. D. Lee and M. A. Ruderman of Columbia University, New York, for suggesting to extend the relativistic theory to include calculations of the transport coefficients of a neutrino gas.

This investigation is part of the research program of the 'Stichting voor fundamenteel onderzoek der materie (F.O.M.)', which is financially supported by the 'Nederlandse organisatie voor zuiver-wetenschappelÿk onderzoek (Z.W.O.)'.

References

1. L. Onsager. *Phys. Rev.*, **37** (1931), 405; **38** (1931), 2265
2. H. B. G. Casimir. *Rev. Mod. Phys.*, **17** (1945) 343; or Philips *Res. Rep.*, **1** (1945) 185
3. S. R. de Groot and P. Mazur. *Nonequilibrium Thermodynamics*, North-Holland Publishing Co., Amsterdam (1962)
4. P. Mazur. In *Fundamental Problems in Statistical Mechanics*, NUFFIC Summer Course, Nijenrode, Netherlands (1961); compiled by E. G. D. Cohen, North-Holland Publishing Co., Amsterdam (1962)
5. S. R. de Groot, Ch. G. van Weert, W. Th. Hermens and W. A. van Leeuwen. *Physica*, **43** (1969), 109
6. S. R. de Groot, Ch. G. van Weert, W. Th. Hermens and W. A. van Leeuwen. *Physica*, **40** (1969), 581
7. W. A. van Leeuwen and S. R. de Groot. *Lettre al Nuovo Cimento*, **6** (1973), 470

8. Ch. G. van Weert. *Proc. Kon. Ned. Akad. Wet.*, B **73** (1971), 381, 397, 500, 517 (thesis, Amsterdam)
9. W. Th. Hermens. *Proc. Kon. Ned. Akad. Wet.*, B **74** (1971), 376, 387, 461, 478 (thesis, Amsterdam); W. Th. Hermens, W. A. van Leeuwen, Ch. G. van Weert and S. R. de Groot, *Physica*, **60** (1972), 472
10. Ch. G. van Weert, P. C. de Jagher and S. R. de Groot. *Physica*, in print
11. J. Meixner. *Ann. Physik*, **39** (1941), 333; **41** (1942), 409; **43** (1943), 244; *Z. Phys. Chem.*, B **53** (1943), 235
12. J. Meixner and H. G. Reik. *Encyclopedia of Physics*, **III-2** (1959)
13. I. Prigogine. *Etude Thermodynamique des Phénomènes Irréversibles*, Dunod, Paris and Desoer, Liège (1947)
14. S. R. de Groot. *Thermodynamics of Irreversible Processes*, North-Holland Publishing Co., Amsterdam (1951)
15. P. Mazur and S. R. de Groot. *Physica*, **19** (1953), 961
16. S. R. de Groot and P. Mazur. *Phys. Rev.*, **94** (1954) 218; P. Mazur and S. R. de Groot. *Phys. Rev.*, **94** (1954), 224
17. R. Fieschi, S. R. de Groot and P. Mazur. *Physica*, **20** (1954), 67
18. R. Fieschi, S. R. de Groot, P. Mazur and J. Vlieger. *Physica*, **20** (1954), 245
19. S. R. de Groot and N. G. van Kampen. *Physica*, **21** (1955), 39
20. E. P. Wigner. *J. Chem. Phys.*, **22** (1954), 1912; an early discussion of this point
21. J. Meixner. *Ann. Phys.*, **43** (1943), 244
22. G. J. Hooyman and S. R. de Groot, *Physica*, **21** (1955), 73
23. J. Meixner. *Advances in Molecular Relaxation*, (1973), in print
24. N. G. van Kampen. *Physica*, **20** (1954), 603; *Fortschritte der Physik*, **4** (1956), 405
25. J. Vlieger, P. Mazur and S. R. de Groot. *Physica*, **27** (1961), 353, 957, 974
26. K. M. van Vliet. *Phys. Rev.*, **110** (1958), 50; **133** (1964), A1182; **138** (1965), AB3
27. K. M. van Vliet and J. R. Fassett. In *Fluctuation Phenomena in Solids*, ed. by R. E. Burgess, Academic Press, New York, 267–359, (1965)
28. K. M. van Vliet. *J. Math. Phys.*, **12** (1971), 1981, 1998
29. H. B. Callen and T. A. Welton. *Phys. Rev.*, **83** (1951), 34
30. M. S. Green. *J. Chem. Phys.*, **19** (1951), 1036
31. H. B. Callen and R. F. Greene. *Phys. Rev.*, **86** (1952), 702
32. H. B. Callen, M. L. Barasch and J. L. Jackson. *Phys. Rev.*, **88** (1952), 1382
33. R. F. Greene and H. B. Callen. *Phys. Rev.*, **88** (1952), 1387
34. R. Kubo. *J. Phys. Soc. Japan*, **12** (1957), 570; Lectures *Theor. Phys.*, Boulder Summer School, **1** (1958)
35. J. Meixner. *Macroscopic and Microscopic Reversibility*, preprint
36. Other work, relevant to the problem treated here, was performed by authors, quoted in the references given above. Let me mention a number of the most important names: E. P. Wigner, J. Meixner, I. Prigogine, L. Waldmann, S. Machlup, R. Defay, P. Outer, Cl. Herbo, R. Buess, M. S. Green, C. Eckart, H. G. Reik, J. Ross, S. Ono, G. J. Hooyman, H. Holtan Jr., G. A. Kluitenberg, R. Fieschi, H. A. Tolhoek, J. Th. G. Overbeek, L. Jansen, A. J. Staverman, N. G. van Kampen, H. König, P. J. Dunlop, L. J. Gosting, K. J. Hansen, F. Schwarzl, D. Polder, A. N. Gerritsen, G. Falk, B. Manz, R. Haase, W. Hackenbroch, C. A. Domenicali, G. M. Rancoita, N. Hashitsume, E. P. Rastogi, R. C. Srivastava, W. A. Day and M. E. Gurtin
37. The work on relativistic kinetic theory was done mainly by A. Lichnerowicz, R. Marrot, W. Israel, J. Guichelaar, W. Th. Hermens, P. C. de Jagher, A. J. Kox, W. A. van Leeuwen, P. H. Meltzer, P. H. Polak and Ch. G. van Weert. For detailed references, see the review articles: S. R. de Groot, *Acta Physica Austriaca Suppl.*,

10 (1973), 529; *Physica*, (1973); and *Zeitschr. Physik.*, (1973); the latter two are in print. See also: S. R. de Groot, W. A. van Leeuwen and Ch. G. van Weert. Elements of relativistic kinetic theory, in *A. Katzir-Katchalsky Memorial Volume*, (1973). The reciprocal relations 9.46 were verified by A. J. Kox through explicit calculation of the transport coefficients L_{iq} and L_{qi}.

For particles without internal degrees of freedom volume viscosity is shown to be a relativistic phenomenon in the framework of kinetic theory; thus also the reciprocal relation mentioned in section 9.3.4, which arises if volume viscous flow and a relaxation process occur together.

38. J. Bernstein, G. Feinberg and T. D. Lee. *Phys. Rev.*, **139** (1965), B 1650; L. Wolfenstein. *Phys. Rev. Lett.*, **13** (1964), 562; D. Bailin. *Rep. Prog. Phys.*, **35** (1971), 491

Discussion

CALLEN

Professor de Groot has given two derivations of the Onsager relations, basing each in the μ-space of Boltzmann, in accordance with the spirit of this symposium. He has referred only in passing to the more penetrating statistical mechanical analyses to which he has himself contributed so importantly. I think it useful briefly to recall the latter, particularly as I note that Professors Miller and Mason will appeal for a more transparent foundation of the Onsager relations.

The Onsager reciprocal relations are embedded in a more general result—the so-called fluctuation–dissipation theorem. That theorem establishes a relation between the response to applied forces and certain correlation functions in the equilibrium ensemble. The derivation makes remarkably few assumptions. One assumes a canonical distribution and one adjoins to the Hamiltonian a set of external coupling terms of the form

$$\mathscr{H} \rightarrow \mathscr{H} + \sum_i X_i F_i(t)$$

Here the X_i are state functions and the $F_i(t)$ are externally controlled amplitudes (such as magnetic fields, surfaces stresses, etc.). The time-dependences of the $F_i(t)$ are assumed to be controllable by the experimenter. The response of the density operator is determined by the Bloch equation and hence the response $\langle X_j(t) \rangle$ is determined. One expands this response in powers of the $F_i(t)$ by standard perturbation theory. It is not assumed that the system is linear, but the response does contain linear terms as well as higher-order terms. The linear terms in the response are best expressed in terms of the Fourier amplitudes $\langle X_j(\omega) \rangle$

$$\langle X_j(\omega) \rangle = \mathrm{a}(\omega) \sum_i \langle X_i X_j(\omega) \rangle_0 F_i(\omega)$$

where $a(\omega)$ is a (known) universal function of ω, $\langle X_i X_j(\omega) \rangle_0$ is the Fourier amplitudes of the unperturbed correlation function $\langle X_i X_j(t) \rangle_0$, and $\mathrm{F}_i(\omega)$ is the Fourier amplitude of $F_i(t)$. Hence the response functions are found to be proportional to the unperturbed correlation functions

$$L_{ij}(\omega) \alpha \langle X_i X_j(\omega) \rangle_0$$

The familiar Onsager argument on the time-symmetry of the correlation functions then implies the symmetry of the response-function $L_{ij}(\omega)$

(assuming it is even under time-reversal for simplicity)

$$L_{ij}(\omega) = L_{ji}(\omega)$$

The purpose of this vague repetition of the proof is to make the following points.

(1) The result follows for the linear terms in the response even though higher-order terms may be present and, indeed, large.

(2) No assumptions of *local state* need be separately introduced. The result is a consequence of perturbation theory around the equilibrium state, and the convergence of such a perturbation theory is assumed, but this is a much less mysterious statement than the presumption of *local equilibrium* or *local state.*

(3) The relationship of response functions to equilibrium correlations is a *result* not an assumption. It justifies Onsager's assertion that the macroscopic processes follow the same laws as the regression of fluctuations—an assertion which has been questioned by some.

(4) The role of these equilibrium correlations is clarified by virtue of their appearance as Fourier components. The physics is suggested by the quantum field theoretic picture of *spontaneous* emission of excited atoms; that picture is that the transitions are *induced* by the fluctuations of the zero-point fluctuations of the vacuum radiation field. Similarly the applied forces $F_i(t)$ can be thought of as being generated by a set of macroscopic oscillators (or *signal generators*). Transitions of these oscillators are *induced* by the thermodynamic fluctuations in the spectral region of the oscillators.

(5) It is clear that the Onsager reciprocity applies to processes which may be either irreversible or purely reversible when driven slowly. Thus the force can be a magnetic field and the response a magnetic moment, the response function L_{11}, then vanishing at zero frequency. This is in contrast to the process of electrical current flow which may have a non-zero *d.c. response*, and which is dissipative even at zero frequency.

(6) The criterion for choice of forces and responses is shifted from the level of a phenomenological entropy production function to a Hamiltonian formalism.

Admittedly, there are shortcomings to this approach. Driving temperatures or driving chemical potential variations cannot be represented by additive coupling terms adjoined to the Hamiltonian. I think this difference is real and that the failure of TIP to distinguish them is an intrinsic imprecision within TIP. To derive the relevant Onsager relations we presumably would have to interpose an auxiliary thermodynamic system. This auxiliary system must be supposed to have very short relaxation times and to be in intimate thermal contact with the primary system. Then we drive the auxiliary system by Hamiltonian coupling. Its temperature follows *instantly* because of the assumed short relaxation time and it, in turn, drives the primary system. This mathematical stratagem in fact mirrors physical reality.

The extension of the method to gradient forces has been discussed by Professor de Groot in a reference quoted in his paper.

Thus questions concerning the Onsager relations, more or less obscure at the microscopic level, appear in a different and sometimes clearer perspective at the statistical mechanical level. The inverse is also true.

DE GROOT

I thank Professor Callen for his interesting comments and for his kind opinion of the account by Mazur and myself (references 3 and 4) of the fluctuation–dissipation theorem. I had indeed counted on him discussing this important subject, as a result of his work with Greene, and limited myself to the derivations of the Onsager relations in the frameworks of the statistical theory of macroscopic variables and the kinetic theory of gases.

PRIGOGINE

I would like to present a few small remarks

(1) The reciprocity relations had been discussed prior to Onsager, by Lorentz and Bohr in the frame of kinetic theories for dilute gases. Already Bohr had observed that they were based solely on microscopic reversibility. The great merit of Onsager was to present a proof independent of any kinetic model and therefore applicable to all states of matter.

(2) While there is no doubt about the validity of the original proof due to Onsager, in the proofs presented by de Groot one would like to have an even more direct derivation. For example in the frame of weakly coupled quantum systems, the Onsager relations reduce to Fermi's *golden rule* for transition probabilities. This type of proof, in which Onsager's relations become a theorem in dynamics, can now be extended to more general situations (see Prigogine, George, Henin, Rosenfeld, Royal Swedish Academy, *Classica Scripta*).

(3) Many people have written Boltzmann's equation in covariant form. This is however, only one aspect of the problem. Another very important aspect is the discussion of the Lorentz invariance of the reduced description of dynamics in terms of velocity distribution. These deeper aspects have been studied by R. Balescu and his coworkers in the last years. A remarkable result is, for example, that relaxation times are *scalars* (and not fourth components of vectors in space time).

(4) As Professor Callen has pointed out, there is a difference between mechanical variables (such as electric fields) and nonmechanical variables

(such as temperature gradients). In the first case the application of the Callen–Green–Kubo response formalism is obvious, in the second it is not. A few years ago Résibois gave the first general proof, to my knowledge, of the validity of the response formalism to thermal variables. He also more recently introduced a new technique which simplifies greatly the classical Chapman–Enskog method. This new technique deserves to be widely known, as it shows that the Chapman–Enskog method can be reduced to an elementary problem identical to that of quantum mechanical perturbation theory.

DE GROOT

(1) In discussions of the historical background of the reciprocal relations, remarks similar to Professor Prigogine's have been made before (see, for example, reference 14). I shall suppose that in his remark rather than 'the frame of kinetic theories of dilute gases' the electron theory of metals is meant, since both Lorentz and Bohr wrote papers on the latter subject, not on the former. The problem concerned is Thomson's (Kelvin's) second relation (connecting thermoelectric power and Peltier heat), which today is understood as an Onsager reciprocal relation. Lorentz treated the problem in 1905 in the context of his electron theory. He does show that the second Thomson relation is satisfied, as does Bohr in his doctor's dissertation (1911). However, I have not been able to find the alleged statement 'that they (the reciprocal relations) were based solely on microscopic reversibility', neither in the original papers, nor in the lectures and review articles of these authors. (Only in a paper by E. A. Uehling of 1932 reference is made to the principle of detailed balancing. But this paper is posterior to Onsager, and Uehling quotes Onsager's proof.) In this light there seems no doubt of the priority of Onsager's insight, which at any rate was much more general, even if the claim discussed above, were true.

(2) A slight misunderstanding might arise from the first phrase of this remark. The first proof which I gave *is* the original proof due to Onsager, as I indicated in my paper, the only difference residing in the notation and in the clarification of Onsager's use of formula, equation 9.10, which had been criticised in the past.

Prigogine refers to the theory of weakly coupled quantum systems. While it is indeed possible to derive Onsager relations, albeit from detailed balancing and not from time reversal invariance, this procedure constitutes a serious limitation, because one can only treat *grazing* collisions instead of the arbitrarily strong collisions which may be treated in the kinetic theory. An extension to more general situations is then indeed needed.

(3) It is true that many people have written Boltzmann's equation in

covariant form. They are all quoted in the papers referred to in reference 37. It is also true that this is only one aspect of the problem: the proof of the covariance of the various quantities and equations is indeed one of the problems. However, many more people than the authors quoted in your remark have written on this problem. I mention J. L. Synge, *The Relativistic Gas*, North-Holland Publishing Co., Amsterdam (1957) (only for free particles); R. Hakim, *J. Math. Phys.*, **8** (1967), 1315; N. G. van Kampen, *Physica*, **43** (1969), 244; Ch. G. van Weert, *Proc. Kon. Ned. Akad. Wet.*, B **73** (1970), 381; S. R. de Groot and L. G. Suttorp, *Foundations of Electrodynamics*, North-Holland Publishing Co., Amsterdam (1972); S. R. de Groot, W. A. van Leeuwen and Ch. G. van Weert, in Volume dedicated to the memory of Aharon Katzir-Katchalsky (Foreword: D. Gabor; ed. by B. Gal-Or), Jerusalem (1973). Moreover many other results have been obtained: the laws of relativistic thermodynamics and hydrodynamics were derived and values were given for the relativistic transport coefficients of a number of systems (see references 6–10 and 37 and papers quoted therein).

(4) This is a remark on Professor Callen's intervention. I suppose that he will give a reply to this question.

MÜLLER

(1) From Professor de Groot's lecture and a talk I had with Professor de Groot afterwards I conclude that in the relativistic kinetic theory which he uses, the heat flux in a body at rest comes out as proportional at the gradient of temperature. Now, according to the results which Chernikov derives from the relativistic kinetic theory, the heat flux should be a linear combination of the gradients of temperature and density. This by itself, of course, would raise some problems in regard to Onsager relations; however, my question is a different one.

Chernikov's form of the heat flux is perfectly consistent with Tolman's result that, in equilibrium, the temperature in a gravitational field is nonuniform; now it seems to me that Professor de Groot's form of the heat flux is not consistent with that result and I should like to hear Professor de Groot's comments on that.

(2) In reaction to this discussion I should like to call attention to the fact, or what I think is a fact, that it is not only the assumption of a linear regression of fluctuation that goes into the Onsager relations, but rather the assumption that that linear regression has the same relaxation time as the regression of macroscopic deviations from equilibrium. In other words: we have here two distinct questions, the concentration of a chemical constituent, (say) in relaxation toward equilibrium, and a function constructed from many fluctuations which describe the mean regression of fluctuations. Both functions are assumed not only to be exponential but the *same* exponential,

and this to me seems to be the steepest assumption in the statistical motivation of the Onsager relations.

DE GROOT

(1) The point raised is important. I shall therefore briefly indicate why the inconsistency which Professor Müller thinks there is, does not exist. N. A. Chernikov[a] and before him W. Israel[b]† use as thermodynamic driving force in their expression for the heat flow (in a single system) the quantity

$$\Delta^{\alpha\beta}\partial_\beta\left(\frac{\mu}{T}\right) \tag{9.59}$$

(see list of symbols at the end of this reply). An alternative form of this force is our result

$$-\frac{h}{T^2}\Delta^{\alpha\beta}\left(\partial_\beta T+\frac{TDU_\beta}{c^2}\right) \tag{9.60}$$

as follows if one eliminates the pressure from the relativistic Gibbs–Duhem relation

$$\rho^{-1}\partial_\alpha p = s\partial_\alpha T+\partial_\alpha\mu \tag{9.61}$$

with the help of the connection[c]

$$DU^\alpha = -\frac{c^2}{\rho h}\Delta^{\alpha\beta}\partial_\beta p \tag{9.62}$$

In 9.60 the Eckart term DU_β/c^2 occurs[d]. It does not vanish for a system at rest, as may be seen from equation 9.62. If one consistently uses the combination $\partial_\beta T+TDU_\beta/c^2$ (or μ/T) no problems arise with regard to the Onsager relations[e]. Since moreover the thermodynamic force, 9.60, occurring in our treatment is proportional to the form 9.59 used by Chernikov (and others), our theory is also consistent with Tolman's work.

Still another form, linear in the gradients $\partial_\alpha T$ and $\partial_\alpha\rho$ may be obtained for the thermodynamic force, if one uses the expression

$$\mu = \frac{kT}{m}\ln\frac{A\rho}{4\pi m^3 ckTK_2(mc^2/kT)} \tag{9.63}$$

for the thermodynamic potential[c].

Symbols

Metric $g_{\alpha\beta} = \mathrm{diag}(-1, 1, 1, 1)$; speed of light c; hydrodynamic velocity U^α; projector $\Delta_{\alpha\beta} = g_{\alpha\beta}+U_\alpha U_\beta/c^2$; time-space coordinates $x^\alpha = (ct, \mathbf{r})$; time-

† See references at end of this section.

space derivatives $\partial_\alpha \equiv \partial/\partial x^\alpha$; thermodynamic potential μ; temperature T; enthalpy h; mass density ρ; pressure p; enthalpy s; particle mass m; Boltzmann's constant k; Bessel function of second order $K_n(x)$; and the arbitrary constant A, which makes the argument of the logarithm in equation 9.63 dimensionless.

References

a N. A. Chernikov. *Acta Physica Polonica*, **27** (1964), 465. Comparison of equations 4.4 and 8.16 with equation 88 of reference c leads to 9.59
b W. Israel. *J. Math. Phys.*, **4** (1963), 1163
c S. R. de Groot, Ch. G. van Weert, W. Th. Hermens and W. A. van Leeuwen. *Physica*, **40** (1968), 257. Equations 9.61 to 9.63 correspond to equations 86, 116 and 129 of this article
d C. Eckart. *Phys. Rev.*, **58** (1940), 919. A macroscopic treatment
e S. R. de Groot, Ch. G. van Weert, W. Th. Hermens and W. A. van Leeuwen. *Physica*, **40** (1969), 581

(2) In the statistical theory the same linear regression law is indeed assumed to hold for the mean regression of fluctuations and for the regression of macroscopic deviations from equilibrium. The limits of the validity of this hypothesis, which does not seem unreasonable, can strictly be assessed only on the basis of a purely microscopic theory. Experimental support comes from Svedberg's and Westgren's experiments on colloid statistics, which show that the behaviour of *small* density fluctuations is on the average in perfect agreement with the macroscopic law of diffusion (*cf.* reference 3, in particular pages 100–103).

GERMAIN

I would like you to comment on a statement that, if I am not mistaken, you made earlier on volumetric viscosity. It seems to me it was said that kinetic theory shows that volumetric viscosity is zero in the nonrelativistic case. Phenomenologically speaking we know that, for isotropic fluids, two viscosity coefficients are needed. Have some measurements been made? What precisely are the results you can derive from a statistical theory or from a kinetic theory as far as the volumetric viscosity is concerned?

DE GROOT

Volume viscosity vanishes in the nonrelativistic kinetic theory of gases, but is different from zero in the relativistic version of that theory. This is not to say that it is a relativistic effect. It may occur in systems, which are not described by the kinetic theory of gases. In fact, the dense state theory of Enskog does yield a nonvanishing volume viscosity. Its effect is also observed in the absorption of sound waves.

GERMAIN

I was quite interested by your lecture in which you produce various proofs of the Onsager reciprocal relations (ORR) all starting from a microscopic description.

Now, people working in continuum mechanics are mostly interested in the application of the ORR they may have to use after writing their entropy production as a sum of products of so-called *fluxes and forces*. How is your derivation related to this kind of application? Is it possible to give a good and complete recipe to people who have to apply ORR without introducing microscopic considerations but resting on pure macroscopic concepts? Maybe this question will be clarified by Dr. Miller and Dr. Mason in chapters 10 and 11. But I want to insist that, in my view, it is very important to clarify, as much as possible, the structure of ORR on a purely macroscopic level.

DE GROOT

The Onsager reciprocal relations really are postulates in the framework of macroscopic theory (thermodynamics of irreversible processes), as explained in the textbooks (for example, references 3, 12, 13, 14) and mentioned in your remark. In a microscopic model they may be derived (see chapter 9, and reference 3). It then turns out that their validity seems fairly general, so that one may trust the postulate of macroscopic physics to hold under a large variety of circumstances. Indeed, as Professor Miller's paper brilliantly shows (chapter 10), the Onsager relations are experimentally confirmed for vastly differing examples under an extremely wide class of physical circumstances.

MEIXNER

I believe I understand Professor Germain's question. If the entropy production is given by

$$\sigma = X_1 Y_1 + X_2 Y_2$$

where restriction to two fluxes X_i and two forces Y_i is made, are these the fluxes and forces for which in the rate equations Onsager–Casimir reciprocal relations (OCRR) hold? This question is justified because one could also write

$$\sigma = X_1(Y_1 + \alpha X_2) + X_2(Y_2 - \alpha X_1)$$

with the fluxes X_1, X_2 and the forces $Y_1 + \alpha X_2$, $Y_2 - \alpha X_1$ where α is an arbitrary constant, and for these new fluxes and forces the OCRR may not hold if they hold for the original fluxes and forces.

But it is clear that the OCRR can be applied only if the fluxes and forces have definite parity with respect to time reversal, that is, are even or odd, and the first thing to examine is whether the forces $Y_1 + \alpha X_2$ and $Y_2 - \alpha X_1$ have definite parity if the X_i, Y_i have.

Assume for instance, X_1, X_2 even, Y_1, Y_2 odd. Then $Y_1 + \alpha X_2$ and $Y_2 - \alpha X_1$

have no definite parity and the OCRR cannot be applied at all with the second form of the entropy production. But if X_1 is even, X_2 odd, and correspondingly Y_1 is odd, Y_2 even, then $Y_1+\alpha X_2$ and $Y_2-\alpha X_1$ have obviously definite parity. But then one can prove that the OCRR hold in the second choice of forces and fluxes if they hold in the first choice.

A general discussion of the linear transformations, which transform fluxes and forces of definite parities to others of definite parities and which consequently preserve the OCRR, is given in a forthcoming paper.

RIVLIN

In this note I shall derive a theorem which has recently been proven by Edelen, and which may have some interest in connection with the extension of the Onsager–Casimir relations to the nonlinear case.

Edelen's Theorem

We consider a set of constitutive equations for which the ν *forces* $J_\alpha(\alpha = 1, \ldots, \nu)$ are functions of the ν *fluxes* $v_\beta(\beta = 1, \ldots, \nu)$ and of μ further variables $\omega_\gamma(\gamma = 1, \ldots, \mu)$, so that

$$J_\alpha = J_\alpha(v_\beta, \omega_\gamma) \tag{9.64}$$

It is assumed that v's and ω's can be varied independently. We may regard the J_α and v_α as the components of vectors $\boldsymbol{J}$ and $\boldsymbol{v}$ in a ν-dimensional space, and ω_β as the components of a vector $\boldsymbol{\omega}$ in a μ-dimensional space. Then equation 9.64 may be written as

$$\boldsymbol{J} = \boldsymbol{J}(\boldsymbol{v}, \boldsymbol{\omega}) \tag{9.65}$$

The power P of the *forces* is given by

$$P = v_\alpha J_\alpha \tag{9.66}$$

or, in vector notation, by

$$P = \boldsymbol{v}\cdot\boldsymbol{J} \tag{9.67}$$

We now define a scalar function Ψ of $\boldsymbol{v}$ and $\boldsymbol{\omega}$ by

$$\Psi = \int_0^1 \boldsymbol{v}\cdot\boldsymbol{J}(\tau\boldsymbol{v}, \boldsymbol{\omega})\,d\tau \tag{9.68}$$

Then

$$\begin{aligned}\frac{\partial\Psi}{\partial v_\alpha} &= \int_0^1 J_\alpha(\tau\boldsymbol{v}, \boldsymbol{\omega})\,d\tau + \int_0^1 \tau v_\beta \frac{\partial J_\beta(\tau\boldsymbol{v}, \boldsymbol{\omega})}{\partial(\tau v_\alpha)}\,d\tau \\ &= \int_0^1 J_\alpha(\tau\boldsymbol{v}, \boldsymbol{\omega})\,d\tau + \int_0^1 \tau v_\beta \frac{\partial J_\alpha(\tau\boldsymbol{v}, \boldsymbol{\omega})}{\partial(\tau v_\beta)}\,d\tau \\ &\quad + \int_0^1 \tau v_\beta \left\{\frac{\partial J_\beta(\tau\boldsymbol{v}, \boldsymbol{\omega})}{\partial(\tau v_\alpha)} - \frac{\partial J_\alpha(\tau\boldsymbol{v}, \boldsymbol{\omega})}{\partial(\tau v_\beta)}\right\} d\tau\end{aligned} \tag{9.69}$$

We note that

$$\int_0^1 \tau v_\beta \frac{\partial J_\alpha(\tau \boldsymbol{v}, \boldsymbol{\omega})}{\partial(\tau v_\beta)} \mathrm{d}\tau = \int_0^1 \tau \frac{\mathrm{d}}{\mathrm{d}\tau}[J_\alpha(\tau \boldsymbol{v}, \boldsymbol{\omega})] \mathrm{d}\tau \tag{9.70}$$

Denoting the last integral in equation 9.69 by $-U_\alpha$, we note that

$$v_\alpha U_\alpha = 0 \tag{9.71}$$

With equation 9.70, we can rewrite equation 9.69 as

$$\frac{\partial \Psi}{\partial v_\alpha} = \int_0^1 J_\alpha(\tau \boldsymbol{v}, \boldsymbol{\omega}) \mathrm{d}\tau + \int_0^1 \tau \frac{\mathrm{d}}{\mathrm{d}\tau}[J_\alpha(\tau \boldsymbol{v}, \boldsymbol{\omega})] \mathrm{d}\tau - U_\alpha \tag{9.72}$$

From equation 9.72, we obtain

$$J_\alpha = \frac{\partial \Psi}{\partial v_\alpha} + U_\alpha \tag{9.73}$$

where Ψ is given by equation 9.68 and U_α satisfies equation 9.71. Thus, the *force* vector is expressible as the sum of the gradient, with respect to the *flux* vector $\boldsymbol{v}$, of a scalar function of $\boldsymbol{v}$ and $\boldsymbol{\omega}$ and a powerless term.

If the constitutive equation does not contain a powerless term, that is $U_\alpha = 0$, then

$$\frac{\partial J_\alpha}{\partial v_\beta} = \frac{\partial J_\beta}{\partial v_\alpha} \tag{9.74}$$

and the constitutive equation satisfies a generalised Onsager relation. The relation 9.74 is, of course, the Onsager relation, if the J's are linear in the v's. In the linear case, in which we can write

$$J_\alpha = A_{\alpha\beta} v_\beta \tag{9.75}$$

where $A_{\alpha\beta}$ are constants, Edelen's theorem reduces to the well-known fact that any square matrix $A_{\alpha\beta}$ can be expressed as the sum of a symmetric and a skew-symmetric matrix.

It can easily be shown that the decomposition 9.73 is unique. Suppose there are two such decompositions $\Psi^{(1)}$, $\boldsymbol{U}^{(1)}$ and $\Psi^{(2)}$, $\boldsymbol{U}^{(2)}$. From equation 9.73, we obtain

$$\frac{\partial}{\partial V_\alpha}(\Psi^{(1)} - \Psi^{(2)}) = -(\boldsymbol{U}^{(1)} - \boldsymbol{U}^{(2)}) \tag{9.76}$$

From this, it follows that

$$V_\alpha \frac{\partial}{\partial V_\alpha}(\Psi^{(1)} - \Psi^{(2)}) = 0 \tag{9.77}$$

Thus, from Euler's theorem, $\Psi^{(1)} - \Psi^{(2)}$ is a constant and the decomposition 9.73 is unique.

The above results are contained in a paper by D. G. B. Edelen, which is pending publication in the *Archive for Rational Mechanics and Analysis.*

DE GROOT

Edelen's treatment is an example of a theory in which the Onsager relations are not derived from a microscopic basis, but from an appropriate set of macroscopic assumptions, valid also for nonlinear phenomena.

SIDOROFF

If I correctly understood what was said, the situation is the following: when from a macroscopic point of view we derive the entropy production inequality by using a nonequilibrium entropy and Gibbs' relations, then we must use linear rate equations in order to be consistent with statistical mechanics. In other words, we cannot claim the support of statistical mechanics for assuming nonlinear rate equations and some kind of nonlinear generalisation of Onsager's relation from this expression of $T\sigma$. Am I correct?

DE GROOT

Linear regression laws are consistent with bilinear entropy production expressions and with the validity of the Gibbs entropy law, as was proved in kinetic theory by Prigogine for the ordinary transport processes, such as heat conduction, diffusion, viscous flow and their cross-effects. For chemical reactions however, exponential regression laws are consistent with the Gibbs law and bilinear entropy production.

Inversely, if one used nonlinear laws, one would also have to modify the Gibbs relation: the local entropy would then no longer depend on the local energy and the local mass density only (in the example of a one-component system) but also explicitly on the gradients of the latter quantities.

10. The Onsager Relations; Experimental Evidence

Donald G. Miller†

Abstract

The Onsager reciprocal relations (ORR) are a postulate of a linear thermodynamic theory of irreversible processes. This postulate states roughly that the matrix of linear coefficients L between properly chosen *flows* J and *forces* X is symmetric, that is

$$L_{ij} = L_{ji}$$

The concept of *proper choice* has been criticised and will be briefly discussed.

Many phenomena are linear in the normal ranges of *force* variables, such as diffusion, thermal diffusion, transport in electrolyte solutions, heat and electrical conduction in solids, electrokinetic effects, and thermogalvanomagnetic effects. Appropriate experimental evidence in these cases will be reviewed, including recent experiments. The conclusion is that the ORR are valid within acceptable error limits.

Workers in continuum mechanics are challenged to find by their rigorous methods the macroscopic origin of this fundamental symmetry principle.

10.1 Introduction

Irreversible processes are now usually described macroscopically in two major forms. One is the *thermodynamics of irreversible processes* (TIP) as originally set out by Onsager[1], and developed by Meixner[2], Prigogine[3], de Groot[4], and others[5,6]. The other, *continuum thermodynamics* (CT) is based on more general analysis of the mechanical and constitutive equations describing continuum processes[7,8,9]. Some of the major contributors to this theory are Truesdell[10], Coleman and Noll[11], Gurtin[12,13,14], and Müller[15].

The TIP is a simpler, linear theory whose origins lie in the 19th century. It is based on the linear laws of Ohm[16], Fick[17] and Fourier[18]; the entropy production calculations of Bertrand[19], Duhem[20], Natanson[21], Jaumann[22,23] and Lohr[24]; and the symmetry or reciprocity relations originally developed on an *ad hoc* basis, such as Kelvin's for thermoelectricity[25], Saxèn's for electrokinetics[26], Stokes' for the heat conductivity tensor[27], Helmholtz's for the cell and Hittorf transference numbers[28], and Wegscheider's for chemical reactions[29]. All these different phenomena can be neatly described by the

† Lawrence Livermore Laboratory, University of California, Livermore.

same TIP formalism, which emphasises the Onsager reciprocal relations (ORR), namely, the symmetry of the linear coefficient matrix. Onsager[1] based his generalisation of these special case symmetries on statistical mechanical arguments, which have been extended and elaborated by others[30,31,32]. However, the formalism is entirely macroscopic; it is based on thermodynamic equations and assumptions; and it can be treated axiomatically as an empirical theory whose consequences are subject to experimental verification.

Linear theories are, of course, only approximations in a nonlinear world. The concepts of CT are more general and have been applied to nonlinear materials, including those with memory. The notation and arguments are naturally more complex and more difficult as befits a more general theory. The CT approach makes use of the following general principles[9]

(1) Balances of mass, energy, and momentum.

(2) Equipresence, that is, all variables are present in every constitutive equation unless prohibited by other principles.

(3) Objectivity, that is, properties are independent of the observer's reference frame.

(4) Entropy production (dissipation) is positive definite.

These principles (especially 4) are a powerful tool for the logical analysis of the effects of various constitutive assumptions and the general limitations on constitutive equations. So far, however, despite the generality of CT, none of its practitioners has shown in general how to obtain the ORR in linear approximations. Some special results do exist based on differing special hypotheses[33,34,35].

The TIP has been criticised by some CT workers, especially by Truesdell[9]. He has stated that

(1) The foundations are vague and uncertain.

(2) There exists no logical way to choose the *forces* and *flows* so as to require the ORR.

(3) Experiments to test the ORR are either inapplicable or too inaccurate.

(4) Some kinetic theories may not yield symmetry relations.

(5) *Curie's theorem* is never proved.

(6) TIP does not do anything new.

Some criticisms have merit, but others are overstated and ultimately ignore a fundamental symmetry property that is not now present in the CT formalism.

In this paper we shall briefly review the fundamental equations, describe the choice of *flows* and *forces* of the linear constitutive equations, and discuss the empirical and axiomatic aspect of Onsager's hypothesis that the linear coefficient matrix is symmetric. We will then briefly exhibit some of the experimental evidence of this symmetry (that is, the ORR) for various cases such as diffusion, thermoelectricity, etc. Some detail will be provided for electrical transference in electrolyte solutions and for heat conduction in anisotropic crystals. We will then consider and try to answer some of the criticisms of TIP. We conclude that experiment shows the validity of the ORR for a large number of linear processes, and challenge the workers in rational mechanics to find general and more fundamental macroscopic hypotheses that will yield the ORR from their formulation of thermodynamics.

10.2 General Notions of TIP

10.2.1 Basic equations

The general thermodynamic assumptions of TIP are that thermodynamic variables, including entropy, have meaning away from equilibrium, and that in a system of varying properties, local equilibrium holds in a small enough subvolume so that the equations of thermodynamics are valid.

With these assumptions, the entropy production σ of a subvolume can be calculated

$$\sigma = \frac{1}{V}\left[\frac{\mathrm{d}S}{\mathrm{d}t} - \sum \frac{1}{T}\frac{\delta q}{\mathrm{d}t}\right] \tag{10.1}$$

where S is the entropy of the system of volume V, t is the time, and T is the temperature of the surroundings at the boundary across which the heat δq is transported into the system. The $\sum$ allows for different boundaries at different temperatures and δ refers to an inexact differential (that is, δq depends on the path of the process).

In simple cases, $T\sigma$ is a product of easily recognisable *forces* and *flows*. Thus, for electrical and heat conduction, respectively, in one dimension

$$T\sigma = IE \tag{10.2}$$

$$T\sigma = J_q\left(-\frac{1}{T}\frac{\mathrm{d}T}{\mathrm{d}x}\right) \tag{10.3}$$

where I is the current, E is the emf $(-\mathrm{d}\phi/\mathrm{d}x)$, x is the distance, ϕ is the electrical potential, and J_q is the flow of heat. For more complicated systems with more than one irreversible process occurring, $T\sigma$ can be recognised as the sum of such product terms. Thus, for a nonviscous fluid of $(l+1)$ constituents in a gravitational field with m chemical reactions and with gradients of concentration and temperature, we find that in one dimension and in molar units[36]

$$T\sigma = \left(-\frac{1}{A}\frac{\delta q}{\mathrm{d}t}\right)\left[-\frac{1}{T}\frac{\mathrm{d}T}{\mathrm{d}x}\right] + \sum_{k=0}^{l}\left(-\frac{1}{A}\frac{\mathrm{d}n_k}{\mathrm{d}t}\right)\left[-\left(M_k g + e_k\frac{\mathrm{d}\phi}{\mathrm{d}x} + T\frac{\mathrm{d}(\mu_k/T)}{\mathrm{d}x}\right)\right] + \sum_{j=1}^{m}\left(\frac{\mathrm{d}\xi_j}{\mathrm{d}t}\right)\left[-\mathscr{A}_j\right] \quad (10.4)$$

where A is the cross-section, n_k is the number of moles of constituent k, M_k is the molecular weight, e_k is the electrical charge in faradays, μ_k is the chemical part of the chemical potential, g is the acceleration due to gravity, and ξ_j is the advancement of chemical reaction j. The *affinity* $\mathscr{A}_j$ is defined by

$$\mathscr{A}_j = \sum_i r_{ji}\mu_i \quad (10.5)$$

where r_{ji} is the stoichiometric coefficient of constituent i in chemical reaction j. Thus, $T\sigma$ has the form

$$T\sigma = \sum_i J_i X_i \quad (10.6)$$

where the J_i and X_i correspond to the ( ) and [ ] terms of equation 10.4, respectively. Note that the matter flows are not independent in equation 10.4 because of the Gibbs–Duhem equation.

Ohm[16], Fick[17], and Fourier[18] noticed long ago that in the simple cases, the forces and flows are linearly related to one another. For example, Ohm's Law is

$$I = (1/R)E \quad (10.7)$$

where $1/R$ is a linear phenomenological coefficient; namely, the reciprocal of the resistance. In general, one would expect the different irreversible processes of a more complex system to interfere with one another, so that each flow would have contributions from the forces of all the other processes. Thus, one should write the linear laws as

$$J_i = \sum_j L_{ij} X_j \quad (10.8)$$

where the L_{ij} are phenomenological coefficients which may be functions of thermodynamic variables. This equation in CT terminology is a linear constitutive equation, and we note that Onsager's use of this form[1] is an early statement of the equipresence principle.

Onsager[1] and others[30,31,32,37] have derived the following statement from statistical mechanics

S. *Provided the J_i and X_i of equation 10.8 are properly chosen from the ex-*

pression for $T\sigma$ and are independent, the linear coefficients L_{ij} satisfy the symmetry relation

$$L_{ij}(B) = \varepsilon_i \varepsilon_j L_{ji}(-B) \qquad (10.9)$$

where B is the magnetic induction and ε_i is $+1$ for even time-reversal flows and -1 for odd time-reversal flows.

Equation 10.9 is called the Onsager reciprocal relations or the Onsager–Casimir relations, and represents the symmetry of the linear coefficient matrix. The requirement of independence is essential.

The experimental validity of equation 10.9 is the subject of this paper, and some of the evidence will be summarised in section 10.3.

Note that TIP is a linear theory based on local equilibrium and thus does not treat more general systems such as materials with memory or systems which are very far from equilibrium. Nonetheless, the large class of materials and irreversible processes to which it does apply includes much of physical and chemical interest. Consequently, TIP is in fact non-trivial.

10.2.2 Proper choice of flows

Since there are many ways to transform equation 10.4, how does one properly pick out independent flows from an arbitrary $T\sigma$ expression? (Once the flow part of a $T\sigma$ term is chosen, the force part is determined.) Coleman and Truesdell[38] have severely criticised the arbitrariness of choices and emphasised that common choices of J_i, such as the vector flows of heat, matter, and electricity of equation 10.4, do not correspond to Onsager's original statistical mechanical variables. Moreover, Coleman and Truesdell invented formal combinations of flows and forces which, when treated as flows, leave $T\sigma$ invariant but destroy the symmetry of equation 10.9.

To avoid the criticism of arbitrariness, a recipe is necessary for choosing flows. This recipe, which has been used implicitly by all TIP workers, is the following.

R. After the dependencies of $T\sigma$ are removed by use of the Gibbs–Duhem equation and by a choice of reference frame (such as volume, solvent, or mass-fixed frames), the flows are chosen as follows

$$\begin{cases} \text{Scalar process (chemical reactions)} \quad J_i = \dfrac{\mathrm{d}\xi_i}{\mathrm{d}t} & (10.10) \\[2ex] \text{Vector processes} \quad (J_i)^* = -\dfrac{1}{A}\dfrac{\mathrm{d}Z_i}{\mathrm{d}t} & (10.11) \end{cases}$$

where Z_i is an *extensive* quantity of classical thermodynamics from the set (q, n_k), and the * refers to one of the above reference frames for matter flows.

We make the following observations. These flows are odd under time reversal, as is clear from equations 10.10 and 10.11. We shall not discuss viscosity further, but the pressure tensor is defined as the *flow* and is even[4]. Equation 10.4 is not an example of $T\sigma$ in the form which exhibits proper flows because the dependencies have not yet been removed. Since the flow of electricity is defined as

$$I = \sum_k e_k J_k \tag{10.12}$$

it is not a basic flow for the recipe. While the heat q is not one of the *state* variables of thermodynamics, it is nonetheless an *extensive* quantity of thermodynamics.

It is our position that statement **S** *plus the recipe* **R** *form an empirical axiom, which is open to experimental test just as are the axioms of classical thermodynamics.*

There are, of course, many sets of flows for which the associated linear matrix satisfies the ORR. There is a special type of transformation called a Meixner transformation which, when applied to J and X, leaves $T\sigma$ invariant and preserves the symmetry of the matrix. In an obvious matrix notation, Meixner's theorem[4,39] is: If J and X have the following properties

$$j = PJ \quad x = QX; \qquad J = LX \quad j = lx; \qquad L = \tilde{L} \text{ (symmetry of } L) \tag{10.13a}$$

and if

$$Q = \tilde{P}^{-1} \text{ (Meixner's transformation)} \tag{10.13b}$$

then

$$T\sigma = \tilde{J}X = \tilde{j}x \qquad l = PL\tilde{P} \qquad l = \tilde{l} \tag{10.14}$$

where $\tilde{M}$ and M^{-1} are the transpose and inverse of a matrix M. In the various experimental tests below, the sets of flows (and thus forces) are not all the same. However, they can all be obtained from the flows 10.10 and 10.11 (and their associated forces) by means of Meixner transformations. In particular, we note that the volume, solvent, and mass-fixed flows all transform into one another by Meixner transformations.

Aside from our empirical axiom approach, there are two other ways of justifying flows like 10.10 or 10.11. First, Onsager relations between either this set of flows and forces or Meixner-connected ones can be obtained by statistical mechanics derivations more general than Onsager's[30,32,40,41] Second, it is possible to take Onsager's original form of $T\sigma$ and the associated linear laws and transform to 10.10 and 10.11 flows. The ORR are preserved in this process subject to the further hypotheses that the L_{ij} do not depend on the shape of the sample and are zero in a vacuum[30,37,40,41,42,43].

10.3 Experimental Evidence for the ORR

In this section we will exhibit typical evidence for the ORR, including some data obtained since our more complete papers of 1960[44] and 1969[45]. The derivations of the appropriate equations are available elsewhere[44,45].

10.3.1 Thermoelectricity

The analysis of either a metallic or electrolytic thermocouple yields $T\sigma$ and linear laws that involve J_q and the electric current I (equation 10.12), and their associated forces $-(1/T)(\mathrm{d}T/\mathrm{d}x)$ and $-\mathrm{d}\phi/\mathrm{d}x$. It can be shown easily that the Peltier heat π and the thermoelectric power $\mathrm{d}E/\mathrm{d}T$ are related to the L_{ij} as follows[46]

$$\pi = \frac{L_{12}}{L_{22}} \qquad T\frac{\mathrm{d}E}{\mathrm{d}T} = \frac{L_{21}}{L_{22}} \tag{10.15}$$

For Kelvin's relation[25]

$$\frac{\pi}{T} = \frac{\mathrm{d}E}{\mathrm{d}T} \tag{10.16}$$

to hold, it is necessary and sufficient that the ORR be valid. Because of the large effect of minor impurities, it is essential that both experiments be performed on the same sample for a valid test of equation 10.16.

In table 10.1[47,48] and figure 10.1[49] are the metallic thermocouple experiments performed on the same sample since 1935, and in table 10.2 is the latest electrolytic thermocouple data. Older data for both types of thermocouple show similar behaviour, with most data giving L_{12}/L_{21} to within 1 to 3 per cent[44,45]. Most of the uncertainties are associated with the very difficult measurements of Peltier heats. Within the relatively small error of these experiments, the ORR are satisfied.

TABLE 10.1 TEST OF KELVIN'S RELATION FOR METALLIC THERMOCOUPLES

Couple	Temp. (°C)	π/T (μV/deg)	$\mathrm{d}E/\mathrm{d}T$ (μV/deg)	L_{12}/L_{21}	Ref.
Cu–Constantan	20	37.7	38.9	0.97	47
	30	40.5	41.8	0.97	47
	40	43.2	44.6	0.97	47
$Bi_2Te_{2.4}Se_{0.6}$ (doped 0.05 wt.% $CuBr_2$)	1	15.85†	15.7†	1.01	48

† Thermal conductivities whose ratio is L_{12}/L_{21}.

10.3.2 Electrokinetics

Electrokinetic systems consist of a fluid of one or more components (some of which may be charged), divided into two reservoirs which are separated by a porous diaphragm. The diaphragm may be a capillary, a frit, or

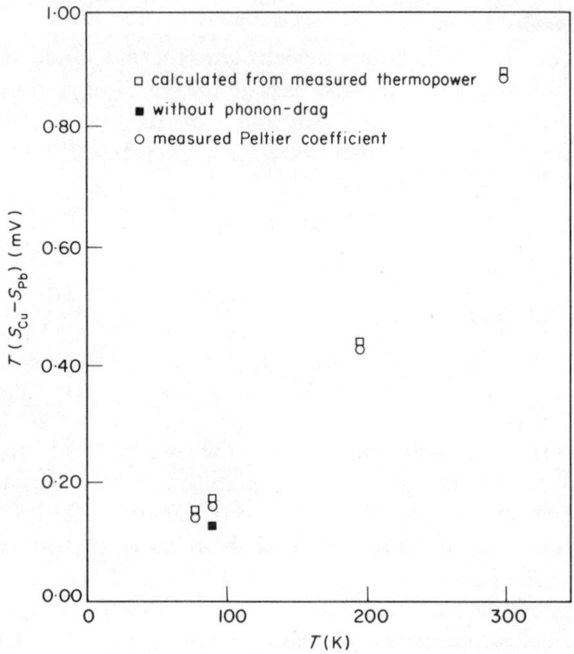

Figure 10.1 A comparison of the measured Peltier coefficient of a lead-copper junction with that calculated from the absolute thermopowers of lead and copper[49]. *The* ORR *are valid to 1 per cent within experimental error.*

TABLE 10.2 TEST OF KELVIN'S RELATION FOR ELECTROLYTIC THERMOCOUPLE

Couple	Concentration (moles/litre)	Temp. (°C)	π (kcal/mole)	$zF(\mathrm{d}E/\mathrm{d}T)$† (kcal/mole)	L_{12}/L_{21}	Ref.
Ag–$AgNO_3$	0.01	25	−4.65	−4.47	1.03	50
	0.1	25	−2.93	−2.89	1.02	50
	0.316	25	−2.30	−2.13	1.08	50
	1.0	25	−1.82	−1.38	1.32	50

† z is the number of electrons in the electrode reaction and F is the value of the faraday.

powdered materials. If an emf E is impressed across electrodes immersed in the fluids, a fluid flow J occurs as a consequence of the current I, and a pressure difference ΔP builds up. Similarly a ΔP will result in a J, E, and I. The TIP analysis of this system yields the flows J and I and associated forces

ΔP and E respectively[51,52]. The large number of experimental quantities which can be defined are given elsewhere[44,52], and include the electrosmotic pressure (EOP), streaming current (SC), electrosmosis (EO), and streaming potential (SP). Related quantities are sedimentation potential (sedP)[53] and electrophoresis (EP)[53].

The ratios of various such quantities are equal to L_{12}/L_{21}. Table 10.3 shows typical values of L_{12}/L_{21} for

TABLE 10.3 TEST OF ELECTROKINETIC RELATIONS

System	Experiments	Temp. (°C)	L_{12}/L_{21}	Ref.
Clay plug, 1% $ZnSO_4$	EOP, SC	—	0.98	54
1% $CuSO_4$	EOP, SC	—	0.95	54
Glass capillary (5 micro-equiv/litre)				
KCl	EO, SP	22.5	0.97	55
HCl		22.5	0.96	55
KOH		22.5	0.97	55
$CaCl_2$		22.5	0.99	55
$Al(NO_3)_3$		22.5	0.94	55
KOH		19	0.99	56
$Ca(NO_3)_2$		19	0.99	56
Pyrex powder–water	sedP, EP	35	1.09±0.08†	57
Isotropic pyrex, various solvents	EOP, SC	35	0.98±0.06†	58
Anisotropic quartz	EOP, SC	40	$\overrightarrow{0.99}$±0.06†	58
			$\overleftarrow{0.96}$±0.02†	58

† The ± values correspond to the maximum deviation from the average and are not true estimated experimental errors. Saxèn's relation is for the EOP and SC experiments.

various systems and various experiment types selected from data collected since 1946. As with the thermocouples, it is essential that both types of measurement be done at the same temperature and on the same sample and diaphragm. The ORR are again verified within experimental uncertainties for these difficult experiments. Other data show similar results[44,45].

10.3.3 Isothermal diffusion

Interdiffusion in an isothermal $(n+1)$ component system provides a good example of a vector transport process in a continuum. The calculation of $T\sigma$ leads to the flows and forces J_i and $-\partial\mu_i/\partial x$ respectively, summed for *all* the $(n+1)$ components, where J_i is the flow of component i referred to the centre of mass frame of reference[59]. However, statement **S** refers to independent flows, whereas the set

$$\left(J_{i,} - \frac{\partial \mu_i}{\partial x}\right) \quad \text{for } i = 0, 1, \ldots, n$$

is a dependent set owing to the Gibbs–Duhem equation. Using the Gibbs–Duhem equation and recognising the resulting combination of flows for each i as the solvent-fixed flow $(J_i)_{sf}$, we find[60] that the solvent term (with subscript 0) disappears and

$$T\sigma = \sum_{i=1}^{n} (J_i)_{sf}\left(-\frac{\partial \mu_i}{\partial x}\right) \tag{10.17}$$

Equation 10.17 now contains an independent set of flows to which statement S applies.

The reference frame closest to experiment is the volume-fixed frame[61]. As shown elsewhere[60], equation 10.17 can be transformed by a Meixner transformation to another n term form involving volume-fixed flows; namely

$$T\sigma = \sum_{i=1}^{n} (J_i)_v Y_i \tag{10.18}$$

where

$$Y_i = \sum_{j=1}^{n} \left(\delta_{ij} + \frac{c_j \bar{v}_i}{c_0 \bar{v}_0}\right)\left(\frac{-\partial \mu_i}{\partial x}\right) \tag{10.19}$$

and δ_{ij} is the Kronecker delta, c_j is the concentration and $\bar{v}_j$ the partial modal volume of constituent j, and 0 refers to the solvent.

The linear coefficient matrices associated with equations 10.17 and 10.18 should both be symmetric, but corresponding entries will have different numerical values. The first nontrivial ORR arises in a ternary system, and all tests have been done on ternaries. Four component diffusion measurements are so difficult that no four component diffusion coefficients have yet been reported.

Data presented in 1960[44] were all based on volume-fixed calculations[61]. Other tests between 1960 and 1969 were done with varying formats[62]. Since 1969, L_{ij} data have been presented for 13 systems. Only six of them have estimated errors for comparison[63,64], and these are given in table 10.4. All six are well within experimental error, and the equality $L^0_{12}/L^0_{21} = 1$ is within ± 5 per cent. Although the other seven[65] have L^v_{12}/L^v_{21} reasonably close to 1.0, no real evaluation can be made without knowledge of experimental errors. Here L^0_{ij} and L^v_{ij} are solvent-fixed and volume-fixed coefficients, respectively.

Accurate ternary diffusion measurements are difficult. Moreover, the calculation of L_{ij} from measured diffusion coefficients D_{ij} requires derivatives of osmotic coefficients or activity coefficients[61]. This differentiation magnifies the experimental errors of the original data. Consequently, estimated errors of no greater than 10 per cent in table 10.4 actually represent fairly tight error limits.

TABLE 10.4 TEST OF ORR FOR DIFFUSION (25°C)

System	$\bar{c}_1$†	$\bar{c}_2$†	L^0_{12}	L^0_{21}	L^0_{12}/L^0_{21}	Estimated error in L^0_{12}/L^0_{21}	Ref.
H_2O–KBr–HBr	0.25	0.1	−1.845	−1.785	1.034	±0.048	63
H_2O–KCl–HCl	0.3	0.2	−2.596	−2.563	1.013	±0.050	64
H_2O–KCl–HCl	1	0.1	−2.917	−2.896	1.007	±0.060	64
H_2O–NaCl–HCl	0.3	0.2	−1.848	−1.765	1.047	±0.099	64
H_2O–NaCl–HCl	0.5	0.5	−3.308	−3.240	1.021	±0.065	64
H_2O–NaCl–HCl	1.9	0.1	−2.011	−2.021	0.995	±0.049	64

† $\bar{c}$ are average concentrations of solutes in moles/litre.

In 1969[45], 30 of 33 systems satisfied the ORR and only 1 was seriously out. The situation now is 36 out of 39 systems satisfy the ORR with only 1 seriously out. The one seriously out has estimated activity coefficient derivatives and was one of the first ternary diffusion systems done. Re-evaluation of that system would be in order. We may conclude that the ORR are verified within experimental error.

10.3.4 Chemical reactions

The linear laws are a very poor approximation for chemical reactions, except when the system is so close to equilibrium that these laws are essentially without practical value. Nevertheless sufficiently close to equilibrium the linear approximation is satisfactory[66], and we may seek a test of the ORR. The first nontrivial ORR arises from a triangular chemical reaction system with first order reactions[1]. The $T\sigma$ for this system involves the three advancement rates $\mathrm{d}\xi_{ij}/\mathrm{d}t$ as flows and the three associated forces, $-(\mu_j - \mu_i)$[67]. Since the three $(\mu_j - \mu_i)$ terms are dependent, the expression for $T\sigma$ can be written in terms of only two of them. When this is done, the advancements combine in such a way that the combinations are two $\mathrm{d}c_i/\mathrm{d}t$, where c_i are concentrations as before. (This of course can be done in two other ways to get the other two pairs of $\mathrm{d}c_i/\mathrm{d}t$.) Consequently we obtain, for example

$$T\sigma = \frac{\mathrm{d}c_1}{\mathrm{d}t}(\mu_3 - \mu_1) + \frac{\mathrm{d}c_2}{\mathrm{d}t}(\mu_3 - \mu_2) \tag{10.20}$$

If the reactions are first order, the kinetic equations can also be written in terms of the rate constants k_{ij}, $\mathrm{d}c_i/\mathrm{d}t$, and c_i. If the c_i are expanded in terms of $\mu_i - \bar{\mu}_i$ (where $\bar{\mu}_i$ is μ_i at the equilibrium concentrations), then the expression for dc_i/dt, etc., can be obtained in terms of the kinetic constants, equilibrium concentrations $\bar{c}_i$, and the $\mu_3 - \mu_i$ of equation 10.20[67]. Comparing these expressions with the linear laws for equation 10.20 leads to the following results[68], which we will not write out in detail; namely that *the* ORR, *detailed balance, and the Wegscheider relation are equivalent.*

We shall test the Wegscheider relation[29], which is

$$k_{12}k_{23}k_{31} = k_{21}k_{32}k_{13} \tag{10.21}$$

where k_{ij} represents the reaction rate constant of constituent 1 going to form constituent 2, etc. Appropriate reactions are the isomerisations of the three normal butenes. The data[69] are subject to much experimental error, but the results[70] are given in table 10.5. Subject to the relatively large errors, the Wegscheider relation, and thus the ORR, is satisfied.

TABLE 10.5 TEST OF THE ORR FOR THE CHEMICAL REACTIONS: ISOMERISATION OF THE NORMAL BUTENES

Catalyst	$\frac{k_{12}}{k_{13}}$	$\frac{k_{23}}{k_{21}}$	$\frac{k_{32}}{k_{31}}$	$\frac{k_{12}k_{23}k_{31}}{k_{21}k_{32}k_{13}}$
Al_2O_3	2.4	1.0	2.5	0.96
Na–Al_2O_3	4.0	0.77	3.6	0.85

10.3.5 Thermomagnetism and galvanomagnetism

The flow of heat and electricity through solids becomes a more complicated problem in the presence of a magnetic field. Even an isotropic substance requires consideration of at least two dimensions, and some of the linear coefficients change sign with field reversal. The expression for $T\sigma$ can be written in terms of current flow and heat flow in their full three-dimensional component forms with their associated forces[40,71,72,73]

$$\frac{-\partial\phi}{\partial x}, \quad \frac{-\partial\phi}{\partial y}, \quad \frac{-\partial\phi}{\partial z}; \qquad \text{and} \qquad \frac{-1}{T}\frac{\partial T}{\partial x}, \quad \frac{-1}{T}\frac{\partial T}{\partial y}, \quad \frac{-1}{T}\frac{\partial T}{\partial z}$$

The magnetic field B does not appear explicitly in $T\sigma$ or the linear laws, but the linear coefficients are all functions of B. The ORR is equivalent to the symmetry of the 6×6 coefficient matrix.

For convenience in defining experimental quantities, the linear laws are transformed so that $\boldsymbol{J}$ and $\boldsymbol{E}$ are the *flows* and $\boldsymbol{I}$ and $\boldsymbol{G} = -(1/T)\,\mathbf{grad}\,T$ are the associated *forces*, where boldface quantities are vectors[44,72,73]. This partial inversion transforms the old ORR matrix into a new one. Thus if the new linear laws are

$$\begin{aligned} \mathbf{E} &= l_{ee}\mathbf{I} + l_{eq}\mathbf{G} \\ \mathbf{J} &= l_{qe}\mathbf{I} + l_{qq}\mathbf{G} \end{aligned} \tag{10.22}$$

then the new forms of the ORR are[44]

$$\begin{gathered} l_{ee}(B) = \tilde{l}_{ee}(-B) \qquad l_{qq}(B) = \tilde{l}_{qq}(-B) \\ l_{eq}(B) = -\tilde{l}_{qe}(-B) \end{gathered} \tag{10.23}$$

where again $\tilde{M}$ is the transpose of M.

In an isotropic metal, many relations from equation 10.23 result from crystal symmetry considerations alone. However, there remain two nontrivial ORR for transverse effects and one for a longitudinal effect[74]. These are the Bridgman relation[75], a transverse Kelvin type relation, and a longitudinal Kelvin type relation

$$p^t k_i / T Q_i^t = 1 \text{ (Bridgman)} \tag{10.24}$$

$$\frac{\pi^t}{T} \bigg/ \frac{\mathrm{d}E^t}{\mathrm{d}T} = 1 \tag{10.25}$$

$$\frac{\pi^l}{T} \bigg/ \frac{\mathrm{d}E^l}{\mathrm{d}T} = 1 \tag{10.26}$$

where superscript t and l refer to transverse and longitudinal; subscript i means a temperature gradient in only one direction; p^t is the Ettinghausen coefficient (a measure of the temperature gradient in the y direction when a current flows in the x direction and B is in the z direction); Q_i^t is the Ettinghausen–Nernst coefficient (a measure of the potential gradient in the y direction when heat flows in the x direction and B is in the z direction); and k_i is the thermal conductivity in the x direction when heat flows in the x direction (no electrical currents and B is in the z direction).

Just as with thermoelectric experiments, thermogalvanomagnetic ones are very difficult and must be done on the same sample to avoid impurity effects. Thus, in 1960[44], the test of equation 10.24 showed a lot of scatter. However, the one substance As, for which all experiments had been done on the same sample[76], gave 0.98 for equation 10.24. Similarly, the only transverse Kelvin relation data obtained on the same sample was within 5 per cent[77].

Since then equation 10.25 has been tested on Bi at 78 K, with the value 1.0 and an estimate of 5 per cent error[78]. Another recent test of both equations 10.24 and 10.25 was carried out on Zn at 3 K[79]. All the coefficients show a strong oscillatory behaviour as the external field increases, as shown in figures 10.2 (equation 10.25) and 10.3 (equation 10.24). In figure 10.2 the two curves can be superposed to 5 per cent and in figure 10.3 to

1 per cent. The authors[79] believe the constant offset to be a result of a residual Thomson effect or temperature drift. Despite this offset, the fact that the appropriate quantities follow each other so closely in this low temperature, quantum mechanical oscillation region is a clear sign of a direct connection between them.

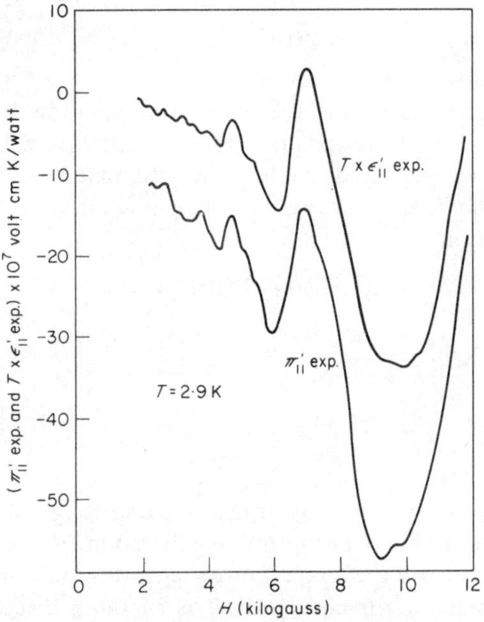

Figure 10.2 The experimental thermoelectric coefficient and Peltier coefficient against magnetic field at $T = 2.9$ K[79]. The upper curve represents the apparent adiabatic thermoelectric coefficient ε'_{11} multiplied by the mean temperature T of the crystal. The lower curve represents the apparent adiabatic Peltier coefficient π'_{11} at the same temperature T.

In sufficiently anisotropic media, none of equation 10.23 should hold on purely crystal symmetry grounds. Consequently a test of the ORR can be carried out on the *diagonal blocks* l_{ee} and l_{qq} of the overall tensor equation 10.22. Gallium has a low enough symmetry in the presence of a magnetic field to allow such a test. The appropriate data for l_{ee} (the Hall tensor) in two investigations[80,81] show adequate agreement, especially considering that different crystal specimens were used for the various coefficients and the errors of alignment are large. Figures 10.4 and 10.5 show comparisons from one investigation[80], and the ORR were satisfied within 30 per cent for another[81].

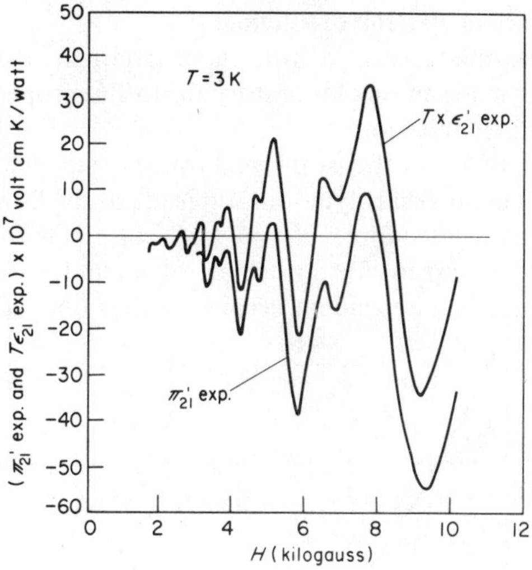

Figure 10.3 *The experimental Ettingshausen–Nernst coefficient and Ettingshausen coefficient at 3 K against magnetic field*[79]*. The upper curve represents the apparent adiabatic Ettingshausen–Nernst coefficient ε'_{21} multiplied by the mean temperature of the crystal. The lower curve represents the apparent adiabatic Ettingshausen coefficient π'_{21} at the same temperature.*

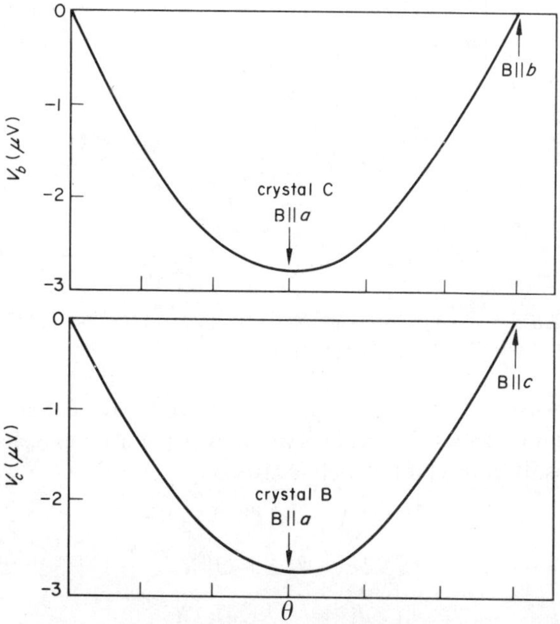

Figure 10.4 *Hall voltages against magnetic field directions for Ga at 77 K and 10 kG*[80]*. Equality of Hall voltages for these two crystals corresponds to one* ORR *in the Hall tensor.*

10.3.6 Transference in electrolyte solutions

We shall describe this case in a little more detail than others because a special effort was made in our laboratory to do the proper experiments as precisely as possible for an ORR test[82].

The calculation of $T\sigma$ for the isothermal transport of electricity (by means of ions) and mass in an electrolyte solution leads to the flows of solvent and of ions and their associated forces $X_i = -(\partial\mu_i/\partial x + z_i F \partial\phi/\partial x)$, where z_i is the signed valence of ion i (zero for a nonelectrolyte) and F is the value of the faraday[83]. The forces are dependent because of the Gibbs–Duhem equation.

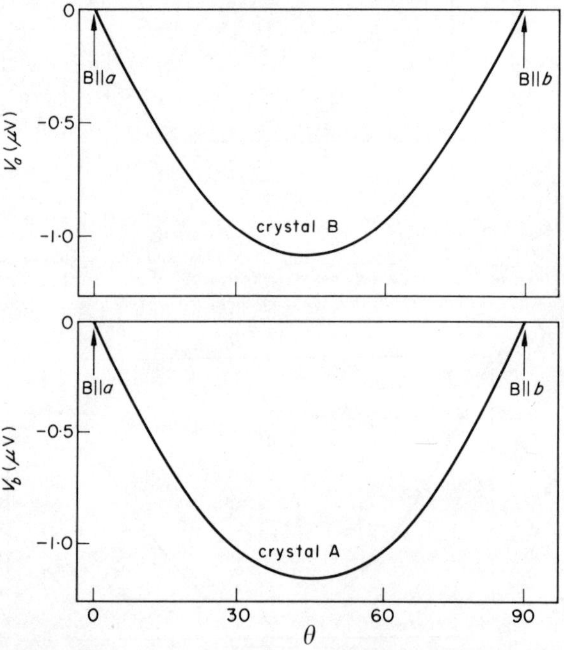

Figure 10.5 Hall voltages against magnetic field directions for Ga at 77 K and 12 kG[80]. Equality of Hall voltages in these two crystals corresponds to a second ORR *in the Hall tensor.*

When the solvent term is eliminated, only the independent solvent-fixed flows of the ions remain[84]. In the simplest case of a binary electrolyte (such as NaCl dissolved in H_2O) which ionises as

$$C_{r_1}A_{r_2} = r_1 C^{z_1} + r_2 A^{z_2} \tag{10.27}$$

one has

$$T\sigma = J_1^0 X_1 + J_2^0 X_2 \tag{10.28}$$

$$J_1^0 = l_{11} X_1 + l_{12} X_2 \tag{10.29}$$

$$J_2^0 = l_{21} X_1 + l_{22} X_2 \tag{10.30}$$

where 1 refers to the cation C and 2 to the anion A, and the X_i are the same as above; r_i are the stoichiometric coefficients for the ionisation, and superscript 0 refers to solvent-fixed flows. This case is complex enough to have a nontrivial ORR[84]. The solvent-fixed flows and forces satisfy statement **S**, so that the ORR is

$$l_{12} = l_{21} \tag{10.31}$$

It can be shown by analysis of the classical Hittorf transference number experiment and concentration cell with transference experiment that[44, 84]

$$\frac{t_1^h}{t_1^c} = \frac{z_1(l_{11}/N) + z_2(l_{12}/N)}{z_1(l_{11}/N) + z_2(l_{21}/N)} \tag{10.32}$$

where t_1^h and t_1^c are the experimental Hittorf and cell transference numbers, and N is the total number of equivalents of ions per litre.

From equations 10.31 and 10.32, it is clear that the necessary and sufficient condition for the ORR is[1, 44, 84]

$$t_1^h = t_1^c \tag{10.33}$$

This was the equation used for the test in 1960[44]. However both theory[85, 86] and experiment[84] show that l_{11}/N is finite and not very dependent on concentration, whereas l_{12}/N is zero at infinite dilution and increases rapidly with concentration, occasionally reaching a maximum at higher concentrations. Because l_{11} is relatively larger than l_{12} and l_{21}, it follows that a good percentage test of equation 10.33 does not imply a good percentage test of equation 10.31. Moreover, the higher the concentration and thus the larger value of l_{12} relative to l_{11}, the better will be the test.

To get a direct test of equation 10.31, it is necessary to calculate the l_{ij}/N from other experimental data. It has been shown[84] that the l_{ij} can be written in terms of classical experiments as

$$l_{ij} = \frac{t_i^h t_j^c N \Lambda}{1000 z_i z_j F^2} + \frac{r_i r_j c D^0}{1000 \hat{R}\, \mathrm{Tr}\,(1 + c\, \mathrm{d} \ln y/\mathrm{d}c)} \tag{10.34}$$

where Λ is the equivalent conductance, $N = r_1 z_1 c_1$ is the concentration in equivalents/litre, c is the concentration in moles/litre, D^0 is the solvent-fixed binary diffusion coefficient, $\hat{R}$ is the gas constant, $r = r_1 + r_2$, and y is the molar activity coefficient. Consequently, to calculate the four l_{ij}, it is necessary to have four independent experimental transport quantities at each concentration of interest; namely, D^0, Λ, t_i^h, t_j^c, as well as activity coefficient derivatives.

Some observations on the experimental determination of these transport quantities follow

(1) The accurate determination of Λ, while not routine, is fairly straightforward.

(2) Diffusion coefficients require some care and elaborate optical apparatus, and not much data is available at high concentrations.

(3) Activity coefficients, or alternatively osmotic coefficients, can be measured with reasonable precision. However, the need for derivatives of these data imposes an accuracy on the initial data that is an order of magnitude higher than is needed for the derivatives themselves.

(4) The cell transference number can be written in c, y units as

$$t_2^c = \frac{F}{r\hat{R}T}\frac{\mathrm{d}E}{\mathrm{d}\ln(cy)} \tag{10.35}$$

when the two identical electrodes are reversible to the cation. For a binary system, t_1^c is obtained from

$$t_1^c = 1 - t_2^c \tag{10.36}$$

If a good electrode is available, the E's of the appropriate concentration cell are not so hard to measure. However, because t_2^c depends on E derivatives (as well as activity coefficient derivatives), the precision of the cell measurements should be at the 10 to 15 microvolt level, that is, at the limit of current experimental techniques.

(5) The Hittorf transference number experiment can only be described as very unpleasant. The apparatus and theory are simple, but the results depend decisively on the difference of two nearly equal concentrations, which consequently must be determined to nearly the precision of atomic weight determinations. The moving boundary experiment is more accurate and is equivalent to the Hittorf in terms of l_{12}, but is useless at concentrations above ~ 0.2 molar.

Aqueous $AgNO_3$ is a good choice for an experimental test because it is soluble to high concentration ($c = 9$) where the cross-coefficients l_{12}/N and l_{21}/N are larger; it is partially associated so that the cross-coefficients are relatively larger than in strong electrolytes; and it has good electrochemical properties for making reproducible Hittorf and concentration cell electrodes.

The diffusion coefficient[87] and both types of transference number[88] measurements were carried out in our laboratory with as much care as we could provide. Existing literature data for conductance and activity (or osmotic) coefficients were critically reviewed, selected, and assigned estimates of error. The appropriate activity derivatives were calculated numerically, graphically smoothed, and fit by least-square polynomials. These data were combined to yield all four l_{ij}/N at each of several concentrations.

The ratios l_{12}/l_{21} for several concentrations are presented in table 10.6[82].

The error of the ratio is also included and is primarily dependent on the errors in t_1^h and t_1^c. The estimated errors are designated by vertical bars on the Hittorf data and by dotted lines on the cell data, as shown in figure 10.6. Because the error expression for the ratio has l_{12}/N in the denominator and because l_{12}/N goes to zero as c (or N) goes to zero, the error goes up sharply at low concentrations. Consequently, the best test is at higher concentrations where the error limits are much tighter.

Table 10.6 shows that the ORR (equation 10.31) is obeyed for $AgNO_3$ well within the estimated error at all concentrations studied and is within 0.5 per cent for $c > 2$. Table 10.7 provides a test of equation 10.33 using t_1^h and t_1^c from our $AgNO_3$ experiments[82,88] and two from the 1960 compilation[44]. We conclude that the $AgNO_3$ results are a decisive test of the ORR in electrolyte systems because of the tight error bounds.

TABLE 10.6 TEST OF ORR FOR ELECTROLYTE TRANSPORT ($AgNO_3$ AT 25° C)

c (moles/litre)	l_{12}/l_{21}	Estimated error
0.05	1.04_0	$\pm 0.06_7$
0.1	1.00_6	$\pm 0.04_6$
0.5	0.97_7	$\pm 0.04_3$
1.0	0.98_4	$\pm 0.02_8$
2.0	0.99_8	$\pm 0.02_0$
3.0	0.99_9	$\pm 0.01_6$
4.0	0.99_6	$\pm 0.01_5$
5.0	0.99_5	$\pm 0.01_3$
6.0	0.99_7	$\pm 0.01_2$
7.0	0.99_9	$\pm 0.01_3$
8.0	1.00_2	$\pm 0.01_7$

TABLE 10.7 TEST OF EQUATION 10.33

System		Ref.	Concentration (moles/litre) 0.01	0.05	0.1	0.5	1.0	5.0	8.0
LiCl	t_1^c	89	0.333	0.326	0.320	0.307	0.281	—	—
25° C	t_1^h	89	0.329	0.323	0.319	0.301	0.287	—	—
$BaCl_2$	t_1^c	90	0.440	0.427	0.418	0.381	0.353	—	—
25° C	t_1^h	90	0.438	0.425	0.416	0.379	0.353	—	—
$AgNO_3$	t_1^c	82, 88	—	0.468	0.469	0.475	0.487	0.568	0.607
25° C	t_1^h	82, 88	—	0.466	0.468	0.479	0.491	0.565	0.605

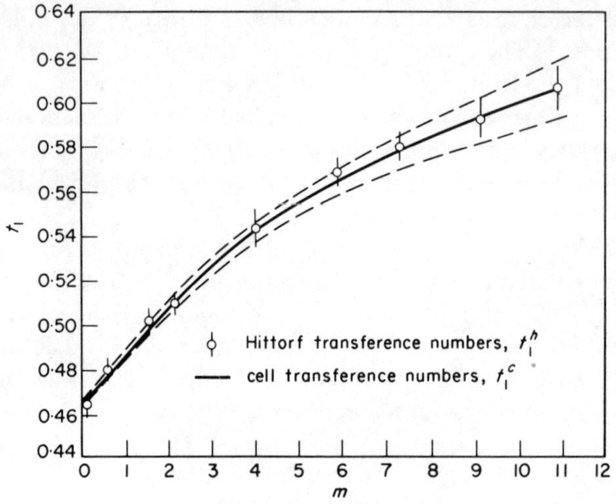

Figure 10.6 Comparison of t_1^c and t_1^h for $AgNO_3$ at 25° C[81]. The dotted lines represent the uncertainties in the cell transference numbers and the error bars represent the uncertainties in Hittorf ones.

10.3.7 Heat conductivity in anisotropic crystals

The calculation of $T\sigma$ for an anisotropic crystal leads to the heat flows in component form of J_1, J_2, J_3 and associated forces[91]

$$-\frac{1}{T}\frac{\partial T}{\partial x_1}, \quad -\frac{1}{T}\frac{\partial T}{\partial x_2}, \quad -\frac{1}{T}\frac{\partial T}{\partial x_3}$$

The assumed linear law is a generalisation of Fourier's law; namely

$$J_i = -\sum_j \frac{L_{ij}}{T}\frac{\partial T}{\partial x_j} \qquad i, j, = 1, 2, 3 \tag{10.37}$$

A search for higher order terms such as $(\partial^2 T/\partial x_i \partial x_j)$ or $(\partial T/\partial x_i)(\partial T/\partial x_j)$ was unsuccessful using reasonable temperature gradients[92].

If we take

$$k_{ij} = \frac{L_{ij}}{T} \tag{10.38}$$

then the usual form for the heat conductivity is obtained[27]

$$J_i = -\sum_j k_{ij}\frac{\partial T}{\partial x_j} \tag{10.39}$$

where the k_{ij} are the elements of the heat conductivity tensor. Statement **S** says that the L_{ij} form of the tensor is symmetric, and therefore so is the k_{ij} tensor. To verify the ORR, we thus need to show that

$$k_{ij} = k_{ji} \tag{10.40}$$

The numerical entries in the conductivity tensor depend on the coordinate axes to which the tensor is referred. If the principal axes are chosen, then the tensor may become greatly simplified[93]. In fact it can be shown that equation 10.40 is satisfied for 19 of the 32 crystal classes by purely geometrical considerations alone. Consequently, any test of equation 10.40 as an ORR must be on one of the 13 remaining classes. The trigonal, tetragonal, and hexagonal members of the 13 have the same and simple form of the tensor:

$$\begin{vmatrix} k_{11} & k_{12} & 0 \\ -k_{12} & k_{11} & 0 \\ 0 & 0 & k_{33} \end{vmatrix} \tag{10.41}$$

For such crystals (classes C_3, C_{3i}, C_4, C_{4h}, S_4, C_6, C_{3h}, C_{6h}), it is clear that k_{ij} can be symmetric for pure heat conduction if and only if

$$k_{12} = 0 \tag{10.42}$$

Here x_3 is the principal axis, and because of the symmetry, x_1 and x_2 can be any pair of orthogonal lines in the x_1x_2 plane.

Now anisotropic heat conduction in a magnetic field has the same form as tensor 10.41 except that the k_{ij} are functions of the magnetic induction B. Furthermore, it is known that when $B \neq 0$ then $k_{12} \neq 0$. Consequently, tensor 10.41 in a magnetic field is *not* symmetric. Righi and Leduc have measured these non-zero coefficients by methods analogous to those discussed below[94]. Similarly the Hall tensor for the electrical conductivity of crystals is asymmetric and its elements can be measured by such methods[94].

The Righi–Leduc and Hall experiments are emphasised because it has been suggested[9,37] that the similar determination of the numerical value of k_{12} in the pure heat conduction case is impossible. The arguments are

(1) Individual heat flows are not observable, only the divergence is. Consequently a divergence-free antisymmetric tensor d_{ij} can be added to k_{ij} yielding an asymmetric tensor but no observable change.

(2) The solutions of the heat conduction equation involve terms which always have $(k_{ij}+k_{ji})$ and never each one separately.

While these statements are true, they are not relevant to the specific experiments used either to determine the Hall and Righi–Leduc coefficients or to prove $k_{12} = 0$ in the absence of a field. Effects of asymmetry do appear when the *direction* of the flow is under consideration.

Let us turn to two experiments which concern flow directions and which can thus distinguish between symmetry and asymmetry of the conductivity tensor. One is by Soret, the other by Voigt.

Soret's is this[95]: consider a thin plate very large in extent (or alternatively surrounded by a circular bounding surface of highly conducting material) which is cut perpendicular to the principal axis (x_3) of a crystal whose tensor is like expression 10.41. In this case, it can be shown that on heating the centre, the resulting isothermals are always circles. If the tensor is symmetric, the flow of heat will be in straight lines away from the centre; if not, the heat will flow away in spirals, figure 10.7[93,96,97].

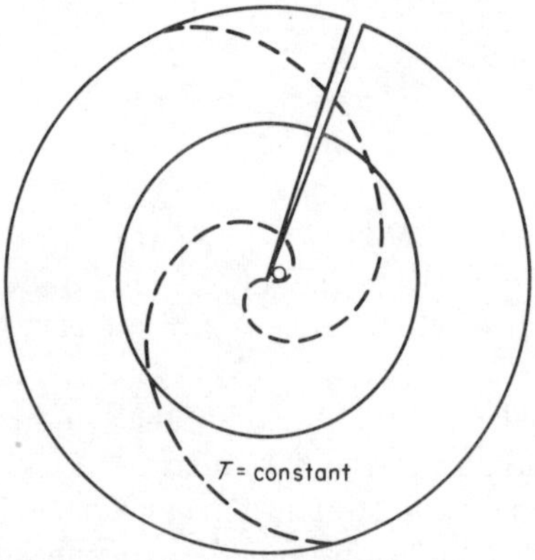

Figure 10.7 Circular plate cut perpendicular to the axis x_3 heated at centre 0. If the tensor 10.41 is not symmetric, heat flow (dotted lines) will be spirals.

Suppose now a very thin sector is cut out of the plate. If the tensor is not symmetric, the spiral heat flow will result in an accumulation of heat on one side of the cut and a loss on the other. One would thus find a temperature difference between the two sides. Soret[95] observed no such difference. The analogous experiment for electrical conductivity in a magnetic field (Hall effect), where $k_{12} \neq 0$, was suggested independently by Boltzmann[98] and carried out by Ettinghausen and Nernst[99].

Voigt's experiment[97,100], suggested also by P. Curie[101], is more direct and more accurate, and is related to the original Hall and Righi–Leduc experiments[94]. Suppose a fixed temperature difference is applied to the ends of a long, narrow, thin plate of a crystal whose tensor is like expression 10.41. Let the axis x_1 be along the length, x_2 along the width, and the principal axis x_3 be perpendicular to the plate (figure 10.8). The solution of the boundary value problem is independent of the symmetry of the tensor and

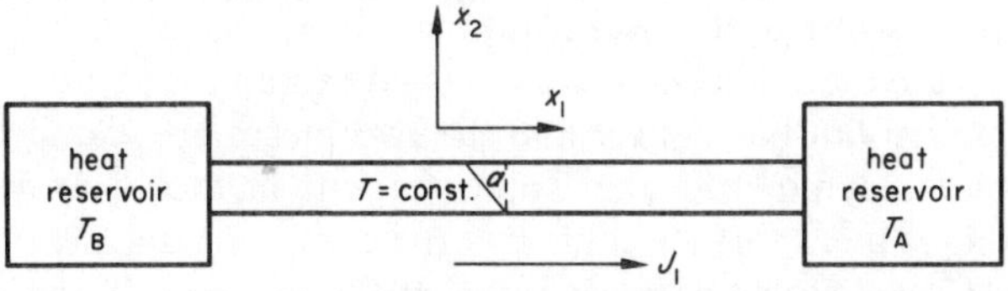

Figure 10.8 Schematic diagram of the Curie-Voigt experiment. The principal axis x_3 comes out of the paper. If the tensor 10.41 is asymmetric, the isothermal lines far from the region of end effects will be inclined away from the normal (dotted line) to the direction of heat flow.

shows that the heat flows only along x_1. Hence for this case

$$\begin{aligned} J_1 &= -k_{11}\frac{\partial T}{\partial x_1} - k_{12}\frac{\partial T}{\partial x_2} \\ 0 = J_2 &= +k_{12}\frac{\partial T}{\partial x_1} - k_{11}\frac{\partial T}{\partial x_2} \\ 0 = J_3 &= -k_{33}\frac{\partial T}{\partial x_3} \end{aligned} \tag{10.43}$$

Consequently from the expression for J_2, one obtains

$$\frac{\partial T}{\partial x_2}\bigg/\frac{\partial T}{\partial x_1} = k_{12}/k_{11} = \tan\alpha \tag{10.44}$$

where α is the angle which the isothermal straight line makes with the normal to the line of heat flow (figure 10.9). By means of the *melting wax* technique, an isothermal is located. If this line is inclined away from the normal, then the tensor is not symmetric, and the ratio of k_{12} to k_{11} is given by equation 10.44.

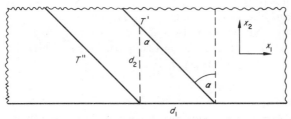

Figure 10.9 Expanded drawing of isothermals show how α is related to the thermal gradients. Since

$$\frac{\partial T}{\partial x_1} = \frac{(T'' - T')}{d_1} = \frac{\Delta T}{(d_2 \tan\alpha)}$$

and

$$\frac{\partial T}{\partial x_2} = \frac{\Delta T}{d_2}$$

clearly

$$\frac{\partial T}{\partial x_2}\bigg/\frac{\partial T}{\partial x_1} = \tan\alpha$$

Because of possible heat losses from the edges, it is more precise to use Voigt's *twin plate* method. The plate is sawed in half along the x_1 axis, one piece is rotated about the x_2 axis, and the two pieces are clamped together. If the tensor is asymmetric, the isotherms will have the form shown in figure 10.10. One measures the angle β at the common edge near the middle, which avoids any distortion due to losses at the edges or due to end effects. The angle α is $[90° - (\beta/2)]$. Voigt[100] found that for suitable crystals of apatite and dolomite, the lines were straight and perpendicular to x_1. More precisely, β was 180° with an error of not more than 4 min (that is, < 0.037 per cent). Therefore, α is less than 2 min, and

$$k_{12}/k_{11} < 0.0005 \tag{10.45}$$

This value implies that $k_{12} = 0$ to less than 0.05 per cent and consequently that the tensor is symmetric.

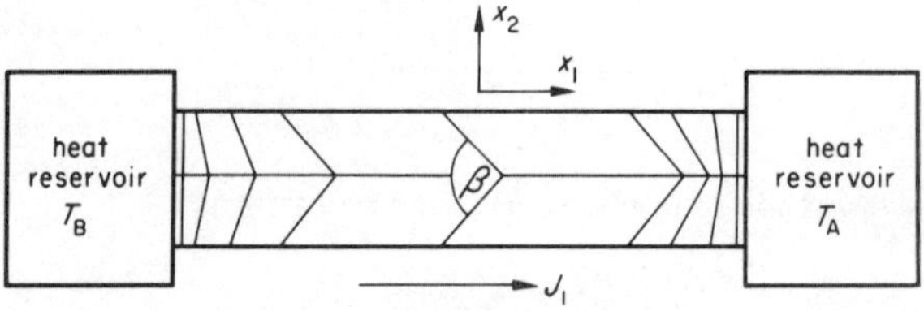

Figure 10.10 Schematic diagram of Voigt's twin-plate experiment. If the tensor 10.41 is not symmetric, the isothermals will form a V symmetric along the x_1 axis with an interior angle β. If symmetric, the isothermals are perpendicular to the x_1 axis.

The Voigt experiment can also yield k_{11} if J_1 and $\partial T/\partial x_1$ are also measured. Of course J_1 is a net flow. However there is no Casimir divergence problem[37] in separating the three x_1, x_2, x_3 flows because the boundary conditions lead to only a single flow in a known direction.

We also note that both Soret's and Voigt's experiments could be used to determine the antisymmetric Righi–Leduc coefficients which arise where the magnetic induction B is not zero.

10.3.8 Conclusion

In view of the experimental evidence presented above (and the other evidence presented in 1960[44] and 1969[45]), we may draw the following conclusion: *the* ORR *are confirmed experimentally within acceptable error limits for the widely different phenomena: thermoelectricity, electrokinetics, isothermal diffusion, chemical reactions, thermomagnetism and galvanomagnetism, transference in electrolyte solutions, and heat conduction in anisotropic solids.*

The flows we have used in the experimental tests are those of recipe **R** in section 10.2.2 or can be obtained from them by Meixner transformations.

Consequently these choices plus the experimental evidence confirm statement S and thus the ORR as an empirical axiom, independent of any statistical mechanical arguments.

10.4 Criticisms of TIP and ORR

As noted earlier, certain criticisms of TIP and ORR have merit, although many are grossly overstated. The following are my observations on these criticisms

(1) Clearly TIP is *not* the most general thermodynamic theory of irreversible processes. In particular, its basic equations cannot describe the nonlinear phenomena often treated by CT.

(2) It is now evident that the fundamental balance equations were constructed and the concept of local equilibrium (Gibbs' equation) was used to some extent in *ad hoc* or intuitive ways. However, recently, a number of authors have shown that the powerful methods of CT rigorously yield the TIP $T\sigma$ equations when applied to simpler linear materials[13,15,102,103,104,105]. This process not only justifies the TIP starting point, but more importantly provides a technique for clarifying exactly what simplifying hypotheses are required and what terms have to be neglected (for example, terms in J_i^2). It has also been shown[13,106] that the TIP balance equations plus CT methods applied to appropriate constitutive equations lead to the TIP bilinear entropy production and to the TIP linear equations. Moreover, a large fraction of materials of experimental interest have simpler and linear constitutive equations.

(3) *Curie's theorem*, although not rigorous as originally proposed[107], can be justified by more elaborate symmetry considerations[108,109,110] and by 'known theorems of algebra[111]'. Consequently it is possible to separate scalar, vector, and tensor flows in linear isotropic cases.

(4) It has been claimed the Soret and Voigt experiments are without content[9]. Earlier we noted that the arguments advanced were not relevant. Moreover, exactly the same types of experiment have been used to find the antisymmetric elements of the Hall and Righi–Leduc tensors. That certain transformations of Onsager's statistical mechanical variables do not lead to an exact preservation of the ORR[37,40,43] is not relevant to our discussion, since we are interested in a macroscopic theory. However, it has been shown that the ORR do transform for a *finite* body[112].

(5) It is correct that $T\sigma$ in the form of equation 10.6 cannot in itself determine forces or flows. There must be a recipe to choose the flows J_i out of an expression for $T\sigma$. We have treated the ORR and choice of flows as empirical macroscopic axioms, and have given such a recipe **R**. As noted

before, our choices of flows and the ORR can be justified by statistical mechanics[30,32,40,41], by transformations of Onsager's original variables subject to hypotheses of shape independence and zero value in a vacuum[30,37,40,41,42,43], or by analysis of $\Delta\dot{S}$ rather than $T\sigma$[113]. Consequently, the fact that Onsager's original variables are not the same as ours, while true, is not relevant to the experimental verification of the ORR.

(6) Whether the experiments really do show the validity of the ORR has been questioned, because L_{12}/L_{21}, etc., are not exactly 1,000 000——. Of course data are never perfect; the required experiments are very difficult and often sensitive to the sample. However, careful experiments, as indicated in section 10.3, do verify the ORR within tight limits of experimental error. Even Newton's laws, when tested experimentally, are subject to similar errors.

(7) The final criticism is that TIP and ORR do not really have any utility. However, as noted earlier, most phenomena studied in chemistry and physics fall into the linear region, with the exception of chemical reactions. TIP gives a relatively simple, unified description of these linear phenomena, applicable to fluids, solids, membrane process, and a host of other systems. The idea of cross-coefficients or interaction coefficients is an elementary version of the equipresence concept; without finite values of such coefficients, thermoelectric, galvanomagnetic, and electrokinetic effects would not even be observable.

The ORR are of substantial value because they result in a simplification and reduction in the number of experimental coefficients necessary to describe a system. They also provide connections between related properties of a given phenomenon in a direct way. Many such connections have been proposed or known for some time; such as the symmetry of the heat conductivity tensor[27], the equality of the Hittorf and cell transference numbers[28], and the relations of Kelvin[25], Bridgman[75], and Saxèn[26]. However, these all had been based either on limited models or on incorrect theories which are much more *ad hoc* than TIP. Some new connections have been found, such as the unsuspected relation between the four diffusion coefficients of a ternary system[85]. (That four diffusion coefficients were required was not even proposed until 1932[85], and the first experiments were not reported until 1955[114,115].)

An advantage of TIP is that the same general formalism applies to widely differing phenomena. Some of these are sufficiently complex as not to have been subjected to any CT analysis.

10.5 Conclusion and Challenge

In section 10.3, we concluded that the ORR are experimentally verified. Despite this experimental evidence, critics pose the fundamental issue whether TIP and ORR have any content or validity. Let us summarise our position.

(1) The basic TIP balance and $T\sigma$ equations can be obtained from very general CT equations with appropriate and reasonable special hypotheses that apply to a large class of typical materials.

(2) A macroscopic recipe can be given for the choice of flows from $T\sigma$ to use in the linear constitutive equations which lead to the ORR.

(3) Given this recipe, experiment confirms the ORR for linear processes within experimental error for a variety of irreversible phenomena. This variety is much greater than CT can presently treat.

(4) The ORR and the choice of flows are supported by statistical mechanics derivations. Moreover, there are kinetic theory special cases[116,117,118] and continuum mechanics special cases with special hypotheses[33,34,35,102,105,119] which also yield the ORR.

In view of the theoretical and experimental evidence for ORR, I would challenge the critics from CT to search actively for the underlying basis for such reciprocal relations. What necessary macroscopic hypotheses or restrictions are required to obtain this apparently fundamental symmetry—which may also extend beyond purely linear processes? What limitations does this symmetry principle really have? Where will these additional restrictions be imposed: with a different form of material objectivity, with different constitutive equations, with a different Clausius–Duhem equation, with new stability conditions, or with time-reversal hypotheses? Day[33,119], Gurtin[33,35], Müller[34], Horne and Ingle[102], and Doria[105] have already provided some possible clues.

Critics must face the facts. The Onsager reciprocal relations are an inescapable, experimentally verified physical principle. The macroscopic origin of this symmetry principle will probably best be found by the techniques of rational continuum mechanics. The challenge thus is to find it in a general form and to determine its region of applicability.

Acknowledgement

This work was performed under the auspices of the United States Atomic Energy Commission.

References

1. L. Onsager. *Phys. Rev.*, **37** (1931), 405; **38** (1931), 2265
2. J. Meixner and H. G. Reik. *Thermodynamik der Irreversiblen Prozesse*, ed. by S. Flügge, vol. III/2, Springer-Verlag, Berlin (1959), p. 413–523

3. I. Prigogine. *Introduction to Thermodynamics of Irreversible Processes*, C. C. Thomas, Springfield, Illinois (1955)
4. S. R. de Groot and P. Mazur. *Non-Equilibrium Thermodynamics*, Interscience, New York (1962)
5. R. Haase. *Thermodynamik der Irreversiblen Prozesse*, Dietrich Steinkopff, Darmstadt (1963); *Thermodynamics of Irreversible Processes*, Addison-Wesley, Reading, Massachusetts (1969)
6. D. D. Fitts. *Non-Equilibrium Thermodynamics*, McGraw-Hill, New York (1962)
7. C. Truesdell and R. Toupin. *The Classical Field Theories, Handbuch der Physik*, vol. III/1, Springer-Verlag, Berlin (1960)
8. C. Truesdell and W. Noll. *The Non-Linear Field Theories of Mechanics, Handbuch der Physik*, vol. III/3, Springer-Verlag, Berlin (1965)
9. C. Truesdell, *Rational Thermodynamics*, McGraw-Hill, New York (1969)
10. C. Truesdell. *Rend. Lincei* (8), **22** (1957), 33; **44** (1968), 381
11. B. Coleman and W. Noll. *Arch. Rat. Mech. Anal.*, **13** (1963), 167
12. M. Gurtin. *Arch. Rat. Mech. Anal.*, **28** (1968), 40
13. M. Gurtin and A. Vargas. *Arch. Rat. Mech. Anal.*, **43** (1971), 179
14. M. Gurtin. *Arch. Rat. Mech. Anal.*, **43** (1971), 198
15. I. Müller. *Arch. Rat. Mech. Anal.*, **28** (1968), 1
16. G. S. Ohm. *Die Galvanische Kette, Mathematisch Behandelt*, Berlin (1827)
17. A. Fick. *Ann. Phys.* (Pogg.), **94** (1855), 59
18. J. Fourier. *Théorie Analytique de la Chaleur*, Paris (1822)
19. J. Bertrand. *Thermodynamique*, Gauthier-Villars, Paris (1887), ch. 12
20. P. Duhem. *Traité d'énergétique*, vol. 2, Gauthier-Villars, Paris (1911), ch. 12, 15
21. L. Natanson. *Z. Physik. Chem.*, **21** (1896), 193
22. G. Jaumann. *Sitzber. Akad. Wiss. Wien. Math.-naturw. Kl.*, Abt. IIA, **120** (1911), 385
23. G. Jaumann. *Denksch. Akad. Wiss. Wien, Math.-naturw. Kl.*, **95** (1918), 461
24. E. Lohr. *Denksch. Akad. Wiss. Wien. Math.-naturw. Kl.*, **93** (1916), 339; **99** (1924), 59
25. W. Thomson. *Proc. Roy. Soc.*, (Edinburgh) **3** (1854), 225
26. U. Saxèn. *Ann. Physik.*, **47** (1892), 46
27. G. Stokes. *Cambridge and Dublin Math. J.*, **6** (1851), 215
28. H. von Helmholtz. *Ann. Physik*, **3** (1878), 201
29. R. Wegscheider. *Z. Physik. Chem.*, **39** (1901), 257
30. S. de Groot and P. Mazur. *Phys. Rev.*, **94** (1954), 218, 224
31. H. Mori. *Phys. Rev.*, **112** (1958), 1829
32. J. Kirkwood and D. Fitts. *J. Chem. Phys.*, **33** (1960), 1317
33. W. Day and M. Gurtin. *Arch. Rat. Mech. Anal.*, **33** (1969), 26
34. I. Müller. *Arch. Rat. Mech. Anal.*, **41** (1971), 319
35. M. Gurtin. *Arch. Rat. Mech. Anal.*, **44** (1972), 387
36. D. G. Miller. *Am. J. Phys.*, **24** (1956), 595
37. H. B. Casimir. *Rev. Mod. Phys.*, **17** (1945), 343
38. B. D. Coleman and C. Truesdell. *J. Chem. Phys.*, **33** (1960), 28
39. J. Meixner. *Ann. Physik*, **43** (1943), 244
40. R. Fieschi, S. de Groot and P. Mazur. *Physica*, **20** (1954), 67, 245, 259
41. S. de Groot and N. van Kampen. *Physica*, **21** (1955), 39
42. P. Mazur and S. de Groot. *Physica*, **19** (1953), 961
43. Reference 4, p. 69–77
44. D. G. Miller. *Chem. Rev.*, **60** (1960), 15
45. D. G. Miller. In *Transport Phenomena in Fluids*, ed. by H. Hanley, Marcel Dekker

Inc., New York (1969), ch. 11. This chapter is a reprinting of the essential parts of ref. 44 plus new experimental evidence collected between 1960 and 1969
46. Reference 4, p. 350–1
47. A. Woodall. *Proc. Phys. Soc.*, (London) **47** (1935), 615
48. F. Donohoe and L. Testardi. *J. Appl. Phys.*, **31** (1960), 1304
49. W. Henry. *Canad. J. Phys.*, **41** (1963), 1094
50. E. Lange and T. Hesse. *Z. Elektrochem.*, **38** (1932), 428
51. P. Mazur and T. Overbeek. *Rec. Trav. Chim.*, **70** (1951), 83
52. P. Lorenz. *J. Phys. Chem.*, **45** (1952), 775
53. S. de Groot, P. Mazur and J. Overbeek. *J. Chem. Phys.*, **20** (1952), 1825
54. U. Saxèn. *Ann. Phys.*, **47** (1892), 46
55. A. Rutgers and M. de Smet. *Trans. Faraday Soc.*, **43** (1947), 102
56. P. Wijga. *Stromungspotentialen, Electroendosmose en Oppervlaktegeleiding*, Thesis, Amsterdam (1946)
57. R. Rastogi and B. Misra. *Trans. Faraday Soc.*, **63** (1967), 584
58. R. Rastogi, M. Srivastava and S. Singh. *J. Phys. Chem.*, **74** (1970), 2960
59. Reference 4, p. 24, 239
60. L. Woolf, D. Miller and L. Gosting. *J. Am. Chem. Soc.*, **84** (1962), 317
61. D. G. Miller. *J. Phys. Chem.*, **63** (1959), 570; (corrections) **63** (1959), 2089; (recalculated results) **69** (1965), 3374
62. References in reference 45
63. A. Revzin. *J. Phys. Chem.*, **76** (1972), 3419
64. H. Kim, G. Reinfelds and L. Gosting. *J. Phys. Chem.*, **77** (1973), 934
65. T. Kett and D. Anderson. *J. Phys. Chem.*, **73** (1969), 1268
66. I. Prigogine, P. Outer and I. Herbo. *J. Phys. Chem.*, **52** (1948), 321
67. K. G. Denbigh. *Thermodynamics of the Steady State*, Wiley, New York (1951), p. 31–6, 44–9
68. T. Bak. *Bull. Classe Sci., Acad. Roy. Belg.*, **45** (1959), 116
69. W. Haag and H. Pines. *J. Am. Chem. Soc.*, **82** (1960), 387, 2488
70. R. Maurel and D. G. Miller. *Comptes Rend.*, **255** (1962), 1266
71. Reference 4, p. 344–8, 355–64
72. H. Callen. *Phys. Rev.*, **73** (1948), 1349; **85** (1952), 16
73. P. Mazur and I. Prigogine. *J. Phys. Radium*, **12** (1951), 616
74. J. Jan. *Solid State Physics*, **5** (1957), 1
75. P. Bridgman. *Thermodynamics of Electrical Phenomena in Metals*, MacMillan, New York (1934), ch. 7. See also *Phys. Rev.*, **24** (1924), 644
76. N. Little. *Phys. Rev.*, **28** (1926), 418
77. L. Houlliwegue. *J. Phys.*, **5** (1896), 53
78. R. Wolfe and G. Smith. *Phys. Rev.*, **129** (1963), 1086
79. C. Grenier, J. Reynolds and N. Zebouni. *Phys. Rev.*, **129** (1963), 1088
80. W. Reed and J. Marcus. *Phys. Rev.*, **130** (1963), 957
81. J. Yahia and J. Marcus. *Phys. Rev.*, **113** (1959), 137
82. D. G. Miller and M. J. Pikal. *J. Soln. Chem.*, **1** (1972), 111
83. Reference 4, p. 27
84. D. G. Miller. *J. Phys. Chem.*, **70** (1966), 2639; **71** (1967), 616
85. L. Onsager and R. Fuoss. *J. Phys. Chem.*, **36** (1932), 2689
86. M. Pikal. *J. Phys. Chem.*, **75** (1971), 3124
87. J. G. Albright and D. G. Miller. *J. Phys. Chem.*, **76** (1972), 1853
88. M. J. Pikal and D. G. Miller. *J. Phys. Chem.*, **74** (1970), 1337
89. G. Jones and B. C. Bradshaw. *J. Am. Chem. Soc.*, **54** (1932), 138

90. G. Jones and M. Dole. *J. Am. Chem. Soc.*, **51** (1929), 1073
91. Reference 4, p. 235–8
92. M. Jannettaz. *Comptes Rend.*, **114** (1892), 1352
93. H. S. Carslaw and J. C. Jaeger. *Conduction of Heat in Solids*, 2 ed., Oxford Univ. Press, London (1959), sections 1.17–1.20
94. L. L. Campbell. *Galvanomagnetic and Thermomagnetic Effects*, Longmans, New York (1923), ch. II and XIII
95. C. Soret. *Arch. Sci.*, (Geneva) **29** (1893), 355
96. J. F. Nye. *Physical Properties of Crystals*, Oxford Univ. Press, London (1957), ch. XI
97. W. Voigt. *Lehrbuch der Kristallphysik*, Teubner, Leipzig (1910)
98. L. Boltzmann. *Sitzber. Akad. Wiss. Wien, Math.-naturw. Kl.*, Abt. II, **94** (1886), 644
99. A. von Ettinghausen and W. Nernst. *Sitzber. Akad. Wiss. Wien, Math.-naturw. Kl.*, Abt. II, **94** (1886), 560
100. W. Voigt. *Göttingen Nachr.* (1903), 87
101. P. Curie. *Arch. Sci.*, (Geneva) **29** (1893), 342
102. F. Horne and S. Ingle. *Rational and Practical Nonequilibrium Thermodynamics*, Thesis, Michigan State Univ. (1971)
103. F. Horne and J. Bartelt. *Nonequilibrium Thermodynamics of Fluid Mixtures: Principles, Perturbation Methods, and Parameter Estimation*, Thesis, Michigan State Univ. (1968)
104. F. Horne and J. Bartelt. *Pure App. Chem.*, **22** (1970), 349
105. M. Doria. *Arch. Rat. Mech. Anal.*, **32** (1969), 343
106. Reference 101, Appendix C
107. I. Prigogine. *Etude Thermodynamique des Phénomènes Irréversibles*, Desoer, Liège (1947), p. 114
108. Reference 6, p. 35–6
109. Reference 4, p. 57–64
110. Y. Yao. *J. Chem. Phys.*, **48** (1968), 537
111. Reference 9, p. 135–7
112. S. Crandall. *Physica*, **28** (1955), 251
113. G. Hooyman, S. de Groot and P. Mazur. *Physica*, **21** (1955), 360
114. R. L. Baldwin, P. J. Dunlop and L. J. Gosting. *J. Am. Chem. Soc.*, **77** (1955), 5235
115. P. J. Dunlop and L. J. Gosting. *J. Am. Chem. Soc.*, **77** (1955), 5238
116. I. Müller. *Arch. Rat. Mech. Anal.*, **31** (1968), 255
117. J. Hirschfelder, C. Curtiss and R. Bird. *Molecular Theory of Gases and Liquids*, Wiley, New York (1954), section 11.2
118. Reference 4, p. 184–7
119. W. Day. *Arch. Rat. Mech. Anal.*, **40** (1971), 155

Copyright Authorisation

11. The Onsager Reciprocal Relations—Experimental Evidence; Discussion Paper

E. A. Mason†

11.1 Introduction

One good way to start a lively discussion is for the opening discussor to disagree sharply with the speaker. Unfortunately, I happen to agree with Dr. Miller's point of view, so that I must adopt the alternative technique of arousing discussion by re-emphasising some of Dr. Miller's points as sharply as possible.

The most fundamental point to be emphasised, it seems to me, is that the *thermodynamics of irreversible processes* (TIP) can be put on an entirely macroscopic basis. In this formulation the Onsager reciprocal relations (ORR) are to be regarded as an empirical postulate, in the same sense as are the laws of *classical equilibrium thermodynamics* (CET), and as such are subject to experimental test. If the experimental tests are sufficiently convincing, such an empirical postulate may be elevated to the status of a law, in which it becomes a tautology in the logical sense, incapable of being disproved, and thenceforth serving instead as a framework for the description of a wide variety of phenomena.

Let me put the thesis, for the sake of arousing discussion, that it is now time to elevate TIP and the ORR to the status of tautology, or to put it more elegantly, to the status of a *paradigm* in the sense of T. S. Kuhn[1]. To support this thesis, let me first make a few remarks on the advantages of a completely macroscopic formulation of TIP and ORR, second, comment on some previous criticisms of the macroscopic approach, and third, offer some further remarks on the experimental evidence for the ORR and the useful range of the linear laws. Finally, I shall hazard a few semiphilosophical remarks on the present status and possible future development of TIP and ORR.

11.2 Advantages of a Macroscopic Viewpoint

Although I believe strongly in atoms and molecules, and have devoted much of my scientific lifetime to kinetic theory and statistical mechanics, I nevertheless feel that there is considerable merit in a macroscopic formulation of both CET and TIP. One should not underestimate their power and validity

† Brown University, Providence R.I., USA.

because of the apparent insight offered by those examples simple enough to be dealt with in detail by statistical methods. Probably everyone has at some time seen students emerge from a course in *Statistical Physics* powerless in the face of any problem not involving an ideal gas or a perfect crystal. We need macroscopic formulations to handle those problems and those systems that are too complex and too intractable to be treated by a molecular-scale theory—dense gases, liquid solutions, complicated solids, and so on. We should be able to use CET and TIP to find results in which we have full confidence, because they are free from special simplifying assumptions about details on the molecular scale, and free from the severe mathematical approximations that often have to be made to extract an answer from a microscopic theory.

To illustrate another advantage of the macroscopic viewpoint, let me quote from a general introduction given by Professor Scatchard to a Faraday Society Discussion in 1956 on Membrane Phenomena[2].

> I think a much more important contribution of thermodynamics to science is the time of imaginative investigators which has been saved for useful work by the denial of the possibility of perpetual motion. I do not expect the complete devastation of a criticism such as, 'If that were so I could devise a perpetual motion machine,' but perhaps the statement 'This does not prove your special theory, but only proves the Onsager relations' may become nearly as effective as 'This only proves the second law'.

In other words, if we can agree on the validity of ORR, let's get on with it and use them for something other than the production of journal articles.

11.3 Criticism of Macroscopic Formulation

Dr. Miller has commented on several criticisms of TIP and ORR. From a macroscopic viewpoint the most fundamental of these seems to be the claim that there is no unique way to choose the forces and fluxes without recourse to some statistical–mechanical argument, and so no completely macroscopic formulation is even possible. One of the more dramatic arguments along this line was the demonstration by Coleman and Truesdell (reference 38 of chapter 10) that new forces and flows could be chosen which would preserve the entropy production equation but would *not* lead to ORR. This is, if

$$T\sigma = \sum_i J_i X_i \tag{11.1}$$

and

$$J_i = \sum_j L_{ij} X_j \tag{11.2}$$

with

$$L_{ij} = L_{ji} \tag{11.3}$$

then new fluxes and forces J_i' and X_i' could be defined as

$$J_i' \equiv J_i + \sum_j W_{ij} X_j \qquad X_i' \equiv X_i \tag{11.4}$$

where W_{ij} represents *any* non-zero skew matrix ($W_{ij} = -W_{ji}$). From this it is easy to show that

$$T\sigma = \sum_i J_i' X_i' \tag{11.5}$$

$$J_i' = \sum_j L_{ij}' X_j' \tag{11.6}$$

but
$$L_{ij}' = L_{ij} + W_{ij} \neq L_{ji} \tag{11.7}$$

The converse can also be proved straightforwardly. The flaw, if it may be called that, in this argument lies in equation 11.4, which suggests that we are so ignorant concerning fluxes and forces that we cannot tell one from the other, and end up defining a new set of fluxes which include some of the original forces. It is not hard to escape this trap—we merely are obliged to supply a macroscopic recipe for distinguishing between forces and fluxes. Dr. Miller has supplied one such recipe in his talk, and others are clearly possible. The recipe need not supply a unique definition of individual forces and fluxes, it must merely distinguish between the two categories.

The macroscopic recipe supplied by Dr. Miller is based essentially only on classical thermodynamics, in the sense that one must know enough about the system to identify the deformation variables that characterise the state of the system, and hence be able to write expressions for reversible and irreversible work. It is not even necessary to go through the formality of writing the explicit expression for the entropy production. This recipe is sometimes paraphrased by saying that the fluxes are true derivatives of extensive thermodynamic quantities, and the forces are gradients of intensive thermodynamic properties. Once we have escaped the Coleman–Truesdell trap, it is a question of deciding on the validity of the ORR by experiment, a question that has been handsomely reviewed for us by Dr. Miller.

Another cutting criticism is that there is virtually no new physical content in TIP. There is something to this criticism. Except for the ORR, there is nothing new in TIP that was not already present in CET, except the concept of local state. That is, TIP without ORR is just quasithermodynamics. In short, the ORR are the only new physical results in TIP—they are its heart and soul. I think this is less a criticism of TIP than a motivation to subject the ORR to careful experimental scrutiny. This is precisely what Dr. Miller has done for us.

11.4 Experimental Evidence for ORR

There are a few more experimental tests of the ORR that might be mentioned. These are all concerned with gases, and are seldom mentioned in connection with TIP. Perhaps the reason is that gases can generally be described by a highly developed kinetic theory, and so the question of using TIP does not arise. Nevertheless, these are valid experimental tests.

The first test concerns the relation of thermal diffusion and the diffusion thermoeffect. The corresponding phenomena in liquids are known as the Soret effect and Dufour effect, respectively. In thermal diffusion a temperature gradient gives rise to a mass flow; an initially uniform gas mixture will thus undergo partial separation when subjected to a temperature difference. In the diffusion thermoeffect a composition gradient gives rise to a heat flow; a diffusing gas mixture thus develops a small temperature difference. The coefficients describing these two effects should be equal, according to ORR. Most of the experimental work on the diffusion thermoeffect was reported by L. Waldmann in the years 1943–9 for dilute gases. Comparison with the more extensive thermal diffusion data shows agreement with ORR within experimental error[3], which is in the range of 5 to 10 per cent. A few measurements of the diffusion thermoeffect have also been made up to 20 atm[4], which can be compared with thermal diffusion measurements at high pressures[5,6]. The agreement is not spectacular, but there is certainly no inconsistency with the ORR.

A second test involves isothermal diffusion in ternary gas mixtures. Because of ORR, there are only three independent coefficients, not four. Unfortunately for a direct test of ORR, this result occurs in the kinetic theory of gases almost trivially at the very beginning, and data are analysed not by transport equations of the Onsager form of equation 11.2 but by a set of inverse relations of the form

$$X_i = \sum_j R_{ij} J_j \tag{11.8}$$

known in gas theory as the Stefan–Maxwell equations. The reason is that the composition dependence of the R_{ij} is much simpler than that of the L_{ij}. The experimentally measured mole fractions in the system H_2–N_2–CO_2, with a variety of initial conditions, agreed with the solutions of the Stefan–Maxwell equations to about 0.5 per cent[7]. This result is thus also consistent with ORR, although the data were not analysed in such a way as to provide a direct test.

The third and last test concerns coupling between isothermal transport due to diffusion and to convective flow, a subject that arises frequently in membrane transport. Instead of molar fluxes J_1 and J_2 it is customary to define new fluxes[8]

$$J_V = J_1 \bar{V}_1 + J_2 \bar{V}_2 \tag{11.9}$$

$$J_D = \left(\frac{J_1}{c_1}\right) - \left(\frac{J_2}{c_2}\right) \tag{11.10}$$

where $\bar{V}_i$ is partial molal volume and c_i is concentration. The linear laws are then written as

$$-J_D = L_D RT\left(\frac{\partial c_1}{\partial x}\right) + L_{Dp}\left(\frac{\partial p}{\partial x}\right) \tag{11.11}$$

$$-J_V = L_{pD} RT\left(\frac{\partial c_1}{\partial x}\right) + L_p\left(\frac{\partial p}{\partial x}\right) \tag{11.12}$$

and ORR gives $L_{Dp} = L_{pD}$. Some results for gaseous flow and diffusion through a porous graphite membrane, expressed in the above membrane notation, are shown in figure 11.1. Here pure helium was on one side of the membrane with pure argon on the other side, and the results are plotted in terms of arithmetic-mean values, $\bar{c}_1$, $\bar{c}_2$, and $\bar{p}$. The ORR states that the slope of the J_D against Δp curve should be related to the intercept of the J_V against Δp curve; this relationship is verified within experimental error[9], which is obviously rather large because the slope of the J_D curve is not well-determined. Here there could be a clear experimental utility for ORR—it is obviously more accurate to predict the slope of the J_D curve from the intercept of the J_V curve than to measure it directly.

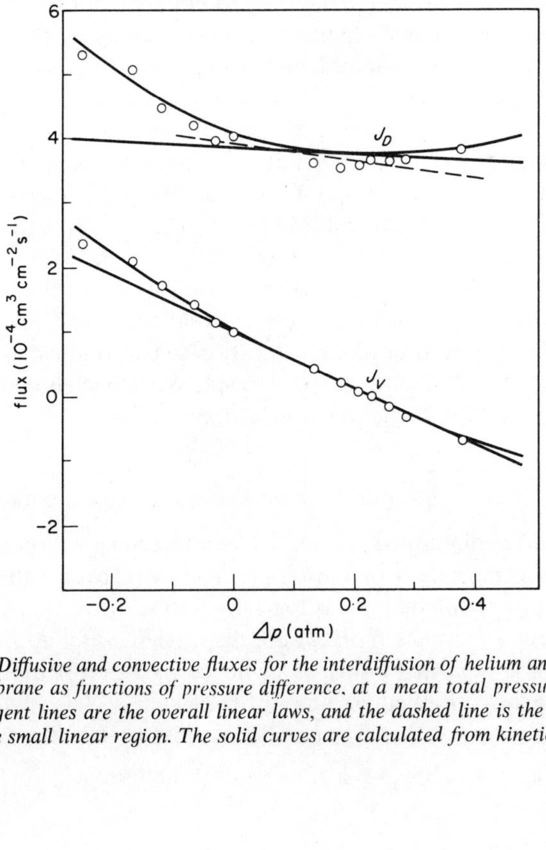

Figure 11.1 Diffusive and convective fluxes for the interdiffusion of helium and argon in a porous graphite membrane as functions of pressure difference, at a mean total pressure of $\bar{p}$ = 1.96 atm. The solid tangent lines are the overall linear laws, and the dashed line is the least-squares fit to the data in the small linear region. The solid curves are calculated from kinetic theory.

A more interesting feature stands out in figure 11.1, however. Because of the large composition difference across the membrane, the curve of J_D against Δp shows only a tiny linear region. For instance, if one looked at the J_V and J_D curves only in the vicinity of $\Delta p = 0.5$ atm, the apparent values of L_{pD} and L_{Dp} would not even agree in sign. One might be tempted to conclude that TIP and ORR had an almost uselessly small range of validity in this case. Somewhat surprisingly, this is not true. If we allow for the composition and pressure dependence of the L_{ij}, as predicted from kinetic theory for instance, and then integrate the linear laws across the membrane, we get the solid curves shown in figure 11.1, which are in very good agreement with the measurements over the whole range. Thus we learn a useful lesson: apparent limitations in the range of validity of the linear laws may really be artifacts of poor integration procedures.

Incidentally, the one type of gas-phase experimental test almost always mentioned in discussions of ORR has still not been done. This involves the thermomechanical effects, such as thermal transpiration or the thermomolecular pressure difference. The ORR predict a relation between the thermomolecular pressure difference and the heat of transport of the gas. The pressure differences are relatively easy to measure, but the heats of transport pose a real experimental challenge. I think it unlikely that anyone will have the motivation to try the heat measurements, especially since there is now a kinetic theory calculation of the heats of transport that covers the range from the free-molecule to the continuum regime[10].

As a final remark on the experimental situation, I would like to emphasise both the variety and the accuracy of the experimental support for the ORR assembled by Dr. Miller. I rather doubt that similar attempts to marshall the experimental evidence in support of the first, second, and third laws of thermodynamics would produce anything much better in the way of either variety *or* accuracy. I am absolutely certain that the experimental evidence for these three laws at the time of their elevation to paradigm status was much inferior to the evidence assembled for the ORR. Why then should we hesitate to accord full paradigm status to the macroscopic ORR?

11.5 Present Status of ORR and Possible Future Developments

Perhaps I should explain further what I mean by the elevation of a relation to the status of a paradigm or tautology. Such a relation cannot possibly be disproved by experiment, for it is logically only a definition. Consider the first law of thermodynamics. You cannot disprove it—any apparent experimental disproof is regarded either as evidence of experimental error or as evidence that an overlooked or new form of energy was involved in the experiments. New forms of energy can be invoked to *save* the law any time it seems to be in serious trouble. If you doubt this statement, consider the history of the neutrino, which was invented by Pauli just to save conservation of energy in nuclear beta-decay, and had to wait about thirty years to find any other independent confirmation of its existence. Similarly, an apparent violation of the second law will be regarded as evidence that some part of a supposedly reversible change in state really involved an irreversible element, possibly due to some previously unidentified internal variable of the system. Thus we never violate the first and second laws, we only discover new forms of energy and new internal variables. In macroscopic mechanics we never can discover violations of Newton's second law of motion, we can only find new forms of forces, for this law is really the definition of force and therefore a tautology.

I do not mean to sound cynical. All science runs in this manner, and there are good reasons for it, as Kuhn has discussed at length[1]. Permit me to quote a passage from a memorial lecture by E. P. Wigner on the development of the compound nucleus model for nuclear reactions[11]:

> The rest of the story is similar in its main lines, and on a small scale, to the story of almost every physical theory. First, the ephemeral and the general elements of the theory are separated. Second, the general elements are formulated in such a general way that they can serve as framework for the description of a wide variety of phenomena. This, unfortunately, also means that the physical content of the framework becomes so small that almost any experimental result can be fitted into it. The interest, therefore, shifts away from the framework to the body of information which can be described in the language given by the framework. Third, an attempt is made to deduce from very general principles the physical content which remains in the framework. The story of almost every physical theory goes along this way; some run through it fast, the more important ones less rapidly.
>
> It may be worthwhile to illustrate this by means of an example. Galileo's discovery of the laws of free fall led to a concrete and definite equation. What was ephemeral in this equation was the constancy of the acceleration. The general part of it was formulated as Newton's second law, the proportionality between acceleration and force. This is the first phase already mentioned. However, Newton's second law is so general that it permits almost any type of motion, it provides a language to *describe* motions rather than *determining* the motion by itself. Hence, the problem after the establishment of the second law shifted from the description of the motion to the determination of the forces between bodies. This shift of the problem is what was called the second phase of the theory. The last phase of the theory is the search for the fundamental reason for those parts of the general physical law which give it whatever physical content it does have. This is, actually, Newton's first law. Its fundamental basis, the equivalence of moving observers, was embodied eventually in the Galilei and Lorentz transformations.

I think TIP and ORR are in the second stage, but not everyone is yet willing to accede to this view. What about the third phase? As Professor de Groot has discussed, this is well-advanced from the statistical–mechanical or kinetic-theory point of view. Dr. Miller has posed a different challenge: can the

ORR be deduced from macroscopic considerations by the techniques of rational continuum mechanics? This would indeed be an interesting result. I am afraid to hazard a guess as to how this might be achieved, but I will offer an opinion on how it will *not* be achieved. It will not be achieved by formulations involving memory functions or time histories. To illustrate my opinion, I invite you to consider that old warhorse of classical thermodynamics, the mass of gas in a cylinder closed by the famous weightless, frictionless piston. Only now let there be a small leak around the edge of the piston. The state of this system at a given time obviously depends on how fast a given load was placed on the piston; clearly the system has a *memory*, for the present state is influenced by the past history. Yet I believe it would be madness to try to reformulate the laws of thermodynamics to accommodate such a system. One should look for the leak, instead.

References

1. T. S. Kuhn. *The Structure of Scientific Revolutions*, Univ. of Chicago Press, 2 ed. (1970)
2. G. Scatchard. *Disc. Faraday Soc.*, **21** (1956), 27
3. K. E. Grew and T. L. Ibbs. *Thermal Diffusion in Gases*, Cambridge Univ. Press, London (1952), ch. 6
4. E. A. Mason, L. Miller and T. H. Spurling. *J. Chem. Phys.*, **47** (1967), 1669
5. T. Makita. *Rev. Phys. Chem. Japan*, **29** (1960), 47, 55
6. T. Makita and T. Takagi. *Rev. Phys. Chem. Japan*, **32** (1963), 1
7. J. B. Duncan and H. L. Toor. *Am. Inst. Chem. Engrs. J.*, **8** (1962), 38
8. A. Katchalsky and P. F. Curran, *Nonequilibrium Thermodynamics in Biophysics*, Harvard Univ. Press, Cambridge, Mass. (1965), ch. 10
9. E. A. Mason, R. P. Wendt and E. H. Bresler. *J. Chem. Soc. Faraday Trans.*, II **68** (1972), 1938
10. A. P. Malinauskas and E. A. Mason. *Trans. Faraday Soc.*, **67** (1971), 2243
11. E. P. Wigner. *Am. J. Phys.*, **23** (1955), 371

Discussion

LOBO

Are the ORR really of any value in measuring diffusion coefficients?

MILLER

The answer is yes and no. *No* for optical measurements, because the nature of the experiments is such that all of the diffusion coefficients (4 for a ternary, 9 for a quaternary) come out simultaneously in the analysis of the fringe patterns. However, Professor Mason mentioned that the ORR should always be used as a consistency check to verify that no gross error has been made.

Yes for diaphragm cell measurements because here fewer experiments would be necessary. However, because diaphragm cell measurements are not very precise, it would be best to do the extra experiments anyway.

GERMAIN

Can a more satisfactory recipe be provided?

MILLER

I have offered one which seems to be macroscopically satisfactory for scalar and vector flows. (I did not discuss higher order tensor flows.) The idea is to calculate $T\sigma$ for the case of interest. The result is always a sum of terms each of which has the time derivative of an extensive thermodynamic variable. Then one must eliminate the Gibbs–Duhem dependence and choose a frame of reference for matter flows among the three prescribed. The result will be either the set of flows I indicated or a combination of them which can be transformed into that set by appropriate divergences, Meixner transformations, etc. which leave $T\sigma$ invariant. In some cases, the flow of electrons may be a matter flow, and it may also be possible to combine terms afterwards to get a current flow. But in all cases, the time derivative of an extensive variable will be found in each of the $J_i X_i$ terms.

PRIGOGINE

While the Onsager relations obviously form an important part of TIP, I would not agree that they are 'its heart-and-soul'. At least in part it is a fact that nonequilibrium thermodynamics permits us—at least in *single* cases—to study the behaviour of matter when deviations for equilibrium are imposed. We may say really that distance from equilibrium plays the role of a new thermodynamic parameter similar in some aspect to temperature and pressure. While in classical thermodynamics irreversibility was a nuisance, a parasitic element which prevented us from obtaining the *maximum yield* in the Carnot cycle, this *is no longer so for* TIP. Here, on the contrary, irreversibility at sufficient distance from equilibrium leads to new structures called the *dissipative structure.* TIP becomes then also the study of the possible occurrence *of those new nonequilibrium* states of matter. The relation with biology is obvious. It is this recent development which is responsible for much of the interest of the scientific community for TIP.

MASON

I would agree absolutely with Professor Prigogine that the greatest scientific interest at present lies in extending TIP to new situations. But in the linear near-equilibrium regime, which is the one discussed by Dr. Miller, the only new macroscopic content beyond the assumption of local state consists of the reciprocal relations. Perhaps we can take Professor Prigogine's remark as tacit agreement that we should accept the reciprocal relations and get on with new things.

MEIXNER

My first remark refers to Professor Mason's presentation. It is a supplement to what I have already said in chapter 7. One should always speak of the Onsager–Casimir relations instead of the Onsager reciprocal relations. Because by simple transformation, for instance exchange of a flux with the respective force as an independent variable, Casimir relations show up even if in the original rate equations there were only Onsager relations. Then there is no sense in a statement that Onsager–Casimir relations are wrong with *fluxes* and *forces* which do not have definite parities.

The second remark concerns Professor Miller's lecture (chapter 10), particularly what he said at the end. One can in fact formulate two macroscopic postulates from which, in essence, (apart from a few exceptional cases) the Onsager–Casimir relations can be derived. One of them has been brought forward in special cases by Day and by Gurtin.

A second formulation is that the passivity integral has for every periodic process (after the transients have died out) the same value as for a properly defined time reversed process. These postulates can be proved by virtue of the fluctuation–dissipation theorem supplemented by microscopic reversibility.

One might, however, be induced to see in these postulates quite general properties of thermodynamic materials. This is not so, rather one can show that the validity of these postulates is restricted to processes which always stay close to a fixed equilibrium state. Details will be given in a forthcoming paper.

MASON

If one can assign definite parities to the forces and fluxes, then there is no difficulty with a macroscopic formulation of TIP. The problem is reduced, therefore, to supplying a *macroscopic* recipe for assigning such parities. I have not yet seen such a recipe, but perhaps one could be formulated.

KESTIN

There are two problems connected with the choice of forces, X_i, and fluxes, J_i: how do we make an *initial* choice and what transformations preserve the validity of the OCRR?

It seems to me that Professor Meixner's two theorems answer the second question. However, the problem of an *initial* choice remains. I submit that the first question must be answered on the basis of our understanding of physics. Since the entropy production at $T = \text{const.}$ is derived from the dissipation rate $(\mathrm{d}W^0 - \mathrm{d}W)/T$, we must trace the physical meaning of X_i and J_i to some expression for work. Now, in all branches of physics (as noted by Carathéodory), the work is given in the form of products $f_i \, \mathrm{d}x_i$ of components of force into increments of distance. Evidently, in most situations encountered in thermodynamics the preceding expression is transformed and written $F_\alpha \, \mathrm{d}a_\alpha$, where each F_α represents some generalised force and a_α represents some generalised displacement. In turn, $F_\alpha \, \mathrm{d}a_\alpha$ is written in a local form applicable at a point in the continuum, the details depending on circumstances. It seems to me that X_i is related to F_α, whereas J_i is related to the time rate of change, $\dot{a}_\alpha$, of the deformation parameter, a_α, in each case. Hence, X_i is an intensity and J_i is a flux of an extensity.

SIDOROFF

I would like to describe an attempt to take up the challenge proposed by both lecturers. L. C. Woods has proposed in his book *The Thermodynamics of Fluid Systems*, which is about to be published, a new macroscopic approach to Onsager's relations. Here is how I interpret his ideas.

From a macroscopic analysis the entropy production $T\sigma$ can be written as

$$T\sigma = \boldsymbol{X}^T \cdot \boldsymbol{x} \tag{11.13}$$

where $\boldsymbol{X} = (X_1, X_2, \ldots, X_n)$ is even and $\boldsymbol{x} = (x_1, x_2, \ldots, x_n)$ is odd. We assume a linear relation

$$\boldsymbol{X} = \psi \boldsymbol{x} \tag{11.14}$$

and the symmetry breaking introduced by Professor Prigogine is quite obvious: under time reversal $\boldsymbol{X}$ must become $\boldsymbol{X}$ and $\boldsymbol{x}$ must become $-\boldsymbol{x}$. Then from equation 11.13 $T\sigma$ becomes $-T\sigma$ in contradiction with the second law. On the other hand if $\boldsymbol{x}$ becomes $-\boldsymbol{x}$, then from equation 11.14, $\boldsymbol{X}$ becomes

$-\boldsymbol{X}$ and $T\sigma$ becomes $T\sigma$. The linear relation, equation 11.14, which accounts for the dissipation breaks the parity of $\boldsymbol{X}$ on a macroscopic scale. In fact, we have to introduce two kinds of time reversal.

(1) A microscopic time reversal (mtr) which determines the parity of the variables: $\boldsymbol{x} \to -\boldsymbol{x}$ and $\boldsymbol{X} \to +\boldsymbol{X}$.

(2) A macroscopic time reversal $(\mathrm{MTR}(\boldsymbol{x}))$ in which $\boldsymbol{x}$ transforms as in a mtr while $\boldsymbol{X}$ transforms according to equation 11.14

$$\mathrm{MTR}(\boldsymbol{x}): \boldsymbol{x} \to -\boldsymbol{x} \qquad \text{and} \qquad \boldsymbol{X} \to -\boldsymbol{X}$$

More generally we can write a linear relation with respect to another set of forces and fluxes: consider the vectors $\boldsymbol{y}$ and $\boldsymbol{Y}$ defined by

$$y_i = x_i \quad \text{or} \quad X_i \begin{cases} \text{if } y_i = x_i & \text{then} \quad Y_i = X_i \quad \text{and} \quad \eta_i = -1 \\ \text{if } y_i = X_i & \text{then} \quad Y_i = x_i \quad \text{and} \quad \eta_i = +1 \end{cases}$$

so that $T\sigma = \boldsymbol{Y}^{\mathrm{T}} \cdot \boldsymbol{y}$

and we assume a linear relation

$$\boldsymbol{Y} = \boldsymbol{L}\boldsymbol{y} \tag{11.15}$$

Using the parity matrix $\boldsymbol{\eta} = \mathrm{diag}(\eta_1, \eta_2, \ldots, \eta_n)$, then in a mtr $\boldsymbol{y} \to \boldsymbol{\eta}\boldsymbol{y}$ and $\boldsymbol{Y} \to -\boldsymbol{\eta}\boldsymbol{Y}$. The macroscopic time reversal associated to y is defined in the following way

$$\mathrm{MTR}(\boldsymbol{y}): \boldsymbol{y} \to \boldsymbol{\eta}\boldsymbol{y} \qquad \boldsymbol{y} \to \boldsymbol{L}\boldsymbol{\eta}\boldsymbol{y}$$

that is $\boldsymbol{y}$ transforms as in a mtr while $\boldsymbol{Y}$ transforms according to equation 11.15.

Of course while there is only one mtr, there are as many MTR as there are possible $\boldsymbol{y}$, that is 2^n. Then we can prove the following theorem.
Theorem: Onsager's reciprocity relations

$$\boldsymbol{L}^{\mathrm{T}} = \boldsymbol{\eta}\boldsymbol{L}\boldsymbol{\eta}$$

are equivalent to the assumption that $T\sigma$ is invariant under any macroscopic time reversal.

This gives a macroscopic status to ORR. We may ignore microscopic aspects completely, except for one thing: we still need to refer to mtr to determine the parity of variables. Once this is done, the 'proper choice of fluxes and forces' becomes an empty problem since they all are equivalent provided we follow the rules indicated by Professor Meixner: conserve the bilinear form for $T\sigma$ and use variables of a definite parity.

MASON

This is a neat and compact formulation of TIP, and in a way is an amplification of Professor Meixner's first remark. But it is still not a completely macroscopic formulation, since the parity of the variables must be found from microscopic considerations.

12. Some Restrictions on Constitutive Equations

R. S. Rivlin†

Abstract

The condition for stability of a homogeneous state of deformation of an elastic body under dead-loading is derived on the basis of the Hadamard criterion. The strong-ellipticity condition then follows as a necessary condition. The pure homogeneous deformation is then discussed, of a cube of incompressible isotropic neo-Hookean elastic material, under dead-loading by three equal pairs of equal and opposite forces applied to the faces of cube. It is shown that the resulting state of pure homogeneous deformation is not uniquely determined. The implications of this result, with respect to the material stability conditions proposed by Coleman and Noll and by Truesdell and Toupin are discussed. Finally, some explicit restrictions on the strain–energy function are given, which result from the consideration that the velocities of propagation of plane waves in the pure homogeneously deformed material must be real.

12.1 Introduction

If the variables entering into a constitutive equation are specified, two types of restriction, arising from consideration of invariance, can usually be placed on the manner in which the dependent variable can depend on the independent variables. One of these arises from a consideration of the effect of an arbitrary rotation on the form of the constitutive equation. A number of methods by which such restrictions can be made explicit have been given, notably by Oldroyd[1], Rivlin and Ericksen[2], Green and Rivlin[3], Noll[4], and Pipkin and Rivlin[5]. The further restrictions, which may be placed on the form of the constitutive equations by any symmetry which the material may possess, have been discussed extensively by Reiner, Rivlin, Ericksen, Green, Pipkin, Smith, Spencer and others (see, for example, references 2, 3 and 5 to 15). We shall not, for lack of space, discuss restrictions of these two types in the present paper. Rather, we shall concentrate on a critical discussion of various inequalities which have been proposed. Although most of these may be loosely described as thermodynamic in character, we shall limit our discussion of them to the situation in which thermal effects are not present or are neglected.

† Center for the Application of Mathematics, Lehigh University, Bethlehem, Pa.

We open our discussion by introducing, in section 12.2, the Hadamard condition for stability of a body in equilibrium under the action of specified forces applied as dead loads. This condition is used, in section 12.3, in the discussion of the problem of the pure homogeneous deformation of a cube of incompressible isotropic elastic material under the action of specified pairs of equal and opposite forces, applied normally to the faces of the cube and distributed uniformly over them. This problem was discussed by Rivlin[16] in 1948, in the case when the material of the cube is an incompressible neo-Hookean material. It was found that if the applied forces are specified, more than one equilibrium configuration of pure homogeneous deformation is possible for certain ranges of values of the applied forces. The stability of these various equilibrium configurations was investigated[16], using essentially the Hadamard condition. It was concluded that for certain ranges of values of the applied forces, more than one stable equilibrium configuration of pure homogeneous deformation is possible. Which one is, in fact, attained depends, of course, on the order in which the forces are applied. In evaluating these results, it must be borne in mind that the neo-Hookean constitutive equation provides a moderately good approximation[17] to the actual behaviour of many rubber-like materials over a wide range of deformation. Also, it is the constitutive equation obtained from statistical–mechanical calculations based on an idealised molecular model of vulcanised rubber[18].

The Hadamard condition is a local convexity condition on the Gibbs free-energy. (Since thermal effects are neglected, the latter is the strain energy minus the work done by the applied forces.) The Coleman–Noll inequality[19], which is discussed in section 12.4, replaces this local convexity condition by a global convexity condition. It is pointed out, in section 12.4, that in application to the pure homogeneous deformation of a cube of isotropic elastic material under dead loading, the Coleman–Noll inequality implies a unique stable equilibrium configuration. This is, of course, in direct conflict† with the earlier result of Rivlin[16] discussed in section 12.2.

Baker and Ericksen[22] put forward inequalities which must be satisfied by the principal components of the Cauchy stress in a deformed isotropic material (see section 12.5). These are equivalent to the condition that the shear modulus be positive for an infinitesimal simple shear superposed on a pure homogeneous deformation, the direction of shear being a principal direction and the plane of shear being a principal plane for the pure homogeneous deformation.

In 1956, in a paper 'Das ungelöste Haupt problem der Endlichen Elastizitätstheorie', Truesdell[23] describes this work of Baker and Ericksen and suggests, as did Baker and Ericksen earlier[22], that it would be interesting

† This conflict was mentioned by Rivlin[20] in a review of the book by Truesdell and Noll[21].

to seek further restrictions of this kind on the constitutive equation for an elastic material. Since 1956 many such restrictions have been suggested, including the Coleman–Noll inequality mentioned. These are mainly due to Truesdell and Toupin[24], and have been discussed at considerable length by Truesdell and Noll[21]†. While one may argue with Truesdell's contention[23] that the discovery of further restrictions of the Baker–Ericksen type was in 1956—or is now—the main unsolved problem of finite elasticity theory, it is nevertheless of some interest to explore those restrictions that have been proposed. This is done, to some extent, in section 12.5, where we discuss certain of the restrictions which are implied by the Coleman–Noll inequality. It is pointed out, as was recognised by Truesdell and Noll (reference 21, section 53), that these restrictions become self-contradictory when applied to an incompressible elastic material. It is also pointed out, in section 12.6, that the contention of Truesdell and Noll (reference 21, section 53), that they are nevertheless applicable to compressible materials, is not, as a general statement, reasonable. They may, of course, apply in particular cases, but validity in this sense is hardly in the spirit of the search proposed by Truesdell[23].

A different approach to the quest for restrictions on the constitutive equations for elastic materials stems from Hadamard's[25] requirement that the speeds of propagation of plane waves of infinitesimal amplitude, in a deformed elastic material, be real for any direction of propagation. This is equivalent to the requirement that the speeds of propagation of plane surfaces of second-order discontinuity in an arbitrary direction be real. In this form it was applied by Ericksen[26] to incompressible isotropic elastic materials, but he did not pursue the analysis to the point of obtaining restrictions on the form of the strain–energy which do not involve the direction of propagation, apart from restrictions equivalent to the Baker–Ericksen condition previously mentioned.

The Hadamard condition was applied to a compressible isotropic elastic material by Hayes and Rivlin[27]. They obtained, in addition to the Baker–Ericksen condition, further explicit conditions on the strain–energy function. These are discussed in section 12.7. More recently, Sawyers and Rivlin[28] have obtained, for an incompressible isotropic elastic material, certain necessary conditions on the strain–energy function for the wave speeds to be real. These are also discussed in section 12.7.

12.2 The Hadamard Stability Condition

From the first law of thermodynamics, it follows that if a body undergoes

† Truesdell and Noll (reference 21, section 87), make the claim: 'After the general problem had been presented by Truesdell . . . in a lecture delivered in 1955, the entire body of the researches reported in Sects. 51, 52 and 87 grew from this beginning'.

deformation, then the difference in the total energy of the body (internal energy plus kinetic energy) at times t_1 and t_2 is equal to the sum of the work done, in the time interval (t_2, t_1), by the forces applied to the body and the heat entering the body in this time interval. We may write this as

$$(\mathscr{U}_1-\mathscr{U}_2)+(\mathscr{T}_1-\mathscr{T}_2) = \mathscr{W}+\mathscr{H} \tag{12.1}$$

where $\mathscr{U}_1$, $\mathscr{U}_2$ denote the internal energy at times t_1 and t_2; $\mathscr{T}_1$, $\mathscr{T}_2$ denote the kinetic energy at times t_1 and t_2; $\mathscr{W}$ denotes the work done by the applied forces and $\mathscr{H}$ denotes the heat entering the body.

If the body is thermally insulated, so that no heat enters it, equation 12.1 may be written as

$$(\mathscr{U}_1-\mathscr{U}_2)+(\mathscr{T}_1-\mathscr{T}_2) = \mathscr{W} \tag{12.2}$$

If the body is in equilibrium at time t_2, then $\mathscr{T}_2 = 0$ and equation 12.2 becomes

$$(\mathscr{U}_1-\mathscr{U}_2)+\mathscr{T}_1 = \mathscr{W} \tag{12.3}$$

If the adiabatic deformation envisaged is carried out reversibly, then it follows from the second law of thermodynamics that the deformation is isentropic. If, on the other hand, we do not consider the deformation to be adiabatic, but rather to be an isothermal deformation, with uniform temperature throughout the body, it follows from the second law of thermodynamics that equation 12.3 is still valid if $\mathscr{U}_1$ and $\mathscr{U}_2$ are interpreted as the Helmholtz free energy of the body at times t_1 and t_2. In either case, in the framework of a purely mechanical theory, we may regard $\mathscr{U}_1$ and $\mathscr{U}_2$ as the strain–energy of the body at times t_1 and t_2.

Since, for any deformation possible in a real body, $\mathscr{T}_1 \geqslant 0$, the state of deformation assumed at time t_1 will be possible only if

$$\mathscr{W} \geqslant \mathscr{U}_1-\mathscr{U}_2 \tag{12.4}$$

We now consider that the force system acting on the body consists of body forces $\boldsymbol{\phi}$ per unit mass and surfaces forces $\boldsymbol{F}$, per unit area measured at some reference time T. We consider that $\boldsymbol{\phi}$ and $\boldsymbol{F}$ are time-independent, so that dead-loading conditions apply. Let $\boldsymbol{x} = \boldsymbol{x}(t)$ and $\boldsymbol{X}$ be the vector positions, with respect to a fixed origin, of a generic particle of the body. Then $\mathscr{W}$ is given by

$$\mathscr{W} = \int_V \mathrm{d}V \int_{\boldsymbol{x}_2}^{\boldsymbol{x}_1} \rho_0 \boldsymbol{\phi}\cdot\mathrm{d}\boldsymbol{x} + \int_A \mathrm{d}A \int_{\boldsymbol{x}_2}^{\boldsymbol{x}_1} \boldsymbol{F}\cdot\mathrm{d}\boldsymbol{x} \tag{12.5}$$

where $\boldsymbol{x}_1 = \boldsymbol{x}(t_1)$, $\boldsymbol{x}_2 = \boldsymbol{x}(t_2)$, ρ_0 is the density of the material of the body at time T, V is the domain occupied by the body at time T and A is the surface of this domain. Since $\boldsymbol{\phi}$ and $\boldsymbol{F}$ are independent of time, equation 12.5 yields

$$\mathscr{W} = \int_V \rho\boldsymbol{\phi}\cdot(\boldsymbol{x}_1-\boldsymbol{x}_2)\,\mathrm{d}V + \int_A \boldsymbol{F}\cdot(\boldsymbol{x}_1-\boldsymbol{x}_2)\,\mathrm{d}A \tag{12.6}$$

The strain energy is assumed to be an extensive quantity, that is, we assume that the strain energy $\mathscr{U}$ of the body at time t can be written in the form

$$\mathscr{U} = \int_V \rho_0 U\,\mathrm{d}V \tag{12.7}$$

where U is the strain energy per unit mass. Then, if U_1 and U_2 are the values of U at times t_1 and t_2 respectively, we can use equations 12.6 and 12.7 to rewrite the inequality 12.4

$$\int_V \rho_0(U_1-U_2)\,\mathrm{d}V \leqslant \int_V \rho\boldsymbol{\phi}\cdot(\boldsymbol{x}_1-\boldsymbol{x}_2)\,\mathrm{d}V + \int_A \boldsymbol{F}\cdot(\boldsymbol{x}_1-\boldsymbol{x}_2)\,\mathrm{d}A \tag{12.8}$$

If the condition 12.8 is violated, then the configuration $\boldsymbol{x}_1$ cannot be reached under the assumed dead-loading condition.

Now let us take configuration $\boldsymbol{x}_1$ infinitesimally different from $\boldsymbol{x}_2$ and write

$$\boldsymbol{x}_2 = \boldsymbol{x}, \quad \boldsymbol{x}_1 = \boldsymbol{x}+\delta\boldsymbol{x}, \quad U_1 = U_2+\delta U \tag{12.9}$$

The inequality 12.8 then becomes

$$\int_V \rho_0\delta U\,\mathrm{d}V \leqslant \int_V \rho_0\boldsymbol{\phi}\cdot\delta\boldsymbol{x}\,\mathrm{d}V + \int_A \boldsymbol{F}\cdot\delta\boldsymbol{x}\,\mathrm{d}A \tag{12.10}$$

If the condition 12.10 is violated for all possible $\delta\boldsymbol{x}$, then no configuration in the neighbourhood of $\boldsymbol{x}_2$ can be reached under dead-loading conditions and, accordingly, the configuration $\boldsymbol{x}$ is a *stable* equilibrium configuration.

If the material of the body is perfectly elastic, U is a function of the deformation gradients $x_{i,A}$ measured in the rectangular cartesian coordinate system x.

We may then write

$$\delta U = \frac{\partial U}{\partial x_{i,A}}\delta x_{i,A} + \frac{1}{2}\frac{\partial^2 U}{\partial x_{i,A}\partial x_{j,B}}\delta x_{i,A}\delta x_{j,B} + 0(\delta x_{i,A})^3 \tag{12.11}$$

Now, if Π_{Ai} is the Piola–Kirchoff stress in the configuration $\boldsymbol{x}$, then

$$\Pi_{Ai} = \rho_0\frac{\partial U}{\partial x_{i,A}} \tag{12.12}$$

Also
$$F_i = \Pi_{Ai}N_A$$
and
$$\Pi_{Ai,A}+\rho_0\phi_i = 0 \tag{12.13}$$

Using equation 12.13 to substitute for F_i and ϕ_i in equation 12.10, and applying the divergence theorem to the surface integral, we can rewrite the condition 12.10 as

$$\int_V \rho_0 \delta U \,\mathrm{d}V \leqslant \int_V \Pi_{Ai} \delta x_{i,A} \,\mathrm{d}V \tag{12.14}$$

Now, introducing equations 12.11 and 12.12 into equation 12.14, we obtain

$$\int_V \rho_0 \frac{\partial^2 U}{\partial x_{i,A} \partial x_{j,B}} \delta x_{i,A} \delta x_{j,B} \,\mathrm{d}V \leqslant 0 \tag{12.15}$$

If this condition is violated for all possible infinitesimal $\delta x_{i,A}$; that is, if the condition

$$\int_V \rho_0 \frac{\partial^2 U}{\partial x_{i,A} \partial x_{j,B}} \delta x_{i,A} \delta x_{j,B} \,\mathrm{d}V > 0 \tag{12.16}$$

is satisfied for all possible infinitesimal $\delta x_{i,A}$, then the configuration $\boldsymbol{x}$ will be one of stable equilibrium. This is Hadamard's condition for stability. Otherwise, the configuration is said to be one of *unstable*† equilibrium, if the strong inequality in equation 12.15 applies for some value of $\delta x_{i,A}$, and one of *neutral* equilibrium, if the strong inequality in equation 12.15 applies for no possible values of $\delta x_{i,A}$, but the equality applies for some possible value of $\delta x_{i,A}$.

If the deformation considered is homogeneous, then a necessary and sufficient condition for equation 12.16 to be valid is

$$\frac{\partial^2 U}{\partial x_{i,A} \partial x_{j,B}} \delta x_{i,A} \delta x_{j,B} > 0 \tag{12.17}$$

at each point of the body, for all non-zero $\delta x_{i,A}$.

In particular equation 12.17 must be satisfied for matrices $\delta x_{i,A}$ which may be expressed as the outer product of two triples χ_i and μ_A, that is, for $x_{i,A} = \chi_i \mu_A$. It follows that a necessary condition for Hadamard's stability

† Strictly, stability may still obtain when

$$\int_V \rho_0 \frac{\partial^2 U}{\partial x_{i,A} \partial x_{j,B}} \delta x_{i,A} \delta x_{j,B} \,\mathrm{d}V = 0$$

for some infinitesimal $\delta x_{i,A}$, if, for example,

$$\int_V \rho_0 \frac{\partial^3 U}{\partial x_{i,A} \partial x_{j,B} \partial x_{k,C}} \delta x_{i,A} \delta x_{j,B} \delta x_{k,C} \,\mathrm{d}V = 0$$

and
$$\int_V \rho_0 \frac{\partial^4 U}{\partial x_{i,A} \partial x_{j,B} \partial x_{k,C} \partial x_{l,D}} \delta x_{i,A} \delta x_{j,B} \delta x_{k,C} \delta x_{l,D} \,\mathrm{d}V > 0$$

for this $\delta x_{i,A}$. We shall, however, ignore special situations of this kind and take equation 12.16 as our definition of stability.

condition 12.17 to be valid is that

$$\frac{\partial^2 U}{\partial x_{i,A} \partial x_{j,B}} \chi_i \chi_j \mu_A \mu_B > 0 \tag{12.18}$$

for all non-zero triples χ_i and μ_A. This condition is sometimes called the *strong-ellipticity* condition for stability.

If the material is incompressible, the condition 12.17 for stability of a homogeneous deformation under dead-loading is somewhat modified, since the nine quantities $\delta x_{i,A}$ cannot be varied independently, but are constrained by the condition that only isochoric deformations are possible in the body. This condition is

$$|x_{i,A}| - 1 = 0 \tag{12.19}$$

from which it follows that

$$\delta |x_{i,A}| = \tfrac{1}{2}\varepsilon_{ijk}\varepsilon_{ABC} x_{j,B} x_{k,C} \delta x_{i,A} + \tfrac{1}{2}\varepsilon_{ijk}\varepsilon_{ABC} x_{k,C} \delta x_{i,A} \delta x_{j,B} + 0(\delta x_{i,A})^3 \tag{12.20}$$

Then, following Beatty[29], we replace $\rho_0 U$ in equation 12.11 by $\rho_0 U - p(|x_{i,A}| - 1)$, where p is an arbitrary quantity, which may vary from point to point of the body. We thus obtain, with equation 12.11, and neglecting terms of $0(x_{i,A})^3$

$$\rho_0 \delta U = \left(\rho_0 \frac{\partial U}{\partial x_{i,A}} - \tfrac{1}{2} p \varepsilon_{ijk}\varepsilon_{ABC} x_{j,B} x_{k,C} \right) \delta x_{i,A} + \tfrac{1}{2} \left(\rho_0 \frac{\partial^2 U}{\partial x_{i,A} \partial x_{j,B}} - p \varepsilon_{ijk}\varepsilon_{ABC} x_{k,C} \right) \delta x_{i,A} \delta x_{j,B} \tag{12.21}$$

In an incompressible material

$$\Pi_{Ai} = \rho_0 \frac{\partial U}{\partial x_{i,A}} - \tfrac{1}{2} p \varepsilon_{ijk}\varepsilon_{ABC} x_{j,B} x_{k,C} \tag{12.22}$$

Using equations 12.21 and 12.22 in equation 12.14, in place of equations 12.11 and 12.12, the stability criterion 12.17 is replaced by

$$\left(\rho_0 \frac{\partial^2 U}{\partial x_{i,A} \partial x_{j,B}} - p \varepsilon_{ijk}\varepsilon_{ABC} x_{k,C} \right) \delta x_{i,A} \delta x_{j,B} > 0 \tag{12.23}$$

We note from equation 12.22 that

$$p = \tfrac{1}{3} x_{m,P} \left(\rho_0 \frac{\partial U}{\partial x_{m,P}} - \Pi_{Pm} \right) \tag{12.24}$$

Introducing equation 12.24 into equation 12.23, we obtain the stability condition

$$\left[\rho_0 \frac{\partial^2 U}{\partial x_{i,A}\partial x_{j,B}} - \tfrac{1}{3}\varepsilon_{ijk}\varepsilon_{ABC} x_{m,P} x_{k,C}\left(\rho_0 \frac{\partial U}{\partial x_{m,P}} - \Pi_{Pm}\right)\right]\delta x_{i,A}\delta x_{j,B} > 0 \quad (12.25)$$

for all $\delta x_{i,A}$ satisfying the incompressibility condition

$$\varepsilon_{ijk}\varepsilon_{ABC} x_{j,B} x_{k,C}\delta x_{i,A} = 0 \quad (12.26)$$

12.3 Pure Homogeneous Deformation of an Isotropic Elastic Cube

For an incompressible isotropic elastic material, subjected to a deformation in which a particle initially at X_A, in a rectangular cartesian coordinate system x, moves to x_i in the same system, U must be expressible in terms of the deformation gradients through the strain invariants I_1 and I_2 defined by

$$I_1 = \operatorname{tr} \boldsymbol{C}, \quad I_2 = \tfrac{1}{2}[(\operatorname{tr} \boldsymbol{C})^2 - \operatorname{tr} \boldsymbol{C}^2] \quad (12.27)$$

where $\boldsymbol{C} = \|C_{AB}\|$ is the Cauchy strain tensor defined by

$$C_{AB} = x_{i,A} x_{i,B} \quad (12.28)$$

Thus

$$U = U(I_1, I_2) \quad (12.29)$$

We consider the pure homogeneous deformation of a unit cube of this material under dead-loading by pairs of forces acting normally on its faces and uniformly distributed over them. The forces $F_i (i = 1, 2, 3)$, which must be applied to the faces of the unit cube, in order to produce in it a pure homogeneous deformation with extension ratios $\lambda_i (i = 1, 2, 3)$, are given by

$$F_i = 2\rho_0\{(U_1 + I_1 U_2)\lambda_i - U_2\lambda_i^3\} - p/\lambda_i \quad (12.30)$$

where p is arbitrary and U_1 and U_2 denote $\partial U/\partial I_1$ and $\partial U/\partial I_2$ respectively. We have, of course,

$$\lambda_1\lambda_2\lambda_3 = 1 \quad (12.31)$$

The Piola–Kirchoff stress Π_{Ai}, in a reference system x whose axes are parallel to the edges of the cube, is given by

$$\Pi_{Ai} = F_i\delta_{Ai} \quad (12.32)$$

In this system, the deformation is, of course, described by

$$x_1 = \lambda_1 X_1, \quad x_2 = \lambda_2 X_2, \quad x_3 = \lambda_3 X_3 \quad (12.33)$$

Rivlin[16] raised the following question. If, in equation 12.30, the forces F_i are specified, are the values of $\lambda_1, \lambda_2, \lambda_3$ uniquely determined? He studied this problem for a particular form of U

$$\rho_0 U = \tfrac{1}{2}C(I_1 - 3) \tag{12.34}$$

Materials for which U has this form are called neo-Hookean materials. In this case, equation 12.30 becomes

$$F_i = C\lambda_i - p/\lambda_i \tag{12.35}$$

It was found that if $F_i (i = 1, 2, 3)$ are specified, the equations 12.35 and 12.31 do not, in general, yield a unique solution for the four quantities λ_i and p. Thus, more than one equilibrium state of pure homogeneous deformation of the cube may be possible for specified values of the forces F_i. The stability of these various states may be investigated using the Hadamard criterion, equation 12.25, which, with equations 12.34 and 12.32, becomes

$$C\delta x_{i,A} x_{i,A} - \sum_{\alpha=1}^{3} \tfrac{1}{3}\lambda_\alpha (CI_1 - F_m\lambda_m)\varepsilon_{ij\alpha}\varepsilon_{AB\alpha}\delta x_{i,A}\delta x_{j,B} > 0 \tag{12.36}$$

This investigation[16] was carried out only for stability with respect to infinitesimal superposed deformations which are pure homogeneous, and which have their principal directions parallel to those of the equilibrium pure homogeneous deformation. The stability criterion, equation 12.36, becomes, in this case, with equation 12.31

$$\sum_{\alpha,\beta=1}^{3} \left[C(\delta\lambda_\alpha)^2 - \tfrac{1}{3}\frac{1}{\lambda_\alpha\lambda_\beta}(CI_1 - F_m\lambda_m)(1-\delta_{\alpha\beta})\delta\lambda_\alpha\delta\lambda_\beta \right] > 0 \tag{12.37}$$

for all $\delta\lambda_\alpha$ satisfying the incompressibility condition

$$\sum_{\alpha=1}^{3} \frac{\delta\lambda_\alpha}{\lambda_\alpha} = 0 \tag{12.38}$$

It was found[16] that for certain ranges of F_i/C, some of the corresponding equilibrium states are stable with respect to the infinitesimal superposed pure homogeneous deformations, while others are unstable.

For example, if $F_1 = F_2 = F_3 = F$ (say), it was found that

(1) If F/C is negative, only one equilibrium state is possible, that for which $\lambda_1 = \lambda_2 = \lambda_3 = 1$, and this is stable with respect to the superposed pure homogeneous deformations.

(2) If $0 < F/C < 3(\frac{1}{4})^{1/3}$, only one equilibrium state is possible, that for which $\lambda_1 = \lambda_2 = \lambda_3 = 1$, and this is stable.

(3) If $3(\frac{1}{4})^{1/3} < F/C < 2$, seven equilibrium states are possible. One of these is the state for which $\lambda_1 = \lambda_2 = \lambda_3 = 1$, and it is stable. Of the remaining six states, two have $\lambda_1 = \lambda_2$, two have $\lambda_2 = \lambda_3$, and two have $\lambda_3 = \lambda_1$, the third principal extension ratio being, in each case, different

from the other two. For each of these pairs of states, one state is stable and the other unstable.

(4) If $F/C > 2$, the possible equilibrium states remain as in case (3). However, in this case, the state for which $\lambda_1 = \lambda_2 = \lambda_3 = 1$ is unstable.

In the Appendix (section 12.8) we give some indication of the manner in which the conditions governing the possibility of multiple equilibrium configurations arise.

The stability of the states for which $\lambda_1 = \lambda_2 = \lambda_3 = 1$ were further investigated by Hill[30], and by Green and Adkins[31]. They considered the stability of the state, not merely with respect to the infinitesimal superposed pure homogeneous deformations employed by Rivlin[16], but with respect to arbitrary superposed deformation fields satisfying the incompressibility condition; that is, they used essentially the condition 12.36. They found that the state is stable if $F/C > 0$ and unstable if $F/C < 0$.

Recently, Rivlin[32], using the same stability criterion as that employed by Hill and by Green and Adkins, investigated the stability of all the equilibrium states which correspond to $F_1 = F_2 = F_3 = F$. He found that the stability conditions remain precisely the same as they were in his earlier investigation, with the exception that the state $\lambda_1 = \lambda_2 = \lambda_3 = 1$ is now unstable if $F/C < 0$.

12.4 The Coleman–Noll Inequality

With the notation $\boldsymbol{g} = \|x_{i,A}\|$, the condition 12.17 for stability under dead-loading may be interpreted as a *local* convexity condition on the U versus $\boldsymbol{g}$ surface, in a ten-dimensional space, at the point corresponding to equilibrium. If the U versus $\boldsymbol{g}$ surface is locally convex at all points, for which the assumed dependence of U on $\boldsymbol{g}$ applies, then the U versus $\boldsymbol{g}$ surface is *globally* convex. Conversely, of course, if the U versus $\boldsymbol{g}$ surface is globally convex, it is locally convex at each point on it. Thus, global convexity implies that every homogeneous equilibrium deformation of an elastic body of the material considered, can be maintained as a state of stable equilibrium under dead-loading.

Global convexity of the U versus $\boldsymbol{g}$ surface can be expressed mathematically (*cf.* Hill[30]) by the condition that

$$U(\bar{\boldsymbol{g}}) - U(\boldsymbol{g}) - \operatorname{tr}\frac{\partial U}{\partial \boldsymbol{g}}(\bar{\boldsymbol{g}} - \boldsymbol{g}) > 0 \tag{12.39}$$

for any pair of values of $\bar{\boldsymbol{g}}$ and $\boldsymbol{g}$. The assumption that U is globally convex, places a severe restriction on the manner in which U can depend on $\boldsymbol{g}$. Hill[30], correctly as we shall see, rejected this restriction on U, as being out of accord with the behaviour of many materials.

Coleman and Noll[19] formulated a slightly different inequality, which they claimed must be satisfied for all materials. They considered two homogeneous equilibrium states, for which the deformation gradient matrices are $\boldsymbol{g}$ and $\bar{\boldsymbol{g}}$ and the entropies are η and $\bar{\eta}$. They regarded the internal energy in any equilibrium state as a function of the deformation gradients and entropy in that state, and formulated a convexity condition which they claimed must be satisfied for any pair of states $(\boldsymbol{g},\eta)$ and $(\bar{\boldsymbol{g}},\bar{\eta})$ for which $\bar{\boldsymbol{g}}$ and $\boldsymbol{g}$ are related to each other by a pure homogeneous deformation. They discussed also the special cases, in which only equilibrium states with the same entropy, or with the same temperature, are considered. Their inequality then takes the form of 12.39, with the condition that it must be satisfied for all $\bar{\boldsymbol{g}}$ and $\boldsymbol{g}$, related by a pure homogeneous deformation, that is, such that

$$\bar{\boldsymbol{g}} = \boldsymbol{s}\boldsymbol{g} \tag{12.40}$$

where $\boldsymbol{s}$ is a symmetric matrix, all of whose principal values are positive. In the case when isentropic deformations are considered, U is the specific internal energy. In the case when isothermal deformations are considered, U is the specific Helmholtz free energy. In either case, U may be regarded as the strain–energy per unit mass.

We now apply the inequality given in 12.39 with equation 12.40 to a unit cube of isotropic material and take $\bar{\boldsymbol{g}}$ and $\boldsymbol{g}$ to be pure homogeneous deformations for which the principal directions are parallel to the edges of the cube. We denote the principal extension ratios in the two states by the triples $\bar{\boldsymbol{\lambda}}$ and $\boldsymbol{\lambda}$ and the resultant forces, acting normally on the three pairs of opposite faces of the cube, when it is in equilibrium with principal extension ratios $\boldsymbol{\lambda}$, by the triple $\boldsymbol{F} = \rho_0 \partial U/\partial \boldsymbol{\lambda}$. The inequality then becomes

$$U(\bar{\boldsymbol{\lambda}}) - U(\boldsymbol{\lambda}) - \frac{1}{\rho_0}\boldsymbol{F}\cdot(\bar{\boldsymbol{\lambda}} - \boldsymbol{\lambda}) > 0 \tag{12.41}$$

for all triples of possible quantities $\bar{\boldsymbol{\lambda}}$ and $\boldsymbol{\lambda}$ which are allowable in the material. This is a statement that the U versus $\boldsymbol{\lambda}$ surface is globally convex. Since $\boldsymbol{F} = \rho_0 \partial U/\partial \boldsymbol{\lambda}$, it follows trivially that, for specified $\boldsymbol{F}$, only one equilibrium state of pure homogeneous deformation, with principal directions parallel to the edges of the cube, can exist.

This result is in direct conflict with the conclusions of the earlier work of Rivlin[16], discussed in section 12.3, that, for a cube of isotropic incompressible neo-Hookean elastic material, if the applied forces $\boldsymbol{F}$ satisfy certain conditions, more than one equilibrium state of pure homogeneous deformation may correspond to a specified value of $\boldsymbol{F}$. This conflict will be discussed further in section 12.6.

12.5 Further Inequalities for Pure Homogeneous Deformation of an Isotropic Elastic Cube

In this section, we again consider the pure homogeneous deformation of a unit cube of isotropic elastic material, with principal directions parallel to the edges of the cube. The principal Cauchy stresses are denoted by σ_α and the principal extension ratios and the resultant forces are denoted by λ_α and F_α respectively. Then

$$F_1 = \sigma_1 \lambda_2 \lambda_3, \quad F_2 = \sigma_2 \lambda_3 \lambda_1, \quad F_3 = \sigma_3 \lambda_1 \lambda_2 \tag{12.42}$$

Truesdell and Noll (reference 21, sections 51, 52) have given a number of inequalities which they claim must be satisfied by σ_α, F_α and λ_α. We shall discuss some of these in the various subsections of the present section. It will be seen that, for the most part, those discussed are incorrect or meaningless. Many of the other inequalities presented in reference 21 are open to the same objection, but limitations of space prevent discussion of them in the present paper.

12.5.1 Pressure–compression (P–C) inequalities

These inequalities, which were first advanced by Truesdell and Toupin[24] (see, also, Truesdell and Noll reference 21, section 51), may be expressed, in our notation, as

$$\sum_{\alpha=1}^{3} \sigma_\alpha(\lambda_\alpha - 1) > 0 \tag{12.43a}$$

and

$$\sum_{\alpha=1}^{3} F_\alpha(\lambda_\alpha - 1) > 0 \tag{12.43b}$$

provided that at least one of the λ's is not unity. It can be seen that neither of these inequalities is necessarily valid.

First let us assume that the condition 12.43*a* is satisfied for some force system, that the material is incompressible and $\sum_{\alpha=1}^{3} (\lambda_\alpha - 1) > 0$. We may add to the assumed force system an arbitrary hydrostatic pressure p, so that σ_α is replaced by $\sigma_\alpha - p$. Since the material is incompressible, the λ's remain unchanged. The left-hand side of inequality 12.43*a* becomes

$$\sum_{\alpha=1}^{3} \sigma_\alpha(\lambda_\alpha - 1) - p \sum_{\alpha=1}^{3} (\lambda_\alpha - 1) \tag{12.44}$$

Since p may be made as large as we please, this quantity may certainly be made negative, so that the condition 12.43*a* is violated for the new force system. If $\sum_{\alpha=1}^{3} (\lambda_\alpha - 1)$ is negative, we take p to be a large enough negative quantity and again expression 12.44 may be made negative, so that the condition 12.43*a* is violated for the new force system.

We now suppose that the condition 12.43*b* is satisfied for some force system, that the material is incompressible, and $\sum_{\alpha=1}^{3}(1-1/\lambda_\alpha)>0$. For an incompressible material, addition of a hydrostatic pressure p to the assumed force system changes F_α to $F_\alpha-p/\lambda_\alpha$. The left-hand side of the inequality 12.43*b* then becomes

$$\sum_{\alpha=1}^{3}F_\alpha(\lambda_\alpha-1)-p\sum_{\alpha=1}^{3}(1-1/\lambda_\alpha) \tag{12.45}$$

If p is taken to be a large enough positive quantity, expression 12.45 may be made negative and the condition 12.43*b* is then violated. If $\sum_{\alpha=1}^{3}(1-1/\lambda_\alpha)$ is negative, then we take p to be a large enough negative quantity and again expression 12.45 may be made negative, so that the condition 12.43*b* is violated for the new force system.

12.5.2 The ordered-force (O-F) inequality

This inequality is expressed as

$$(F_1-F_2)(\lambda_1-\lambda_2)>0 \qquad \text{if} \qquad \lambda_1\neq\lambda_2 \tag{12.46}$$

It was first given by Coleman and Noll (reference 19, section 12) (see, also, Truesdell and Noll, reference 21, section 51). That this inequality cannot be generally true is evident from the following consideration. If the material is incompressible, then the addition, to the assumed forces F_α, of a hydrostatic pressure p changes them to $F_\alpha-p/\lambda_\alpha$. The left-hand side of inequality 12.46 then becomes

$$(F_1-F_2)(\lambda_1-\lambda_2)+\frac{p}{\lambda_1\lambda_2}(\lambda_1-\lambda_2)^2 \tag{12.47}$$

If 12.46 is valid for the force system initially assumed, then expression 12.47 may be made negative by giving p a sufficiently large negative value, and the condition 12.46 is violated for the new force system. It can easily be shown (reference 21, section 87) that the inequality 12.46 is a consequence of the Coleman–Noll inequality given by equations 12.39 and 12.40.

A somewhat similar inequality, which is far more reasonable, was advanced earlier by Baker and Ericksen[22]. This is the inequality

$$(\sigma_1-\sigma_2)(\lambda_1-\lambda_2)>0 \tag{12.48}$$

We see that it is not open to the same criticism as expression 12.46, since, in an incompressible material, addition of an arbitrary hydrostatic pressure to the assumed force system leaves $\sigma_1 - \sigma_2$ unchanged. For a compressible material, U must depend on the λ's through I_1, I_2 and I_3 defined by

$$I_1 = \lambda_1^2 + \lambda_2^2 + \lambda_3^2 \quad (12.49a)$$

$$I_2 = \lambda_2^2\lambda_3^2 + \lambda_3^2\lambda_1^2 + \lambda_1^2\lambda_2^2 \quad (12.49b)$$

$$I_3 = \lambda_1^2\lambda_2^2\lambda_3^2 \quad (12.49c)$$

Then, with the notation $u_\alpha = \partial u/\partial I_\alpha (\alpha = 1, 2, 3)$

$$\sigma_\alpha = \frac{2\rho_0}{I_3^{\frac{1}{2}}}[(U_1 + I_1 U_2)\lambda_\alpha^2 - U_2\lambda_\alpha^4 + I_3 U_3] \quad (12.50)$$

It follows that the inequality 12.48 may be written as

$$U_1 + \lambda_3^2 U_2 > 0 \quad (12.51)$$

This is, in fact, the condition that the shear modulus be positive, for an infinitesimal simple shear superposed on a pure homogeneous deformation with extension ratios $\lambda_1, \lambda_2, \lambda_3$, the direction of shear being the 1-direction and the plane of shear being the 12-plane.

12.5.3 The GCN$_0$ condition

We now consider two states of pure homogeneous deformation of the unit cube of isotropic elastic material with principal extension ratios $\bar{\lambda}_\alpha$ and λ_α. The corresponding forces which must be applied to the faces of the cube are $\bar{F}_\alpha$ and F_α. The GCN$_0$ condition, which was apparently first given by Truesdell and Toupin[24] (see, also reference 21, section 51), is then expressed by

$$\sum_{\alpha=1}^{3} (\bar{F}_\alpha - F_\alpha)(\bar{\lambda}_\alpha - \lambda_\alpha) > 0 \quad (12.52)$$

It is apparent from an argument, similar to those already used, that this relation cannot be generally valid. We again suppose the material to be incompressible. We keep the force system F_α unchanged and add an arbitrary hydrostatic pressure p to the force system $\bar{F}_\alpha$. The $\bar{\lambda}$'s are, of course, unchanged and $\bar{F}_\alpha$ is changed to $\bar{F}_\alpha - p/\bar{\lambda}_\alpha$. The left-hand side of expression 12.52 becomes

$$\sum_{\alpha=1}^{3} (\bar{F}_\alpha - F_\alpha)(\bar{\lambda}_\alpha - \lambda_\alpha) - p\sum_{\alpha=1}^{3}\left(1 - \frac{\lambda_\alpha}{\bar{\lambda}_\alpha}\right) \quad (12.53)$$

Accordingly as $\sum_{\alpha=1}^{3}\left(1 - \frac{\lambda_\alpha}{\bar{\lambda}_\alpha}\right)$ is positive or negative, we take p to be a sufficiently large positive or negative quantity, so that expression 12.53 is negative and the condition 12.52 is violated for the new force system.

12.5.4 Extension–tension (E–T) inequality

We again consider two states of pure homogeneous deformation of the unit cube, as in section 12.5.3. Now, however, we assume that $\bar{F}_2 = F_2$ and $\bar{F}_3 = F_3$. Truesdell and Toupin[24] (see also reference 21, section 51) suggest that it is reasonable to expect that if $\bar{F}_1 > F_1$, then $\bar{\lambda}_1 > \lambda_1$, that is

$$(\bar{F}_1 - F_1)(\bar{\lambda}_1 - \lambda_1) > 0 \qquad (12.54)$$

This they call the E–T inequality.

We can argue that this cannot be valid generally in a manner similar to that already used in discussing the P–C, O–F and GCN$_0$ inequalities. Suppose the inequality 12.54 is valid for two force systems $\bar{F}_\alpha$ and F_α, for which $\bar{F}_2 = F_2$ and $\bar{F}_3 = F_3$, and suppose also that $\bar{\lambda}_2 = \bar{\lambda}_3$ and $\lambda_2 = \lambda_3$. Now, let us add, to the force systems $\bar{F}_\alpha$ and F_α, hydrostatic pressures $\bar{p}$ and p respectively, such that $\bar{p}/\bar{\lambda}_2 = p/\lambda_2$. Since the material is incompressible, the $\bar{\lambda}$'s and λ's remain unchanged. Also, the forces which replace $\bar{F}_2$ and F_2 remain equal and those which replace $\bar{F}_3$ and F_3 remain equal. However, the forces $\bar{F}_1$ and F_1 become $\bar{F}_1 - \bar{p}/\bar{\lambda}_1$ and $F_1 - p/\lambda_1$ respectively. The left-hand side of expression 12.54 then becomes

$$\left[(\bar{F}_1 - F_1) - \left(\frac{\bar{p}}{\bar{\lambda}_1} - \frac{p}{\lambda_1}\right)\right](\bar{\lambda}_1 - \lambda_1) \qquad (12.55)$$

which may be expressed as

$$(\bar{F}_1 - F_1) - \frac{p}{\lambda_2}(\bar{\lambda}_2^3 - \lambda_2^3)(\bar{\lambda}_1 - \lambda_1) \qquad (12.56)$$

If $\bar{\lambda}_1 > \lambda_1$, then $\bar{\lambda}_2 < \lambda_2$. Accordingly, by choosing p to be sufficiently large and negative, we can make the quantity 12.56 negative, so that the new forces violate the E–T inequality.

12.5.5 The IFS condition (invertibility of the force–stretch relations)

The forces F_α, which must be applied normally to the faces of a unit cube of isotropic elastic material, in order to produce in it a pure homogeneous deformation, with principal extension ratios λ_α and principal directions parallel to the edges of the cube, are expressible, in general, in the form

$$F_1 = F(\lambda_1, \lambda_2, \lambda_3), \quad F_2 = F(\lambda_2, \lambda_3, \lambda_1), \quad F_3 = F(\lambda_3, \lambda_1, \lambda_2) \qquad (12.57)$$

Truesdell and Toupin[24] (see also reference 21, section 51) state† 'It may be reasonable to expect that if given pairs of opposing normal forces of magnitude F_α are applied to the faces of a unit cube of isotropic elastic material, one and only one pure homogeneous deformation will result'. In

† In this quotation, the symbol F_α replaces the symbol T_α used by Truesdell and Toupin in reference 24 without change of meaning.

other words, if F_α is specified in expression 12.54, the λ's are uniquely determined. Truesdell and Toupin[24] call this the invertibility of force–stretch (IFS) condition. We have already seen that this condition is implied by the Coleman–Noll inequality (Truesdell and Noll, reference 21, section 87).

If the material is incompressible, the relations 12.57 must be replaced by

$$F_1 = F(\lambda_1, \lambda_2, \lambda_3) - p/\lambda_1 \tag{12.58a}$$

$$F_2 = F(\lambda_2, \lambda_3, \lambda_1) - p/\lambda_2 \tag{12.58b}$$

$$F_3 = F(\lambda_3, \lambda_1, \lambda_2) - p/\lambda_3 \tag{12.58c}$$

and

$$\lambda_1 \lambda_2 \lambda_3 = 1 \tag{12.59}$$

where p is arbitrary. It has already been seen in section 12.3 that, for the particular case when the material is an incompressible neo-Hookean material, if F_α is specified, then the λ's are not necessarily uniquely determined.

12.6 Discussion of the Validity of the Coleman–Noll Inequality and its Implications

The various inequalities given in section 12.5, with the exception of the Baker–Ericksen inequality 12.48, are all implied (reference 21, section 87) by the Coleman–Noll inequality 12.39. We have seen, again with the exception of the Baker–Ericksen condition, that they cannot be valid generally in the case when the material is incompressible.

In the original paper of Coleman and Noll[19], the inequality 12.39, with equation 12.40, was advanced with no restriction as to compressibility or incompressibility of the elastic material considered. The paper was reprinted in a collection edited by Truesdell (reference 33, p. 184) together with an introduction by him. In this introduction, Truesdell remarks 'The paper here reprinted raised thermodynamics, after its slumber of nearly half a century, to the level of a mathematical science. As with any other theory, mathematical correctness does not prove physical relevance; the range of applicability of Coleman and Noll's theory is still not settled'. One wonders in what sense the paper could be considered to 'raise thermodynamics to the level of a mathematical science' should it indeed transpire that it is physically irrelevant. That Truesdell had some misgivings with respect to physical relevance of the theory is evident from the manner in which it, as well as the various inequalities which follow from it, are presented in the volume *The non-linear field theories of mechanics* by Truesdell and Noll[21].

In section 53 of that volume which is titled 'Restrictions upon the response functions, III. Incompressible materials', Truesdell and Noll, following an extensive presentation of the various inequalities we have discussed in section

12.5 and a discussion of the relationships between them, make the statement

> For incompressible materials the requirement of isochoric deformation and its consequence, the presence of the arbitrary hydrostatic pressure in the stress relations (43.14), render inappropriate nearly all of the considerations of the last two sections. The P–C inequality (51.4) is wrong because change of volume is impossible, ... ; and more general conditions such as (51.42), since they are not invariant under change of the arbitrary hydrostatic pressure are meaningless.

It is indeed curious that Truesdell and Noll, while recognising that the various inequalities presented in the previous section of the present paper are meaningless for an incompressible material, should not have realised that this renders them incorrect as general statements for compressible materials. To see this we have only to consider a material which is slightly compressible. It seems far fetched, for example, to consider that the conclusion reached in section 12.3 (that the state of pure homogeneous deformation resulting from the application of specified forces is not necessarily uniquely determined if the material is incompressible) becomes invalid if the material is compressible, however small this compressibility may be.

12.7 Real Wave Speeds

We consider the propagation of a plane sinusoidal wave of infinitesimal amplitude in an elastic material subjected to a static pure homogeneous deformation. The planes of constant amplitude and phase for the wave are assumed to be parallel to each other and to be perpendicular to the unit vector $\boldsymbol{n}$. We assume that the wave is linearly polarised.

In a rectangular cartesian coordinate system x, the pure homogeneous deformation may be described by

$$\boldsymbol{x} = \boldsymbol{g} \cdot \boldsymbol{X} \tag{12.60}$$

where the deformation gradient matrix $\boldsymbol{g}$ is symmetric. We denote the displacement vector associated with the wave by $\boldsymbol{u}$. Then, in the usual complex notation, $\boldsymbol{u}$ may be expressed in the form

$$\boldsymbol{u} = \boldsymbol{A} \exp \imath(k\boldsymbol{n} \cdot \boldsymbol{x} - \omega t) \tag{12.61}$$

where ω is the angular frequency of the wave, k is its wave number and $\boldsymbol{A}$ is a constant vector. With equation 12.60 we can write equation 12.61 as

$$\boldsymbol{u} = \boldsymbol{A} \exp \imath(k\boldsymbol{N} \cdot \boldsymbol{X} - \omega t) \tag{12.62}$$

where

$$\boldsymbol{N} = \boldsymbol{n} \cdot \boldsymbol{g} \tag{12.63}$$

For an elastic material, with strain–energy U per unit mass, which, neglecting thermal effects, may be regarded as a function of the deformation gradients, we can show easily that $\boldsymbol{A}$ must satisfy the vector equation

$$(S^2\boldsymbol{Q}-\boldsymbol{\delta})\boldsymbol{A} = 0 \tag{12.64}$$

where

$$\boldsymbol{Q} = \|Q_{ij}\| = \left\| \frac{\partial^2 U}{\partial x_{i,A}\partial x_{j,B}} N_A N_B \right\| \tag{12.65}$$

$S = k/\omega$ is the slowness of the wave, and $\boldsymbol{\delta}$ is the unit matrix. In order that equation 12.64 have a nontrivial solution for U, the secular equation

$$\det|S^2\boldsymbol{Q}-\boldsymbol{\delta}| = 0 \tag{12.66}$$

must be satisfied. This provides an equation for the possible slownesses with which a wave can be propagated. The principal values of the matrix $\boldsymbol{Q}$ are the values of $1/S^2$ given by equation 12.66 with equation 12.65. Since $\boldsymbol{Q}$ is a symmetric matrix, these principal values are necessarily real. If one of the principal values is negative, it will yield two imaginary values for S of opposite signs. We note that if k is real and S is imaginary, ω must be imaginary. It follows that an initially sinusoidal disturbance will increase exponentially with time for one or other of the imaginary values of S. It has been suggested[25,27] that, for real elastic materials, the dependence of U on the deformation gradients must be such that this does not occur for any propagation direction $\boldsymbol{n}$; that is, that all three values of S^2, given by equation 12.66, must be positive for all directions of the unit vector $\boldsymbol{n}$. A necessary and sufficient condition for this to be the case is that the quadratic form $Q_{ij}\chi_i\chi_j$, where χ_i is an arbitrary triple of non-zero magnitude, be positive definite, that is

$$\frac{\partial^2 U}{\partial x_{i,A}\partial x_{j,B}} \chi_i\chi_j N_A N_B > 0 \tag{12.67}$$

for all χ_i and N_A such that $\chi_i\chi_i \neq 0$ and $N_A N_A \neq 0$. Comparing this condition with inequality 12.18, we see that stability under dead-loading, of the equilibrium state of pure homogeneous deformation considered, ensures that the slownesses are real for all directions of propagation of the superposed infinitesimal sinusoidal wave. However, the converse is not the case. The condition that the slownesses be real is thus a less restrictive condition on U than is the condition that equilibrium states of pure homogeneous deformation be, of necessity, stable under dead-loading.

If the elastic material considered is isotropic, then U must depend on $\boldsymbol{g}$ through the invariants, I_1, I_2 and I_3, of the Cauchy strain tensor $\boldsymbol{C}$. These are defined by

$$I_1 = \operatorname{tr}\boldsymbol{C} \tag{12.68a}$$

$$I_2 = \tfrac{1}{2}\{(\operatorname{tr}\boldsymbol{C})^2 - \operatorname{tr}\boldsymbol{C}^2\} \tag{12.68b}$$

$$I_3 = \det\boldsymbol{C} \tag{12.68c}$$

where
$$C = g^T g \tag{12.69}$$

Thus
$$U = U(I_1, I_2, I_3) \tag{12.70}$$

By introducing equation 12.70 into equation 12.65 and choosing the axes of the reference system x to be parallel to the principal directions of the pure homogeneous deformation, we can, after considerable algebraic manipulation, obtain[27]

$$Q_{\alpha\alpha} = \sum_{\gamma=1}^{3} \Lambda_{\alpha\gamma} n_\gamma^2 \tag{12.71a}$$

$$Q_{\alpha\beta} = \Theta_{\alpha\beta} n_\alpha n_\beta \quad (\alpha \neq \beta) \tag{12.71b}$$

where

$$\tfrac{1}{2}\Lambda_{\alpha\gamma} = \delta_{\alpha\gamma}(\lambda_\gamma^4 U_2 + I_3 U_3 + 2\Psi_{\alpha\gamma}) + \lambda_\gamma^2\{U_1 + (I_1 - \lambda_\alpha^2 - \lambda_\gamma^2)U_2\} \tag{12.72a}$$

$$\tfrac{1}{2}\Theta_{\alpha\beta} = \lambda_\alpha^2 \lambda_\beta^2 U_2 + I_3 U_3 + 2\Psi_{\alpha\beta} \quad (\alpha \neq \beta) \tag{12.72b}$$

and $\Psi_{\alpha\beta}$ is defined by

$$\begin{aligned}\Psi_{\alpha\beta} = {} & \{\lambda_\alpha^2[U_{11} + (I_1 - \lambda_\alpha^2)U_{21}] + I_3 U_{31}\}\lambda_\beta^2 \\ & + \{\lambda_\alpha^2[U_{12} + (I_1 - \lambda_\alpha^2)U_{22}] + I_3 U_{32}\}\lambda_\beta^2(I_1 - \lambda_\beta^2) \\ & + \{\lambda_\alpha^2[U_{13} + (I_1 - \lambda_\alpha^2)U_{23}] + I_3 U_{33}\} I_3\end{aligned} \tag{12.73}$$

In equations 12.72 and 12.73, $\lambda_\alpha (\alpha = 1, 2, 3)$ are the principal extension ratios for the pure homogeneous deformation, $U_\alpha = \partial U/\partial I_\alpha$, $U_{\alpha\beta} = \partial^2 U/\partial I_\alpha \partial I_\beta$, and the summation convention does not apply to Greek subscripts.

From the condition that the principal minors of all orders in $\det \boldsymbol{Q}$ must be positive, a number of necessary conditions on U have been derived[27]. For example, it has been shown[27] that

$$\Lambda_{\alpha\gamma} > 0 \tag{12.74}$$

With equation 12.72a, this yields

$$\begin{aligned}& \lambda_\alpha^2[U_1 + (I_1 - \lambda_\alpha^2)U_2] + I_3 U_3 \\ & \quad + 2\lambda_\alpha^4[U_{11} + 2(I_1 - \lambda_\alpha^2)U_{12} + (I_1 - \lambda_\alpha^2)^2 U_{22}] \\ & \quad + 2[2\lambda_\alpha^2 U_{31} + 2I_3\lambda_\alpha^2(I_1 - \lambda_\alpha^2)U_{32} + I_3^2 U_{33}] > 0\end{aligned} \tag{12.75}$$

and
$$U_1 + (I_1 - \lambda_\alpha^2 - \lambda_\gamma^2)U_2 > 0 \quad (\alpha \neq \gamma) \tag{12.76}$$

Bearing in mind that $I_1 = \lambda_1^2 + \lambda_2^2 + \lambda_3^2$, the inequality 12.76 becomes the Baker–Ericksen inequality 12.51.

Somewhat similar inequalities have recently been obtained by Sawyers and Rivlin[28] for an incompressible isotropic elastic material, from the consideration that the speeds of propagation must be real, for propagation of plane waves of infinitesimal amplitude in a body of the material subjected to pure homogeneous deformation, the directions of propagation and polarisation lying in the same principal plane. For an incompressible material, U is, of course, a function of I_1 and I_2, given by equation 12.68 only. Sawyers and Rivlin[28] obtained the inequalities 12.76 and

$$\frac{U_{11}+2\lambda_\alpha^2 U_{12}+\lambda_\alpha^4 U_{22}}{U_1+\lambda_\alpha^2 U_2} > -\frac{1}{2(I_1-\lambda_\alpha^2-2/\lambda_\alpha)} \tag{12.77}$$

as necessary conditions for stability.

12.8 Appendix

Taking $F_1 = F_2 = F_3 = F$, say, in equation 12.35, we obtain

$$F\lambda_1 = C\lambda_1^2 - p \tag{12.78a}$$
$$F\lambda_2 = C\lambda_2^2 - p \tag{12.78b}$$
$$F\lambda_3 = C\lambda_3^2 - p \tag{12.78c}$$

It follows that

$$\text{either}\quad \lambda_1 = \lambda_2 \quad \text{or} \quad F/C = \lambda_1+\lambda_2 \tag{12.79a}$$
$$\text{either}\quad \lambda_2 = \lambda_3 \quad \text{or} \quad F/C = \lambda_2+\lambda_3 \tag{12.79b}$$
$$\text{either}\quad \lambda_3 = \lambda_1 \quad \text{or} \quad F/C = \lambda_3+\lambda_1 \tag{12.79c}$$

We thus have, with equation 12.31, the four possibilities

$$\lambda_1 = \lambda_2 = \lambda_3 = 1 \tag{12.80a}$$
$$\lambda_1 = \lambda_2 \quad \text{and} \quad F/C = \lambda_2+\lambda_3 \tag{12.80b}$$
$$\lambda_2 = \lambda_3 \quad \text{and} \quad F/C = \lambda_3+\lambda_1 \tag{12.80c}$$
$$\lambda_3 = \lambda_1 \quad \text{and} \quad F/C = \lambda_1+\lambda_2 \tag{12.80d}$$

The possibility 12.80*b* leads, with equation 12.31, to

$$\lambda_3\left(\frac{F}{C}-\lambda_3\right)^2 = 1 \tag{12.81}$$

This equation has one real solution for λ_3 if $F/C < 3(\frac{1}{4})^{1/3}$ and three real solutions if $F/C > 3(\frac{1}{4})^{1/3}$. In the case $F/C < 3(\frac{1}{4})^{1/3}$, the unique real solution of equation 12.81 for λ_3 is greater than F/C, so that $\lambda_1 = \lambda_2 < 0$ and we accordingly discard this solution. In the case $F/C > 3(\frac{1}{4})^{1/3}$, one of the three real solutions of equation 12.81 is greater than F/C, so that $\lambda_1 = \lambda_2 < 0$, and we accordingly discard this solution. For the remaining two solutions $0 < \lambda_3 < F/C$ and $\lambda_1 = \lambda_2 > 0$. In fact, application of the stability criterion discussed in section 12.3 yields the result that one of these two solutions corresponds to a stable equilibrium configuration and the other to an unstable equilibrium configuration. Similar results apply if we take the possibilities 12.80*c* and 12.80*d* with the roles of λ_3 replaced by λ_1 and λ_2 respectively.

As an example, let us take $F/C = 1.95$, satisfying the condition $3(\frac{1}{4})^{1/3} < F/C < 2$. Then, it is easily seen that the solutions of equation 12.81 are

$$\lambda_3 = 0.4366, \quad 0.8900, \quad 2.573$$

and, correspondingly,

$$\lambda_1 = \lambda_2 = 1.513, \quad 1.060, \quad -0.6234$$

The first solution is, in fact, stable; the second is unstable and the remaining solution is discarded since λ_1 and λ_2 are negative.

Acknowledgement

This work was carried out with the support of the Office of Naval Research under Contract No. N00014–67–0370–0001.

References

1. J. G. Oldroyd. *Proc. Roy. Soc.*, **A 202** (1950), 407
2. R. S. Rivlin and J. L. Ericksen. *J. Rat. Mech. Anal.*, **4** (1955), 323
3. A. E. Green and R. S. Rivlin. *Arch. Rat. Mech. Anal.*, **1** (1957), 1
4. W. Noll. *Arch. Rat. Mech. Anal.*, **2** (1958), 197
5. A. C. Pipkin and R. S. Rivlin. *Arch. Rat. Mech. Anal.*, **4** (1959), 129
6. M. Reiner. *Amer. J. Math.*, **67** (1945), 350
7. R. S. Rivlin. *J. Rat. Mech. Anal.*, **4** (1955), 681
8. G. F. Smith and R. S. Rivlin. *Arch. Rat. Mech. Anal.*, **1** (1957), 107
9. R. S. Rivlin. *Arch. Rat. Mech. Anal.*, **4** (1960), 262
10. G. F. Smith, M. M. Smith and R. S. Rivlin. *Arch. Rat. Mech. Anal.*, **12** (1963), 93
11. A. J. M. Spencer and R. S. Rivlin. *Arch. Rat. Mech. Anal.*, **9** (1962), 45
12. G. F. Smith and R. S. Rivlin. *Arch. Rat. Mech. Anal.*, **15** (1964), 169
13. A. J. M. Spencer. *Arch. Rat. Mech. Anal.*, **18** (1965), 51
14. A. C. Pipkin and A. S. Wineman. *Arch. Rat. Mech. Anal.*, **12** (1963), 420
15. A. S. Wineman and A. C. Pipkin. *Arch. Rat. Mech. Anal.*, **17** (1964), 184
16. R. S. Rivlin. *Phil. Trans.*, **A 240** (1948), 491
17. L. Mullins, R. S. Rivlin and S. M. Gumbrell. *Trans. Faraday Soc.*, **49** (1953), 1495
18. L. R. G. Treloar. *The Physics of Rubber Elasticity*, Clarendon Press, Oxford (1949)
19. B. D. Coleman and W. Noll. *Arch. Rat. Mech. Anal.*, **4** (1959), 97
20. R. S. Rivlin. *Q. Appl. Math.*, **25** (1967), 119
21. C. Truesdell and W. Noll. *The Non-Linear Field Theories of Mechanics, Handbuch der Physik*, vol. 3 (3) Springer, Berlin (1965)
22. M. Baker and J. L. Ericksen. *J. Wash. Acad. Sci.*, **44** (1954), 33
23. C. Truesdell. *Z. Angew. Math. Mech.*, **36** (1956), 97
24. C. Truesdell and R. Toupin. *Arch. Rat. Mech. Anal.*, **12** (1963), 1
25. J. Hadamard. *Bull. Soc. Math. France*, **29** (1901), 50
26. J. L. Ericksen. *J. Rat. Mech. Anal.*, **2** (1953), 329
27. M. Hayes and R. S. Rivlin. *Arch. Rat. Mech. Anal.*, **8** (1961), 15
28. K. N. Sawyers and R. S. Rivlin. *Int. J. Solids Structures*, in the press
29. M. F. Beatty. *Int. J. Solids Structures*, **3** (1967), 23
30. R. Hill. *J. Mech. Phys. Solids*, **5** (1957), 229
31. A. E. Green and J. E. Adkins. *Large Elastic Deformations*, Clarendon Press, Oxford (1960)
32. R. S. Rivlin. *Q. Appl. Math.*, in the press
33. C. Truesdell. *Continuum Mechanics III. Foundations of Elasticity Theory*, Gordon & Breach, New York (1965)

13. Some Restrictions on Constitutive Equations; Discussion Paper

E. H. Lee†

13.1 Introduction

This paper presents a clear and concise discussion of concepts associated with the stability of equilibrium configurations of an elastic body subjected to dead-loading conditions which generate finite deformations. Thermal effects are not specifically included, although analogous considerations will arise in the extension to the more general problem of thermodynamic equilibrium. The development of the Hadamard stability condition is presented in terms of the strain energy density, U, a function of the deformation gradient tensor $x_{i,A}$ of the deformed position, x_i, with respect to the reference position, X_A. It is shown that the Hadamard condition constitutes a local convexity condition in the neighbourhood of the equilibrium configuration at each material point of the body.

Certain inequalities restricting the form of elastic constitutive relations are then discussed. These have been analysed extensively by Truesdell and Noll in their *Handbuch der Physik* article[1]. It is shown in chapter 12 of the present volume that many of these inequalities can be demonstrated to be invalid for incompressible media, and that this circumstance can be expected to carry over for compressible media. In fact the multiple equilibrium configurations determined by Rivlin[2] for an initial cube with equal and opposite pairs of constant forces uniformly distributed over opposite faces, is in conflict with considerations which led to the formulation of the inequalities. It is surprising how such a discrepancy has existed in the literature for many years without more comment or without more attempt to reconcile the situation.

It seems to me that a component in this discrepancy is connected with the definition and significance of the term equilibrium. One of the basic steps in formulating the inequalities was presented by Coleman and Noll[3] in a paper on the thermostatics of continuous media. In the Introduction, the authors comment: 'In writing the present paper we have striven for a level of mathematical rigor comparable to that of works in pure mathematics rather than to that customary in physics'. Thus precise definitions are offered, which include *mechanical equilibrium* defined in terms of the balance of forces and moments, and *thermal equilibrium* for a force temperature pair, defined as a state which minimises an appropriate potential. This latter,

† Stanford University, USA.

combined with a postulate that for every local state, defined by a deformation gradient and an entropy to which an energy density corresponds, a force temperature pair exists which establishes a state of thermal equilibrium, yields an inequality which takes the form

$$\hat{\varepsilon}(F^*, \eta) - \hat{\varepsilon}(F, \eta) - \operatorname{tr}\left[(F^* - F)\hat{\varepsilon}_F(F, \eta)\right] > 0 \tag{13.1}$$

where $\hat{\varepsilon}$ is the energy density function, F the deformation gradient, and η the entropy. Inequality 13.1 pertains to the case of uniform entropy. It simply expresses the fact that the value of $\hat{\varepsilon}$ at a point on the energy surface is greater than that for a point with the same F and η lying on a tangent plane through a neighbouring point on the energy surface. A relationship between the values of F at these two neighbouring points, $F^* = GF$, where G is symmetric and positive definite, is also included, the significance of which will be alluded to later. Thus the energy density function is subject to a restricted convexity condition at all points on the energy density surface.

It has been shown by Hill[4] that a globally convex energy density function leads to a unique solution to a mixed (velocity and traction) static boundary value problem, and that the solution is a stable equilibrium state. It is demonstrated by Rivlin in the paper under discussion that the C–N inequality 13.1 leads to uniqueness for the loaded cube problem in conflict with his original work. For such reasons Hill[4] rejects global convexity as a legitimate restriction on elastic energy density functions. The C–N inequality 13.1, however, continues to play a major role in the study by Truesdell and Noll[1]. This thus appears to follow from the particular definition of thermal equilibrium utilised in reference 3.

The presentation in reference 1 is not however unequivocal. The force–stretch invertibility (IFS) is introduced (p. 156) with the comment: 'It is reasonable to expect that if given pairs of opposing normal forces are applied to the faces of a unit cube of isotropic elastic material, one and only one pure homogeneous deformation will result', on p. 157: 'granted that the IFS condition is satisfied, it is reasonable to expect . . .', and p. 161: '. . . (C–N) implies a full set of simple statical conditions laid down earlier as plausible'. And finally on p. 169: 'While there remains uncertainty as to what is the true general condition to be imposed . . .'. This section of reference 1 is thus in some respects in marked contrast with the aim of definiteness sought in the treatise as a whole, although the tentativeness is not uniformly adhered to, and one also gets the feeling that these inequalities are accorded permanent status.

13.2 The Restricted Convexity Condition

It was pointed out in the Introduction, that the convexity condition was restricted to deformation gradients F and F^* coupled by the requirement $F^* = GF$, where G is symmetric and positive definite. It is pointed out in reference 3 that the possibility of G being a rotation matrix must be ruled out since the inequality would then exclude the possibility of thermal equilibrium under compressive forces. Since dead loads with an unrestricted line of action are considered, compressive forces directed towards each other would introduce instability as a result of the work done by them in rotation. But in any practical compressive experiment, the lines of action of the compressive forces would be controlled by guides and this difficulty would not arise in such a definitive form. It is suggested in reference 3 that Hill rejected unrestricted convexity as unacceptable for this reason, but it seems much more likely that he was concerned with the nonuniqueness in the loaded cube problem[2], discussed in Rivlin's paper.

13.3 Compressible Media

It has been suggested[1] that the structure of constitutive inequalities changes completely when consideration is transferred from compressible to incompressible material as does the question of uniqueness of solution. We have seen that these questions are associated with a restricted convexity of the energy density function. For a nearly incompressible material, the strain–energy density of states comprising deformation gradients implying appreciable volume change will be extremely high. Thus, for example, for plane deformation of a cube into a rectangular parallelepiped with $\lambda_3 = 1$, isochoric deformation would correspond to $\lambda_1\lambda_2 = 1$. Contours of a strain–energy surface would then qualitatively have the structure shown in figure 13.1, with rapid growth away from the isochoric line for both increase and decrease of volume. This would clearly not satisfy the inequality 13.1 through-

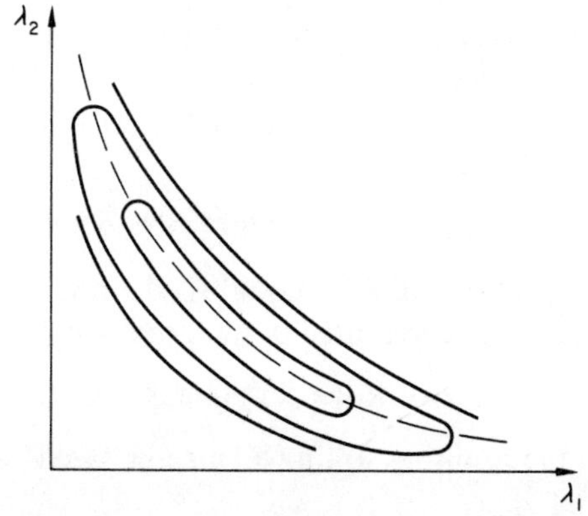

Figure 13.1 Strain–energy contours for a nearly incompressible material.

out the dilated region since the surface would have a saddle point configuration, and the tangent plane would cut the surface. The associated inequalities would then not be valid. A qualitatively similar situation would be expected in more dimensions.

13.4 Discussion

It is clear, for example from the complicated array of equilibrium configurations deduced by Rivlin[2] for a cube subjected to uniformly distributed dead loads, that even simple strain–energy relations in terms of invariants can yield an involved convexity structure even in principal stretch space. This arises in the analysis of the behaviour of solids because of the need to include tensor variables for force and deformation in place of the scalars, pressure and volume, which appear in the analysis of ideal fluids. It seems to me that this circumstance in part answers the complaint of Professor Kestin in his discussion in chapter 8, that researchers in solid mechanics tend to generate theories more complicated than are necessary.

In an analogous manner, time-related properties of solids often require complexities, such as many internal variables, in order to achieve satisfactory representation of material behaviour. A simple linear viscoelastic law, the standard linear solid, is represented by the spring-dashpot model shown in figure 13.2, the deformation of which can be expressed with one internal coordinate, the extension of the dashpot. A readily measured characteristic of a

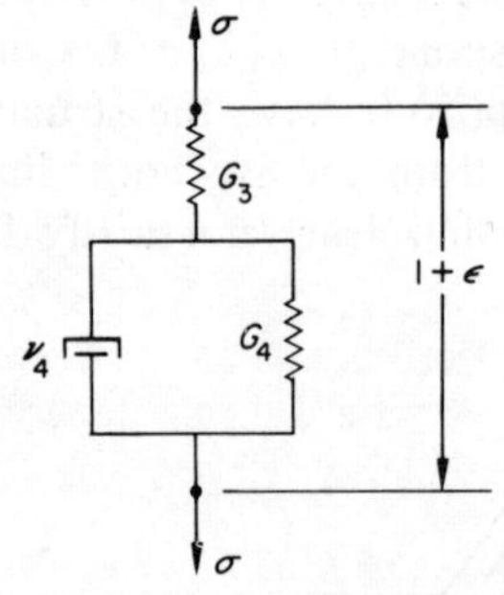

Figure 13.2 The standard linear solid viscoelastic model.

viscoelastic material is the complex modulus, defined as follows. Steady oscillatory stressing can be represented in the usual complex manner as

$$\sigma(t) = \text{Re}\left[\sigma_0 \exp(i\omega t)\right] \tag{13.2}$$

For linear response, the resulting strain will also be steady oscillation at the same frequency

$$\varepsilon(t) = \text{Re}\left[\varepsilon_0 \exp(i\omega t)\right] \tag{13.3}$$

The ratio of the complex stress to the complex strain

$$\frac{\sigma_0}{\varepsilon_0} = G^*(\omega) = G_1(\omega) + iG_2(\omega) \tag{13.4}$$

defines the complex modulus, which is a complex function of frequency, since for viscoelastic specimens there is a phase lag of the strain behind the stress. The variation of the real or imaginary part with frequency provides a representation of the viscoelastic characteristics of the material. As shown in figure 13.3, the variation of $G_1(\omega)$ for the standard linear solid exhibits

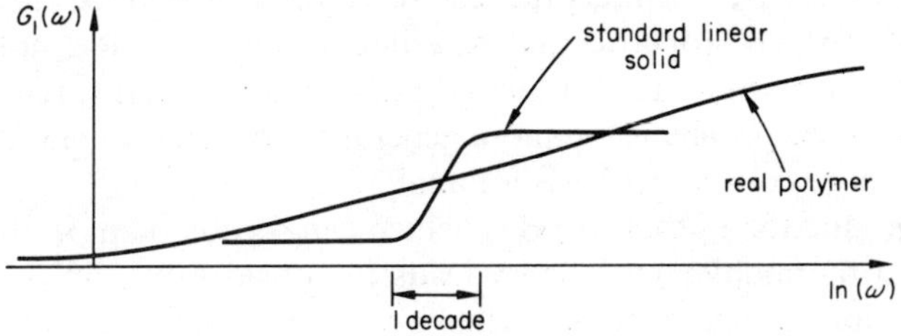

Figure 13.3 Variation of the real part of the complex modulus with frequency.

a step from a low frequency limit to a high frequency limit over a range of about one decade in frequency. In contrast, a real polymer commonly exhibits a gradual increase of G_1 over many decades. To reproduce such behaviour with a spring-dashpot model, it is necessary to introduce a sequence of elements in series, each composed of a spring and dashpot in parallel (Kelvin elements) in place of the single one shown in figure 13.2. Each introduces an internal variable, and a range of characteristic frequencies of the elements is needed to cover the range of variation of $G_1(\omega)$ for the real material. Thus measured material characteristics often demand the introduction of many internal variables. In fact, the discrete spectrum of natural frequencies or characteristic times associated with the sequence of Kelvin elements described, may simply constitute an approximation to a continuous spectrum, and the mathematical representation for arbitrary loading history

$$\varepsilon(t) = \int_{-\infty}^{t} J(t-\tau)\dot{\sigma}(\tau)\,\mathrm{d}\tau \tag{13.5}$$

then replaces the representation in terms of a discrete set of internal variables. For arbitrary kernel function, $J(t)$, this corresponds to the limit of an infinite number of internal variables, the finite case arising when $J(t)$ is a finite sum of exponentials. The circumstance of a broad spectrum of natural times for real polymers is aptly illustrated by the aphorism coined by E. Orwan, that an experiment to measure the relaxation time of a polymer simply yields the result: π times the duration of the experiment, for the material characteristic embodies a wide range of relaxation times available to be stimulated by an appropriate forcing function.

The circumstance of a state defined by a number of external and internal deformation variables is thus transformed naturally into a history or functional law, equation 13.5, on the basis of material properties measurements. For the continuous spectrum case, the full history of loading is needed to define the future response, and hence the redundancy of information concerning the current state mentioned by Professor Kestin in chapter 8 does not arise. Of course, from a practical standpoint, it may be that the consistency of material properties and experimental accuracy does not justify an analysis based on more than a limited number of internal variables. Nonetheless, for some problems the more general form, equation 13.5, may even provide a more convenient basis for analysis[5].

The introduction of these aspects, which can be dominant in the study of solids, into thermodynamic theory leads to considerable difficulties in the representation of real material behaviour. With many internal variables present can we expect the Onsager relations to apply? This circumstance is qualitatively different from those discussed by Dr. Miller. Such difficulties are apparent in the current state of application of the thermodynamics of viscoelasticity and plasticity, which are discussed in chapter 14.

References

1. C. Truesdell and W. Noll. *The Non-Linear Field Theories of Mechanics, Handbuch der Physik*, III/3, Springer, Berlin (1965)
2. R. S. Rivlin. *Phil. Trans. Roy. Soc.*, **A 240** (1948), 491
3. B. D. Coleman and W. Noll. *Arch. Rat. Mech. Anal.*, **4** (1959), 97
4. R. Hill. *J. Mech. Phys. Solids*, **5** (1957), 229
5. E. H. Lee and T. G. Rogers. *J. Appl. Mech.*, **30** (1963), 127–33

Discussion

KESTIN

It happened frequently in the past that certain general principles were first recognised when applied to a restricted field of science. Sometimes the same principle was discovered independently with reference to several diverse fields of science, even though its generalisation to a wide class of problems was already known or discovered at about the same time. Without detracting in any way from Hadamard's contributions to science, I wish to point out that Hadamard's stability condition, equation 12.15, is a special case of Gibbs's general condition of stability of thermodynamic systems.

As we follow the presentation in the paper, we may gain the impression that equation 12.15 is a consequence of equation 12.1 via equation 12.3. In actual fact, as I am sure Professor Rivlin agrees, such a conclusion would not be tenable. The stability condition 12.15 is independent of the first law of thermodynamics, equation 12.1, in the sense that one would not fall into a logical contradiction if one applied equations 12.1 or 12.3 to materials for which condition 12.15 were violated, even though one would fail to observe such systems in the laboratory.

It may also be worth noting that equation 12.15 applies to processes when

$S = \text{const.}$ if U is interpreted as internal energy
$T = \text{const.}$ if U is interpreted as the Helmholtz free energy

This should be borne in mind when the problem is specialised by the introduction of equation 12.34.

RIVLIN

I agree completely with Professor Kestin's remarks that the stability condition is independent of the first law of thermodynamics. I agree also that the Hadamard condition is, indeed, a special case of the Gibbs stability condition.

MEIXNER

Thermostatic stability conditions for solids should be derivable—as in the case of *fluids*—from the idea that a body under conditions of closure (fixed surface and fixed internal energy) should in equilibrium have a greater entropy than in any internally deformed state in which the energy is arbitrarily distributed. One can derive the following stability conditions

$$\int \mathrm{d}m \left\{ s'(\boldsymbol{x}') - s(\boldsymbol{x}) - \frac{}{T}[u'(\boldsymbol{x}') - u(\boldsymbol{x})] + \frac{1}{\rho T} \operatorname{Tr} \boldsymbol{\sigma}(\boldsymbol{x})[\boldsymbol{F}'(\boldsymbol{x}') - \boldsymbol{F}(\boldsymbol{x})]\boldsymbol{F}(\boldsymbol{x})^{-1} \right\} <$$

where $\boldsymbol{x}$ and $\boldsymbol{x}'$ are the coordinates of a mass element dm in the equilibrium state and in the internally deformed state, respectively. s, u, $\boldsymbol{F}$, $\boldsymbol{\sigma}$, are the specific entropy, the specific internal energy, the deformation gradient and the stress tensor, respectively, at position $\boldsymbol{x}$, while the primed quantities are to be taken at position $\boldsymbol{x}'$. In fluids one can conclude that the integrand itself is negative because internal deformations are allowed in which matter is moved along the surface; such a motion does not change the energy because the pressure is normal to the surface and so no work is done in such a motion. In solids the surface tractions may have any direction and therefore only such internal deformations can be permitted for which $\boldsymbol{x} = \boldsymbol{x}'$ over the surface of the body in order that no work is done. No reduction of the above global stability condition to a local one is known at the present time. Incidentally, it is noted that the terms with the internal energies and those with the deformation gradients in the above integral vanish individually as a result of the closure and the equilibrium conditions. Thus the above inequality is in fact recognised to conform with the entropy condition given at the beginning. The given inequality has, however, the advantage that for small departures from the equilibrium state, the integrand is small, of second order.

14. On Nonequilibrium Thermodynamics of Viscoelasticity and Viscoplasticity

S. Nemat-Nasser†

Abstract

The present paper considers macroscopic nonequilibrium thermodynamics of viscoelastic and viscoplastic materials where the nonlinear hereditary effects are accounted for by means of a set of internal variables. On the basis of: the energy balance equation, the assumption that a measurable empirical temperature exists at nonequilibrium states, and the fact that not all *observable* states in any given neighbourhood of a given state are adiabatically attainable, it is shown that, under some mild smoothness conditions

(1) An empirical entropy exists at nonequilibrium states.

(2) This entropy is extensive.

(3) There exists an absolute temperature at nonequilibrium states, which depends on the empirical temperature only.

(4) The entropy function serves as a potential in exactly the same manner as in the thermodynamics of equilibrium.

(5) The entropy is not unique, inasmuch as it depends parametrically on the internal variables in a manner not deducible from the stated assumptions.

(6) For materials with instantaneous elasticity, and certain other materials, the entropy function is monotone, say, nondecreasing, for all adiabatic transitions (which include transitions at constant strains and internal energy), so that the set of all entropy functions satisfies the Clausius–Planck inequality (note that this result is derived rather than assumed).

(7) Because of (6), the set of entropy functions is convex and admits upper and lower bounds which can serve as entropy functions, thus rendering entropy unique.

(8) Both of these bounds can serve as potentials in exactly the same manner as in (4), and hence these bounds can differ from entropy itself by additive functions of the internal variables only.

The final part of the chapter examines a generalisation of the classical approach in which an explicit dissipative mechanism is assumed for a given class of materials.

† The Technological Institute, Northwestern University, Illinois, USA. Part of this paper was completed while the author was on leave at the Technical University of Denmark.

14.1 Introduction

In a mathematical formulation of a physical theory it is desirable that the basic laws are stated in their simplest possible form in such a manner that they contain the maximum possible information, and that the corresponding statements involve only physical quantities that are either directly or indirectly amenable to measurements. Since the second law of thermodynamics is undisputably a major ingredient in a macroscopic thermodynamic theory, its statement should enjoy these qualities.

The present paper complements a recent tentative report[1] by this writer, where a macroscopic nonequilibrium thermodynamic framework was constructed, within which certain thermomechanical properties of viscoelastic and viscoplastic (or elastoviscoplastic) materials can be explored. In reference 1 the statement of the second law, however, involved unobservable quantities, namely internal variables which were introduced in order to account *approximately* for inelastic properties of the considered class of materials. As is shown here, a statement of the second law (a form of Carathéodory's principle) which involves only strains and temperature, not only includes the corresponding statement in reference 1, and an earlier statement employed by Valanis[2], as special cases, but also yields, for a certain class of materials, for example, those with instantaneous elasticity, an additional result that was not apparent in either reference, and hence needed to be stated as a part of an additional assumption. This result is that for adiabatic transitions the entropy is a nondecreasing quantity.

To be more specific, on the basis of: the energy balance equation, the assumption that a measurable empirical temperature exists at nonequilibrium states, and the fact that not all *observable* states in any given neighbourhood of a given state are adiabatically attainable, it will be shown that, under some mild smoothness conditions

(1) An empirical entropy exists at nonequilibrium states.

(2) This entropy is extensive.

(3) There exists an absolute temperature at nonequilibrium states, which depends on the empirical temperature only.

(4) The entropy function serves as a potential in exactly the same manner as in the thermodynamics of equilibria.

(5) The entropy is not unique, inasmuch as it depends parametrically on the internal variables in a manner not deducible from the stated assumptions.

(6) For materials with instantaneous elasticity, and certain other materials, the entropy function is monotone, say, nondecreasing, for all adiabatic transitions (which include transitions at constant strains and internal energy), so that the set of all entropy functions satisfies the Clausius–

Planck inequality (note that this result is derived rather than assumed).

(7) Because of (6), the set of entropy functions is convex and admits upper and lower bounds which can serve as entropy functions, thus rendering entropy unique.

(8) Both of these bounds can serve as potentials in exactly the same manner as in (4), and hence these bounds can differ from entropy itself by additive functions of the internal variables only.†

The final part of the paper examines a generalisation of the classical approach in which an explicit dissipative mechanism is assumed for a given class of materials.

In connection with applications of the theory, the question of fading memory deserves special remarks. Taken at their face value, experiments show that some materials (such as certain polymers) exhibit a fading memory in the sense that if they are kept at given strains and temperature for a sufficiently long time, their future thermomechanical responses then will not reflect what has happened to them in the far past; whereas other materials (such as metals) exhibit a distinct memory, for example, elastic unloading, with a more or less time-independent characteristic. This has led to the introduction of a fading memory as an additional assumption which characterises a specific class of materials.

On physical grounds, however, one observes that the plasticity of metals are often attributable to certain microstructural rearrangements which take place as the material is deformed. Hence, as new complicated rearrangements take place, their influence on the macroscopic responses of the material tends to overshadow the influence of the microstructural rearrangements which had taken place before. Thus, one should have a fading memory effect in metal plasticity, as well as in polymer viscoelasticity, the basic difference being that for the former the time parameter should reflect the extent and the state of microstructural changes, whereas for the latter the real time parameter can be used. In the context of the theory presented in terms of internal variables, the fading memory follows naturally from the dissipative characteristic of the material, and need not be imposed as an additional assumption[3].

Let us now consider a few preliminaries which, to a certain extent, overlap those discussed in reference 1. An important difference, however, is the distinction made here between the *observable* and *unobservable* quantities.

14.2 Preliminaries

Within the context of the continuum approximation, the basic conservation

† It appears that this rather remarkable result has not been proved before.

laws may be written as

$$\rho = \rho^0/\det \boldsymbol{F}, \qquad \operatorname{div} \rho^0 \boldsymbol{T}^R + \rho^0 \boldsymbol{f} = \rho^0 \ddot{\boldsymbol{x}}$$

$$\boldsymbol{F}\boldsymbol{T}^R = (\boldsymbol{F}\boldsymbol{T}^R)^{\mathrm{T}}, \qquad \dot{e} = \boldsymbol{T}^R \cdot \dot{\boldsymbol{F}} - \frac{1}{\rho} \operatorname{div} \boldsymbol{q} + r \tag{14.1}$$

where ρ and ρ^0 are the current and the reference mass-densities, respectively; $\boldsymbol{x} = \boldsymbol{x}(\boldsymbol{X}, t)$ is a one-to-one mapping, giving particle positions $\boldsymbol{x}$ at time t in terms of their positions $\boldsymbol{X}$ in a suitable reference configuration at time $t = 0$, $0 \leqslant t$; $\boldsymbol{F} = \operatorname{div} \boldsymbol{x}$ is the deformation gradient $0 < \det \boldsymbol{F} < \infty$; $\boldsymbol{T}^R$ is the first Piola–Kirchhoff stress tensor (usually $\rho^0 \boldsymbol{T}^R$ is used instead); superposed dot denotes material time derivative; $\boldsymbol{f}$ is body force per unit mass; e is the internal energy-density; $\boldsymbol{q}$ is the heat flux vector; and r is the heat source per unit mass due to radiation absorption. While the heat conduction problem needs special attention in the present context, in order to stress other essential points it will be assumed that $\operatorname{div} \boldsymbol{q} \equiv 0$. Moreover, the term r which relates to radiation absorption, needs careful examination in its own right, but this will not be considered here.

It will be convenient to introduce Green's deformation tensor $\boldsymbol{C} = \boldsymbol{F}^{\mathrm{T}}\boldsymbol{F}$ for a measure of strain, where superposed T denotes transpose, and where matrix multiplication is implied. The last of equations 14.1 then becomes

$$\dot{Q} = \dot{e} - \boldsymbol{T}^R \cdot \dot{\boldsymbol{F}} = \dot{e} - \tfrac{1}{2}\boldsymbol{S} \cdot \dot{\boldsymbol{C}}$$

$$\dot{Q} = -\frac{1}{\rho} \operatorname{div} \boldsymbol{q} + r, \qquad \boldsymbol{T}^R = \boldsymbol{S}\boldsymbol{F}^{\mathrm{T}} \tag{14.2}$$

here $\boldsymbol{S}$ is the (symmetric) second Piola–Kirchhoff stress tensor†, and $\boldsymbol{T}^R \cdot \dot{\boldsymbol{F}} = \frac{1}{2}\boldsymbol{S} \cdot \dot{\boldsymbol{C}}$ denotes the *stress-work* per unit mass.

The basic conservation laws, either in the form given by equation 14.1, or in other fundamentally equivalent forms, are commonly accepted by workers in the field. To construct a nonequilibrium macroscopic thermodynamic framework, one needs additional ingredients, namely temperature, constitutive relations, and a precise statement of the second law, which are unfortunately still subjects of many controversies, and in need of further examination.

14.2.1 Temperature

It will be assumed that a *measurable empirical temperature* θ can be defined as a scalar field at each instant over the body. At nonequilibrium states, this is merely an approximation whose acceptability can be judged on physical grounds only. In the context of the present development, however, this is the most fundamental assumption which brings into the theory a certain ingredient from the classical thermodynamics of equilibria. As will become

† Note that $\boldsymbol{T} = \rho \boldsymbol{F}\boldsymbol{T}^R$ is the true or Cauchy stress tensor.

evident later, the *extensive property* of entropy hinges on, and follows from this assumption†; for a discussion relating to temperature at nonequilibrium states, see reference 3. One should hasten to add that when stress–strain relations in metal plasticity or polymer viscoelasticity under ordinary conditions are involved, the above assumption most probably is quite acceptable. For example, since plasticity in metals is caused by various microscopic defects, and since the density of such defects is (generally) many orders of magnitude smaller than the density of the atoms and molecules, it follows that an empirical temperature which basically characterises the average random vibrational kinetic energy of atoms, is clearly a meaningful macroscopic quantity.

14.2.2 Constitutive relations

The second ingredient relates to constitutive relations. It is a well-known fact that the macroscopic thermomechanical response of most materials depends to a large extent on their past history. Metals and polymers are two significant examples with history-dependent, but dissimilar patterns of behaviour. This history-dependency can be accounted for in one of two ways.

(1) *Explicitly* by writing, say, the stress and the internal energy as functionals of the entire past history of deformation and temperature.

(2) *Implicitly* by introducing additional parameters‡ whose values at a given instant may depend in a certain manner on the history of deformation and temperature.

In this work the second approach is used; for a discussion, comparison of two methods, and relevant references, see reference 3.

The additional parameters mentioned above that enter in the second method, may be introduced quite formally and without any reference to their possible physical origin. It is, however, more convincing if one begins with a certain physical interpretation, as follows.

Many inelastic properties of solids can be explained qualitatively in terms of various microstructural rearrangements. The rearrangements of crystallographic planes due to dislocation motions, grain-boundary slipping, twinning, and phase transformation are microscopic mechanisms which give rise to inelastic behaviour of metals. In polymers the existence of longchain molecules which may straighten or crumple, in addition to sliding relative to each other in response to sustained loads, provides the material with instantaneous elasticity, as well as with nonlinear viscosity. During these

† In more modern continuum thermodynamics, the existence of temperature, the existence of entropy which satisfies the Clausius–Duhem inequality, and the entropy's extensive property, are stated as independent assumptions.

‡ These parameters may be finite or infinite in number, or they may even have continuous spectra.

processes a certain amount of mechanical energy is lost into heat energy. Additionally, the microstructural changes give rise to macroscopic history-dependent material properties.

In a phenomenological approach the effect of the microscopic structural rearrangements may be accounted for by the introduction of additional state variables called *internal* or *hidden coordinates*, and denoted collectively by ξ, which *in a certain average global sense represent the internal changes.* The representation is *macroscopic* in the sense that there may exist multiple (in fact, probably infinitely many) microstates corresponding to the same values of these coordinates. However, inasmuch as these coordinates are usually characterised by certain constitutive relations involving various parameters which are fixed by means of suitable macroscopic experiments, they signify the most phenomenologically dominant aspects of the microstructural changes. It is reasonable to assume that the hidden coordinates are various tensorial quantities. One may, of course, generalise this by considering other alternatives. For instance, it may be useful to consider an infinite set of internal variables, or let these variables have continuous spectra. There are many nontrivial mathematical difficulties that must be overcome in such extensions. For the present discussion, however, a finite number of internal variables will suffice.

In general the selection of the internal variables represents a significant problem. An experimentalist can only monitor certain *inputs* and measure certain *outputs.* The material then represents a black box whose internal structure is manifested through such input–output relations. The optimal selection of suitable internal variables, minimum in number, which provide maximum information for a given input–output setup, is an interesting non-trivial problem outside the realm of thermodynamics. Thermodynamics can only provide a general framework within which one must operate. The detailed selection of the parameters, however, must be guided by other considerations.

Suppose therefore that a set of n internal variables ξ are selected in such a manner that the thermodynamic state at a given particle is defined by $N = m+7$ state variables consisting of six deformation measures such as the components of the Green deformation tensor $\boldsymbol{C}$, one nondeformation measure such as temperature θ, and n hidden coordinates ξ; where $m = n$ if ξ's are all scalars, otherwise m is larger than n. The 7 variables $\boldsymbol{C}, \theta$, however, may be regarded directly (or indirectly) measurable, whereas ξ's which are global average quantities of approximate nature can seldom be endowed with a similar quality. For this and other reasons, it is useful to separate these two sets of variables.

Observable State: For a given particle of a given continuum, the ordered 7 real numbers $\bar{P}_1 \equiv \{\boldsymbol{C}_1, \theta_1\}$ at a given instant t_1, defines the observable state.

Observable Space: Consider the space of all ordered 7 real numbers and its open and connected subspace, called the observable space,

$$\bar{\mathscr{V}} = \{\boldsymbol{C}, \theta \colon \boldsymbol{C} \text{ symmetric and positive-definite, and } 0 < \theta\} \tag{14.3}$$

The observable state for a given particle then is given by a point in $\bar{\mathscr{V}}$. Usually one considers a suitable, open and connected subset $\bar{\mathscr{V}}_1$ of the observable space, in which all possible observable states of a given particle occur.

At this point one should hasten to add that it is neither necessary nor quite correct to endow the observable space (or the thermodynamic space discussed below) with metrical properties. However, with suitable nondimensionalisation and with care, this can be done without adverse effects. With this in mind, one can, for example, consider $\bar{\mathscr{V}}$ as an open and connected subspace of a 7-dimensional Euclidean space. In the following, all spaces may be interpreted in this manner.

The internal energy e can be assumed to be a single-valued, continuously differentiable function of empirical temperature θ—as well as of $\boldsymbol{C}$ and other quantities, as will be discussed later on—and in line with the classical results, one chooses the temperature scale such that e is a strictly increasing function of θ, everywhere in, say, $\bar{\mathscr{V}}_1$. Hence, the roles of e and θ can be interchanged. If this is done, the observable state of the particle will be given by a point $\bar{\bar{P}}_1 \equiv \{\boldsymbol{C}_1, e_1\}$ in the observable space

$$\bar{\bar{\mathscr{V}}} = \{\boldsymbol{C}, e \colon \boldsymbol{C} \text{ symmetric and positive-definite, and } 0 < e\} \tag{14.4}$$

Again, for a given particle, one is often interested in a suitable, open and connected subset $\bar{\bar{\mathscr{V}}}_1$ of the observable space.

Observable Transitions: A set of 7 ordered real-valued continuous and piecewise continuously differentiable functions of the real variable s, $t_0 \leqslant s \leqslant t_1$, written collectively as $\bar{\mathscr{T}}(s) \equiv \{\boldsymbol{C}(s), \theta(s)\}$, defines an observable transition at a given particle whose observable states at times t_0 and t_1 are $\bar{P}_0 \equiv \{\boldsymbol{C}(t_0), \theta(t_0)\}$, and $\bar{P}_1 \equiv \{\boldsymbol{C}(t_1), \theta(t_1)\}$, respectively.

State Space and Thermodynamic State: The thermodynamic state of a given particle can be represented by a point $\hat{P} \equiv \{\boldsymbol{C}_1, \theta_1, \xi_1\}$ in the state space

$$\hat{\mathscr{V}} = \{\boldsymbol{C}, \theta, \xi \colon \boldsymbol{C} \text{ symmetric and positive-definite, and } 0 < \theta\} \tag{14.5}$$

The state space $\hat{\mathscr{V}}$ is therefore the direct product space of the observable space $\bar{\mathscr{V}}$ and the n-dimensional space of internal variables ξ.

When internal energy e is used instead of θ, the state space will be written as

$$\hat{\hat{\mathscr{V}}} = \{\boldsymbol{C}, \theta, \xi \colon \boldsymbol{C} \text{ symmetric and positive-definite, and } 0 < e\} \tag{14.6}$$

A point in this space will be denoted by $\hat{\hat{P}}_1 \equiv \{\boldsymbol{C}_1, e_1, \xi_1\}$.

Transitions: $\hat{\mathscr{T}}(s) \equiv \{\boldsymbol{C}(s), \theta(s), \xi(s)\}$, $t_0 \leqslant s \leqslant t_1$, which is an ordered set of

N continuous and piece-wise continuously differentiable functions, defines a transition from $\hat{P}_0$ to $\hat{P}_1$. The orthogonal projection of a given transition $\hat{\mathscr{T}}$ into the observable space $\mathscr{V}$, gives the corresponding observable transition $\mathscr{T}$.

When e is used as a state variable, a corresponding transition will be denoted by $\hat{\hat{\mathscr{T}}}$ which, of course, will have the same continuity properties defined for $\hat{\mathscr{T}}$.

Constitutive Relations: Since a uniform temperature is assumed, the heat conduction problem does not enter the present discussion. In view of this, therefore, the constitutive relations at a given particle consist of stress and internal energy defined on a suitable subset of $\hat{\mathscr{V}}$ as functions of the state variables $\boldsymbol{C}$, θ, and ξ

$$\boldsymbol{S} = \hat{\boldsymbol{S}}(\boldsymbol{C}, \theta; \xi) \qquad e = \hat{e}(\boldsymbol{C}, \theta; \xi) \tag{14.7}$$

Note that in a physically meaningful theory the parameter ξ must be either implicitly or explicitly suppressed in favour of experimentally measurable quantities.

When internal energy is used instead of temperature, the constitutive relations become

$$\boldsymbol{S} = \hat{\hat{\boldsymbol{S}}}(\boldsymbol{C}, e; \xi) \qquad \theta = \hat{\hat{\theta}}(\boldsymbol{C}, e; \xi) \tag{14.8}$$

which are defined on a suitable subset of $\hat{\hat{\mathscr{V}}}$.

Note that, while the dependency of the above expressions on $\boldsymbol{X}$ which marks a given particle, is not explicitly written out, it should be kept in mind that constitutive expressions, as well as other field quantities, may vary from particle to particle, and hence depend on the considered particle. Throughout this paper attention will be focussed on the thermomechanical properties in the neighbourhood of a fixed particle of a given continuum, and therefore the dependency on this particle will not be written out explicitly.

If the stress tensor is such that $\boldsymbol{FSF}^{\mathrm{T}}$ is symmetric, then body forces $\boldsymbol{f}$ and heat sources r can be adjusted so that the balance equations are identically satisfied along a given transition of a given particle. Hence, in studying the thermomechanical properties of the material at a fixed particle which is at state $\hat{P}_0$ at t_0, and at $\hat{P}_1$ at t_1, one may consider *all* possible transitions (continuous curves) between these two states. *These transitions and the constitutive relations* 14.7 *or* 14.8 *must then be further restricted so that they reflect the intuitive requirement that a certain energy dissipation should accompany all microscopic structural changes, and therefore (almost) all admissible transitions.* This intuitive requirement will be rendered more precise in the statement of the second law, discussed in section 14.3.

Material Systems: Since, for all transitions between states $\hat{P}_0$ and $\hat{P}_1$ of a given particle, the balance laws can be regarded satisfied, one may associate with this particle† a *homogeneous body of unit mass*, called its *material system*, consisting of a material whose thermomechanical properties are *identical* with those of the material at the particle in question, and then consider *homogeneous transitions* of this material system. As the particle goes through a given transition, $\hat{\mathscr{T}}$, its material system is regarded as undergoing a homogeneous transition characterised by $\hat{\mathscr{T}}$. *The thermomechanical properties of the material at the particle are, therefore, described by examining the response of its material system in homogeneous transitions.* In fact, this is exactly what one hopes to accomplish in an experimental setup.

With this definition, certain classical notions become applicable here. For example, two material systems are said to be in *perfect thermal contact* if they maintain common temperatures at each instance along their transitions. Also, one may define an *adiabatic* transition of a material system as the one during which no heat exchange occurs between the material system and its environment. In a similar vein, an *isothermal* transition is the one which occurs at constant temperature.

Elastic Transitions: A transition which occurs at fixed values of ξ's, say $\xi = \xi_0$, will be called elastic. These transitions take place on the hyperplane $\xi = \xi_0$, and therefore during their course there are no microstructural changes occurring in the material. The response of the material in an elastic transition is elastic. It is clear that an elastic transition is identical with its observable transition. Hence, all elastic transitions of a material system are observable, but, of course, the converse is by no means true.

Elastic Materials: These are materials which can undergo *only* elastic transitions with $\xi = 0$. Their states are completely defined by points in observable spaces $\bar{\mathscr{V}}$ or $\bar{\bar{\mathscr{V}}}$, depending on whether θ or e is used as a state variable. Hence, all transitions of an elastic material system are observable.

With the aid of the above preliminaries one is now in a position to consider the most significant ingredient of the theory, namely the second law. This is treated in the following section.

14.3 Second Law and the Existence of Entropy

When a material system is deformed, a certain amount of mechanical work is usually lost into dissipation. If the material system is thermally isolated, that is, the corresponding transitions are adiabatic, the heat so created cannot escape into the environment. Suppose a transition is such that the initial value of the deformation measure is restored at the terminal point. Then, whatever the final values of the internal variables may be, the internal energy of the material system could not have decreased in this adiabatic process.

† Note that the body of which this particle is an element, may itself be heterogeneous. Note also that the unit of mass can be adjusted in order to suit a given situation.

To state this intuitive requirement more precisely, consider a particle and let M be its material system, being at the state $\hat{\hat{P}}_0 \equiv \{\boldsymbol{C}_0, e_0, \xi_0\}$ at the instant t_0. Denote by $\hat{\hat{N}}(\hat{\hat{P}}_0, R)$ an R-neighbourhood of $\hat{\hat{P}}_0$, where R is a suitable positive number. The orthogonal projection of points in $\hat{\hat{N}}(\hat{\hat{P}}_0, R)$ into the observable subspace $\bar{\bar{\mathscr{V}}}$, defines a neighbourhood for the observable state $\bar{\bar{P}}_0 \equiv \{\boldsymbol{C}_0, e_0\}$, which will be denoted by $\bar{\bar{N}}(\bar{\bar{P}}_0)$. The orthogonal projection of points in this latter neighbourhood into the $\boldsymbol{C}$-subspace of $\bar{\bar{\mathscr{V}}}$, defines a neighbourhood for $\boldsymbol{C}_0$, which will be denoted by $\bar{N}(\boldsymbol{C}_0)$. To proceed further, the neighbourhood $\hat{\hat{N}}(\hat{\hat{P}}_0, R)$ must be restricted so that certain *accessibility* conditions are fulfilled. It is clear that, if R is sufficiently small, then all observable states in the observable neighbourhood $\bar{\bar{N}}(\bar{\bar{P}}_0)$ can be regarded as attainable in the sense that each state can correspond to a state in $\hat{\hat{N}}(\hat{\hat{P}}_0, R)$ for a suitable value of ξ. On the other hand, if additional restrictions are imposed, then one may not expect such complete accessibility of points in the observable neighbourhood $\bar{\bar{N}}(\bar{\bar{P}}_0)$. An important restriction is the adiabatic isolation, that is, when only adiabatic transitions are admitted. In this case, one expects that not all states in $\bar{\bar{N}}(\bar{\bar{P}}_0)$ are accessible from $\bar{\bar{P}}_0$, whatever may be the corresponding values of internal variables. Nevertheless, it is reasonable to accept the following basic assumption which may restrict the size of the neighbourhood $\hat{\hat{N}}(\hat{\hat{P}}_0, R)$.

Adiabatic Accessibility: Every ε-neighbourhood of the observable state $\bar{\bar{P}}_0$, which is totally in $\bar{\bar{N}}(\bar{\bar{P}}_0)$, contains a (connected) set of points which can be attained by adiabatic transitions.

It should be noted carefully that, unlike the corresponding statement in reference 1, the above accessibility condition refers to, and is in terms of, only the *observable state variables* of the material system. This is, of course, physically reasonable, since only the observable variables can be regarded as controllable.

It is physically meaningful to make the adiabatic accessibility condition more explicit. To this end, one argues that the six components of the deformation measure, $\boldsymbol{C}$, can be given arbitrary values in the neighbouring $\bar{\bar{N}}(\bar{\bar{P}}_0)$, under adiabatic transitions, provided that the size of this neighbourhood is suitably restricted, and that e together with the internal variables are allowed to take on suitable values. In other words, it is sensible to assume that

> Every state $\hat{\hat{P}}_1 \equiv \{\boldsymbol{C}_1, e_1, \xi_1\}$ in $\hat{\hat{N}}(\hat{\hat{P}}_0, R)$, for which $\boldsymbol{C}_1$ (but not e_1 or ξ_1) is prescribed, can be attained by an adiabatic transition from $\hat{\hat{P}}_0$, provided that e_1 and ξ_1 are suitable. (14.9)

Note that this accessibility condition does not restrict the values of internal variables. This is in accordance with the fact that internal variables are not, in reality, controllable. A similar remark applies to the statements of the second law, that is, statements 14.10 and 14.11 below.

With the above preliminaries out of the way, one can now proceed, and state the second law in a form of *adiabatic inaccessibility, but totally in terms of observable quantities,* as follows

> Second law: Every observable ε-neighbourhood, totally in the observable neighbourhood $\bar{\bar{N}}(\bar{\bar{P}}_0)$, of the observable state $\bar{\bar{P}}_0$ of the material system M, contains a (connected) set of observable states that cannot be attained by M in adiabatic transitions. (14.10)

This statement is somewhat less restrictive than the following alternative which follows directly from the intuitive discussion that occurred at the beginning of this section.

> Second law: From the observable state $\bar{\bar{P}}_0 \equiv \{\boldsymbol{C}_0, e_0\}$ of the material system M, no observable state $\bar{\bar{P}} \equiv \{\boldsymbol{C}_0, e\}$ can be attained in an adiabatic transition, if $e < e_0$, no matter what the corresponding values of the internal variables. (14.11)

This latter form of the second law defines precisely those states that are unattainable adiabatically. From either statement 14.10 or 14.11, and the energy balance equation 14.1, it follows that an entropy function with extensive quality exists. This will be shown below with the aid of the less restrictive statement 14.10.

Existence of Entropy Function: Consider the material system M at state $\hat{\hat{P}}_0$, and confine attention to all (logically possible) adiabatic transitions to neighbouring states, which occur at constant values of internal variables $\xi = \xi_0$. Since no such restriction is imposed in statement 14.10, clearly this additional constraint can only diminish the set of points that is adiabatically accessible from $\hat{\hat{P}}_0$. It follows immediately that, in every ε-neighbourhood of the given state $\hat{\hat{P}} \equiv \{\boldsymbol{C}_0, e_0, \xi_0\}$ of a given material system M, there is a (connected) set of states in the hyperplane $\xi = \xi_0$, which cannot be attained by adiabatic elastic transitions from $\hat{\hat{P}}_0$.

From this statement, the first law written in the differential form

$$\begin{aligned} \mathrm{d}Q &= \mathrm{d}e - \tfrac{1}{2}\hat{\hat{\boldsymbol{S}}} \cdot \mathrm{d}\boldsymbol{C} \\ &= \mathrm{d}e - \hat{\hat{\boldsymbol{T}}}^R \cdot \mathrm{d}\boldsymbol{F} \end{aligned} \tag{14.12}$$

and Carathéodory's theorem on the integrability of differential forms, the existence of an entropy function $\eta = \hat{\hat{\eta}}(\boldsymbol{C}, e; \xi)$ which is extensive, follows immediately. The line of reasoning is precisely that outlined in reference 1.

Briefly, one fixes the internal variables at $\xi = \xi_0$, confines attention to a suitably small neighbourhood of point $\hat{\hat{P}}_0$ in this plane, and observes that for elastic transitions there are points in this neighbourhood that cannot be connected to $\hat{\hat{P}}_0$ by the solution curves of $\mathrm{d}Q = 0$, that is, by adiabatic elastic transitions. This reveals immediately that under suitable smoothness conditions differential form 14.12 has an (and hence, infinitely many) integrating factor $\theta = \hat{\theta}(\boldsymbol{C}, e; \xi_0)$ which renders $\mathrm{d}Q/\hat{\theta} = \mathrm{d}\hat{\hat{\eta}}$ an exact differential form. $\theta = \hat{\hat{\theta}}(\boldsymbol{C}, e; \xi_0)$ is an empirical temperature. Clearly, the entropy will be such that

$$\hat{\hat{\theta}} = \frac{1}{\partial\hat{\hat{\eta}}/\partial e} \qquad \hat{\hat{\boldsymbol{S}}} = -2\frac{\partial\hat{\hat{\eta}}/\partial \boldsymbol{C}}{\partial\hat{\hat{\eta}}/\partial e} \tag{14.13}$$

To show that this entropy function is extensive, one considers two material systems, M' and M'', in *perfect thermal contact*, denotes the combined system by M, and observes that, in any transition to a neighbouring state, heat added to M equals the sum of the heat added to M' and M'', that is

$$\mathrm{d}Q = \mathrm{d}Q' + \mathrm{d}Q'' \tag{14.14}$$

One then applies the second law to the combined system, and with some simple argument which is outlined in detail in reference 1, finally deduces that there exists an absolute temperature, $T = \bar{T}(\theta)$, which depends only on the chosen empirical temperature θ, and that corresponding to this absolute temperature $\bar{T}$ as the integrating factor of the energy equation, there exists a metrical entropy $S = \hat{S}(\boldsymbol{C}', \boldsymbol{C}'', \theta; \xi_0', \xi_0'')$ for the combined system M with the extensive property

$$\hat{S}(\boldsymbol{C}', \boldsymbol{C}'', \theta; \xi_0', \xi_0'') = \hat{S}'(\boldsymbol{C}', \theta; \xi_0') + \hat{S}''(\boldsymbol{C}'', \theta; \xi_0'') \tag{14.15}$$

where primed and doubly primed quantities refer to M' and M'', respectively, and as is clear, θ is used as a state variable.

If the considered neighbourhood in the hyperplane $\xi = \xi_0$ is suitably small, if the value of the entropy is known at one point in this neighbourhood, and if it is assumed (as will be done henceforth) that the entropy is a single-valued, continuous, and, say, continuously differentiable function of all its arguments, then the value of the entropy at all other points in the considered neighbourhood in the hyperplane $\xi = \xi_0$ can be calculated by means of elastic transitions. In particular, one has

$$\hat{\eta}(\hat{P}_1) = \hat{\eta}(\hat{\hat{P}}_0) + \underset{\hat{\hat{P}}_0}{\overset{\hat{P}_1}{\mathscr{C}}}(\hat{\hat{\mathscr{T}}} : \xi = \xi_0) \tag{14.16}$$

where the Clausius integral for the elastic transition $\hat{\hat{\mathscr{T}}}$ at $\xi = \xi_0$ is defined by

$$\mathscr{C}_{\hat{P}_0}^{\hat{P}_1}(\hat{\hat{\mathscr{T}}}:\xi = \xi_0) \equiv \int_{t_0}^{t_1} \frac{1}{\hat{\hat{\theta}}}(\dot{e} - \tfrac{1}{2}\hat{\boldsymbol{S}}\cdot\dot{\boldsymbol{C}})\,dt \tag{14.17}$$

In closing this section, it should be noted carefully that the validity of equation 14.15, that is, the extensivity of entropy, rests on the acceptance of the existence of a common empirical temperature θ, as a careful examination of the details of the argument which leads to equation 14.15 readily reveals[1].

14.4 On the Principle of Nondecreasing Entropy

There are a number of general results which follow from the second law, statement 14.10 without excessive restrictive assumptions on the class of materials. This will now be discussed.

Before one can proceed toward this end, a certain regularity assumption cannot be avoided. The following such assumption, while not totally necessary, is clearly reasonable and quite adequate for present purposes

> Basic regularity assumption: For M in state $\hat{P}_0$ and in a suitable neighbourhood $\hat{N}(\hat{P}_0, R)$, $\eta = \hat{\eta}(\boldsymbol{C}, \theta; \xi)$ is a single-valued, continuous, and continuously differentiable function of $\boldsymbol{C}$, θ, *and* ξ. (14.18)

Assume that the roles of η and θ can be interchanged. Hence, in the space of $\boldsymbol{C}, \eta, \xi$, let $\tilde{P}_0 = \{\boldsymbol{C}_0, \eta_0, \xi_0\}$ represent the given state of M, with the substate $P_0 \equiv \{\boldsymbol{C}_0, \eta_0\}$, and let $\tilde{N}(\tilde{P}_0, R)$ and $N(P_0)$, respectively, be the considered neighbourhood and its orthogonal projection into the $\boldsymbol{C}$, η-subspace.

Attention will be confined to a special class of materials with the following property

> Every state $\tilde{P}_1 \equiv \{\boldsymbol{C}_1, \eta_0, \xi_1\}$ in $\tilde{N}(\tilde{P}_0, R)$, for which $\boldsymbol{C}_1$ (but not ξ_1) is prescribed can be attained by an adiabatic transition from $\tilde{P}_0 \equiv \{\boldsymbol{C}_0, \eta_0, \xi_0\}$, provided that ξ_1 is suitable. (14.19)

This is a more restrictive assumption than the adiabatic accessibility condition 14.9. There are a number of materials which fall into this category, at least with a good degree of accuracy. To see this, observe that, on an adiabatic elastic transition entropy remains constant, that is, all such transitions are *isentropic*, and conversely, all isentropic elastic transitions are adiabatic. With this in mind, one may define

Materials with Instantaneous Elasticity: Material system M is said to have instantaneous elasticity in the suitable neighbourhood $\tilde{N}(\tilde{P}_0, R)$, if from its given state $\tilde{P}_0 \equiv \{\boldsymbol{C}_0, \eta_0, \xi_0\}$, all states in the hyperplane $\eta = \eta_0$ and $\xi = \xi_0$, which are in this neighbourhood, can be attained by suitable transitions which lie totally in this hyperplane, that is, by isentropic elastic transitions.

Many viscoelastic materials behave in this manner with a good degree of accuracy, provided one considers rapid loadings. For such loadings, the material does not have time to undergo internal structural changes, or exchange heat with its environment. Thus it will deform elastically and isentropically, provided that the loading is sufficiently rapid; this argument may even apply to some metals if the loading is rapid enough.

A second class of materials which satisfy condition 14.19, consists of materials with a certain suitable relaxation property. For a material of this kind can be taken from a given state $\tilde{P}_0 \equiv \{\boldsymbol{C}_0, \eta_0, \xi_0\}$ to another state $\tilde{P}_1 \equiv \{\boldsymbol{C}_1, \eta_0, \xi_1\}$, with $\boldsymbol{C}_1$ (but not ξ_1) prescribed, so slowly that the corresponding transition is isentropic (but not elastic). In the classical thermodynamics, this is called a quasistatic process. Such a very slow transition, of course, has only a limiting significance.

Theorem: Let M satisfy condition 14.19; for example, let it have instantaneous elasticity in the neighbourhood $\tilde{N}(\tilde{P}_0, R)$, then for *all* states $\tilde{P} \equiv \{\boldsymbol{C}, \eta, \xi\}$ in this neighbourhood that can be reached from $\tilde{P}_0 \equiv \{\boldsymbol{C}_0, \eta_0, \xi_0\}$ adiabatically, one always has $\eta \geqslant \eta_0$, or else for *all* such states one always has $\eta \leqslant \eta_0$. One then chooses the former.

The proof of this theorem can be sketched as follows. Assume the theorem is false. Then for *any* η_1 sufficiently close to η_0, and *suitable* $\boldsymbol{C}_2$ and ξ_2, state $\tilde{P}_2 \equiv \{\boldsymbol{C}_2, \eta_1, \xi_2\}$ in $\tilde{N}(\tilde{P}_0, R)$ can be attained adiabatically from $\tilde{P}_0$. Now, for *any* $\boldsymbol{C}_1$, the state $\tilde{P}_1 \equiv \{\boldsymbol{C}_1, \eta_1, \xi_1\}$ in $\tilde{N}(\tilde{P}_0, R)$ can be attained from $\tilde{P}_2$ adiabatically (condition 14.19 or instantaneous elasticity with $\xi_1 = \xi_2$). Hence, every point in a suitably small neighbourhood of the state P_0 in the $\boldsymbol{C}, \eta$-subspace, can be attained adiabatically, in contradiction of the second law.

Since an adiabatic elastic transition is isentropic, from this theorem it follows that a change in internal variables in an adiabatic transition cannot result in a decrease in the entropy. If the increase in entropy in an adiabatic transition is interpreted to have been caused by internal dissipation, it follows that the dissipative characteristic of the material is already implied by the rather mild adiabatic inaccessibility which is the content of second law 14.10, and by the assumption 14.19. This is made more explicit in the following discussion.

Returning to the state variables $\boldsymbol{C}$, e, and ξ, and observing the regularity assumption 14.18, calculate the rate of change of entropy $\eta = \hat{\hat{\eta}}(\boldsymbol{C}, e; \xi)$ at a typical state $\hat{\hat{P}}$, as follows

$$\begin{aligned}\dot{\hat{\hat{\eta}}} &= \frac{\partial \hat{\hat{\eta}}}{\partial \boldsymbol{C}}(\hat{\hat{P}})\cdot\dot{\boldsymbol{C}} + \frac{\partial \hat{\hat{\eta}}}{\partial e}(\hat{\hat{P}})\cdot\dot{e} + \frac{\partial \hat{\hat{\eta}}}{\partial \xi}(\hat{\hat{P}})\cdot\dot{\xi} \\ &= \frac{1}{\hat{\hat{\theta}}(\hat{\hat{P}})}\{\dot{e} - \tfrac{1}{2}\hat{\hat{\boldsymbol{S}}}(\hat{\hat{P}})\cdot\dot{\boldsymbol{C}}\} + \frac{\partial \hat{\hat{\eta}}}{\partial \xi}(\hat{\hat{P}})\cdot\dot{\xi} \\ &= \frac{\dot{Q}}{\hat{\hat{\theta}}(\hat{\hat{P}})} + \frac{\partial \hat{\hat{\eta}}}{\partial \xi}(\hat{\hat{P}})\cdot\dot{\xi}\end{aligned} \tag{14.20}$$

where the last line follows from the statement of the first law, equation 14.2, and where $(\partial\hat{\hat{\eta}}/\partial\xi)(\hat{\hat{P}})$, for example, denotes the partial derivative of $\hat{\hat{\eta}}$ with respect to ξ, evaluated at point $\hat{\hat{P}}$. This partial derivative is the gradient of $\hat{\hat{\eta}}$ in the ξ-subspace, that is, with e and $\boldsymbol{C}$ held fixed. With e and $\boldsymbol{C}$ held fixed, $\dot{Q} = 0$, and the rate of change of entropy is then given by the last term in equation 14.20. For such an adiabatic rate of change the theorem above implies that the rate of change of entropy cannot be negative. It thus follows that

> All possible transitions of materials with instantaneous elasticity (or those satisfying 14.19) are such that
>
> $$\frac{\partial \hat{\hat{\eta}}}{\partial \xi}(\hat{\hat{P}})\cdot\dot{\xi} \geqslant 0$$
>
> is not violated anywhere along these transitions. Transitions of this kind will be called *admissible*. (14.21)

Confining attention to a suitably defined neighbourhood in the state space, one concludes from 14.18, 14.20, and 14.21 that

$$\hat{\hat{\eta}}(\hat{\hat{P}}_2) = \hat{\hat{\eta}}(\hat{\hat{P}}_1) + \int_{t_1}^{t_2} \dot{\hat{\hat{\eta}}}\,\mathrm{d}t \geqslant \hat{\hat{\eta}}(\hat{\hat{P}}_1) + \int_{t_1}^{t_2} \frac{1}{\hat{\hat{\theta}}}(\dot{e} - \tfrac{1}{2}\hat{\hat{\boldsymbol{S}}}\cdot\dot{\boldsymbol{C}})\,\mathrm{d}t \tag{14.22}$$

where it is assumed that $\hat{\hat{P}}_1$ is connected with $\hat{\hat{P}}_2$ by an admissible transition $\hat{\hat{\mathcal{T}}}$. For this transition define the Clausius integral

$$\overset{\hat{\hat{P}}_2}{\underset{\hat{\hat{P}}_1}{\mathscr{C}}}(\hat{\hat{\mathcal{T}}}) \equiv \int_{t_1}^{t_2} \frac{1}{\hat{\hat{\theta}}}(\dot{e} - \tfrac{1}{2}\hat{\hat{\boldsymbol{S}}}\cdot\dot{\boldsymbol{C}})\,\mathrm{d}t \tag{14.23}$$

and obtain the Clausius–Planck inequality

$$\hat{\hat{\eta}}(\hat{\hat{P}}_2) \geqslant \hat{\hat{\eta}}(\hat{\hat{P}}_1) + \overset{\hat{\hat{P}}_2}{\underset{\hat{\hat{P}}_1}{\mathscr{C}}}(\hat{\hat{\mathcal{T}}}) \tag{14.24}$$

While 14.21 implies inequality 14.24, the converse is true only subject to certain smoothness conditions. Note that, subject to the restriction 14.19, the Clausius–Planck inequality 14.24 is a *derived* result here.

14.5 Bounds on Entropy[4]

Materials which admit an entropy function satisfying the Clausius–Planck inequality 14.24, may be called *dissipative.* The class of these materials includes those characterised by 14.19, which in turn includes materials with instantaneous elasticity. The Clausius–Planck inequality 14.24, however, is not sufficiently stringent to fix the dependency of the entropy function on the internal variables. This, of course, can be done by special assumptions, as will be mentioned briefly in section 14.6. However, there are a number of interesting results which stem directly from inequality 14.24, without any specific specialised assumptions. These will be discussed below.

14.5.1 Convexity

Let $\{\hat{\hat{\eta}}(\boldsymbol{C}, e;\, \boldsymbol{\xi})\}$ denote, for a given class of materials, the set of all entropy functions which satisfy the Clausius–Planck inequality 14.24. This is then a convex set, in the sense that, if $\hat{\hat{\eta}}_1$ and $\hat{\hat{\eta}}_2$ are two elements of this set, so are $\alpha\hat{\hat{\eta}}_1 + (1-\alpha)\hat{\hat{\eta}}_2$, for all $0 \leqslant \alpha \leqslant 1$. This follows immediately from inequality 14.24.

14.5.2 Bounds

The set of entropy functions admits lower and upper bounds. To show this, let $\bar{\bar{P}}^0 \equiv \{\boldsymbol{I}, e^0, \boldsymbol{0}\}$ denote the natural state of the material system, from which all other states can be reached by means of suitable transitions, where $\boldsymbol{I}$ is the identity tensor. Denote by η^0 the entropy at the natural state. Let $\hat{\hat{N}}(\bar{\bar{P}}^0, R)$ be a neighbourhood of the natural state, every point of which can be reached from this state by suitable transitions. Assume that this neighbourhood admits a subset $\hat{\hat{\mathcal{N}}}$ which has the following properties

(1) It is open and connected.

(2) It contains $\bar{\bar{P}}^0$.

(3) Every state $\hat{\hat{P}}$ in $\hat{\hat{\mathcal{N}}}$ can be attained from $\bar{\bar{P}}^0$ by an admissible transition which is totally in $\hat{\hat{\mathcal{N}}}$, that is, by a transition for which the Clausius–Planck inequality is satisfied.

To obtain the lower bound, consider a closed transition $\hat{\hat{\mathcal{T}}}$ in $\hat{\hat{\mathcal{N}}}$, consisting of two segments: one denoted by $\hat{\hat{\mathcal{T}}}_1$, from $\bar{\bar{P}}^0$ to a typical point $\hat{\hat{P}}_1$, and the other denoted by $\hat{\hat{\mathcal{T}}}_2$, from $\hat{\hat{P}}_1$ to $\bar{\bar{P}}^0$. From the Clausius–Planck inequality one has

$$\mathop{\mathscr{C}}_{\bar{\bar{P}}^0}^{\bar{\bar{P}}^0}(\hat{\hat{\mathcal{T}}}) = \mathop{\mathscr{C}}_{\bar{\bar{P}}^0}^{\hat{\hat{P}}_1}(\hat{\hat{\mathcal{T}}}_1) + \mathop{\mathscr{C}}_{\hat{\hat{P}}_1}^{\bar{\bar{P}}^0}(\hat{\hat{\mathcal{T}}}_2) \leqslant 0 \tag{14.25}$$

or, with $\hat{\hat{\mathscr{T}}}_2$ a *prescribed* (that is, *fixed*) transition

$$-\overset{\hat{\hat{P}}_1}{\underset{\bar{\bar{P}}^0}{\mathscr{C}}}(\hat{\hat{\mathscr{T}}}_1) \geqslant \overset{\bar{\bar{P}}^0}{\underset{\hat{\hat{P}}_1}{\mathscr{C}}}(\hat{\hat{\mathscr{T}}}_2) \tag{14.26}$$

which shows that the quantity on the left side of inequality 14.26 is bounded from below for *all* possible choices of $\hat{\hat{\mathscr{T}}}_1$. Set

$$-\hat{\hat{\eta}}_l(\hat{\hat{P}}_1) = \inf - \overset{\hat{\hat{P}}_1}{\underset{\bar{\bar{P}}^0}{\mathscr{C}}}(\hat{\hat{\mathscr{T}}}_1) = -\overset{\hat{\hat{P}}_1}{\underset{\bar{\bar{P}}^0}{\mathscr{C}}}(\hat{\hat{\mathscr{T}}}_1^l) \tag{14.27}$$

where the infimum is taken over all admissible transitions from $\bar{\bar{P}}^0$ to $\hat{\hat{P}}_1$; it is assumed that an optimum transition $\hat{\hat{\mathscr{T}}}_1^l$ exists, although it may have to be constructed by means of a limiting process. From the Clausius–Planck inequality, on the other hand, it follows that

$$\eta^0 - \hat{\hat{\eta}}(\hat{\hat{P}}_1) \leqslant -\overset{\hat{\hat{P}}_1}{\underset{\bar{\bar{P}}^0}{\mathscr{C}}}(\hat{\hat{\mathscr{T}}}_1) \tag{14.28}$$

so that the left-hand side is a lower bound for the right-hand side. This lower bound cannot be more than the infimum, implying that

$$\eta^0 + \hat{\hat{\eta}}_l(\hat{\hat{P}}_1) \leqslant \hat{\hat{\eta}}(\hat{\hat{P}}_1) \tag{14.29}$$

The quantity

$$\hat{\hat{\mathscr{H}}}_l(\hat{\hat{P}}_1) = \eta^0 + \hat{\hat{\eta}}_l(\hat{\hat{P}}_1) \tag{14.30}$$

is a state function, is the lower bound for entropy, and satisfies the Clausius–Planck inequality. To show this last assertion, consider two successive states, $\hat{\hat{P}}_1$ and $\hat{\hat{P}}_2$, connected by a transition $\hat{\hat{\mathscr{T}}}$. Let the optimum transitions from $\bar{\bar{P}}^0$ to $\hat{\hat{P}}_1$ and $\hat{\hat{P}}_2$ be, respectively, denoted by $\hat{\hat{\mathscr{T}}}_1^l$ and $\hat{\hat{\mathscr{T}}}_2^l$. One then obtains

$$\begin{aligned} -\overset{\hat{\hat{P}}_2}{\underset{\bar{\bar{P}}^0}{\mathscr{C}}}(\hat{\hat{\mathscr{T}}}_2^l) &\leqslant -\overset{\hat{\hat{P}}_2}{\underset{\bar{\bar{P}}^0}{\mathscr{C}}}(\hat{\hat{\mathscr{T}}}_1^l + \hat{\hat{\mathscr{T}}}) \\ &= -\overset{\hat{\hat{P}}_1}{\underset{\bar{\bar{P}}^0}{\mathscr{C}}}(\hat{\hat{\mathscr{T}}}_1^l) - \overset{\hat{\hat{P}}_2}{\underset{\hat{\hat{P}}_1}{\mathscr{C}}}(\hat{\hat{\mathscr{T}}}) \end{aligned} \tag{14.31}$$

so that

$$\hat{\hat{\mathscr{H}}}_l(\hat{\hat{P}}_1) + \overset{\hat{\hat{P}}_2}{\underset{\hat{\hat{P}}_1}{\mathscr{C}}}(\hat{\hat{\mathscr{T}}}) \leqslant \hat{\hat{\mathscr{H}}}_l(\hat{\hat{P}}_2) \tag{14.32}$$

To obtain the upper bound for entropy, from inequality 14.29, with $\hat{\hat{\mathscr{T}}}_1$ *prescribed*, write

$$\overset{\bar{P}^0}{\underset{\hat{P}_1}{\mathscr{C}}}(\hat{\hat{\mathscr{T}}}_2) \leqslant -\overset{\hat{P}_1}{\underset{\bar{P}^0}{\mathscr{C}}}(\hat{\hat{\mathscr{T}}}_1) \tag{14.33}$$

which shows that the left-hand quantity is bounded from above for *all* possible choices of $\hat{\hat{\mathscr{T}}}_2$. Set

$$-\hat{\eta}_u(\hat{\hat{P}}_1) = \sup \overset{\bar{P}^0}{\underset{\hat{P}_1}{\mathscr{C}}}(\hat{\hat{\mathscr{T}}}_2) = \overset{\bar{P}^0}{\underset{\hat{P}_1}{\mathscr{C}}}(\hat{\hat{\mathscr{T}}}{}_2^u) \tag{14.34}$$

where the supremum is taken over all admissible transitions from $\hat{\hat{P}}_1$ to $\bar{P}^0$; it is assumed that the optimum transition $\hat{\hat{\mathscr{T}}}{}_2^u$ exists. From the Clausius–Planck inequality and equation 14.34, it now follows that

$$\hat{\eta}(\hat{\hat{P}}_1) \leqslant \eta^0 + \hat{\eta}_u(\hat{\hat{P}}_1) \tag{14.35}$$

The quantity

$$\hat{\mathscr{H}}_u(\hat{\hat{P}}_1) = \eta^0 + \hat{\eta}_u(\hat{\hat{P}}_1) \tag{14.36}$$

is a state function, is the upper bound for entropy, and satisfies the Clausius–Planck inequality; that is, for any two states, $\hat{\hat{P}}^1$ and $\hat{\hat{P}}^2$, which are connected by an admissible transition $\hat{\hat{\mathscr{T}}}$ one has

$$\hat{\mathscr{H}}_u(\hat{\hat{P}}_1) + \overset{\hat{P}_2}{\underset{\hat{P}_1}{\mathscr{C}}}(\hat{\hat{\mathscr{T}}}) \leqslant \hat{\mathscr{H}}_u(\hat{\hat{P}}_2); \tag{14.37}$$

this can be proved using the same line of thinking as that which led to inequality 14.32[1].

From 14.29, 14.30, 14.35, and 14.36, it now follows that the entropy at a typical state $\hat{\hat{P}}_1$ is such that

$$\hat{\mathscr{H}}_l(\hat{\hat{P}}_1) \leqslant \hat{\eta}(\hat{\hat{P}}_1) \leqslant \hat{\mathscr{H}}_u(\hat{\hat{P}}_1) \tag{14.38}$$

14.5.3 Potential property of bounds

A significant and apparently novel result is that both bounds in inequality 14.38 can serve as potentials in exactly the same manner as does entropy $\hat{\eta}$ itself, that is, equations 14.13. This means that these bounds can differ from $\hat{\eta}$ by functions of ξ's only.

To show this one observes that inequalities 14.32 and 14.37 become strict equalities if states $\hat{\hat{P}}_1$ and $\hat{\hat{P}}_2$ are on the same $\xi = \xi_1$ hyperplane, and that $\hat{\hat{\mathscr{T}}}$ is an elastic transition in this plane. To prove these assertions, consider 14.32 first.

Since $\hat{\hat{P}}_1$ and $\hat{\hat{P}}_2$ are connected by an elastic transition, one has

$$\mathop{\mathscr{C}}\limits_{\hat{P}_1}^{\hat{P}_2}(\hat{\hat{\mathscr{T}}}:\xi=\xi_1)=\eta(\hat{\hat{P}}_2)-\eta(\hat{\hat{P}}_1)$$

and hence 14.31 reduces to

$$-\mathop{\mathscr{C}}\limits_{\bar{P}^0}^{\hat{P}_2}(\hat{\hat{\mathscr{T}}}_2^l)\leqslant-\mathop{\mathscr{C}}\limits_{\bar{P}^0}^{\hat{P}_1}(\hat{\hat{\mathscr{T}}}_1^l)+\eta(\hat{\hat{P}}_1)-\eta(\hat{\hat{P}}_2) \tag{14.39}$$

On the other hand, since $\hat{\hat{\mathscr{T}}}_1^l$ is the optimal transition from $\bar{\bar{P}}^0$ to $\hat{\hat{P}}_1$, one has

$$-\mathop{\mathscr{C}}\limits_{\bar{P}^0}^{\hat{P}_1}(\hat{\hat{\mathscr{T}}}_1^l)\leqslant-\mathop{\mathscr{C}}\limits_{\bar{P}^0}^{\hat{P}_2}(\hat{\hat{\mathscr{T}}}_2^l)+\eta(\hat{\hat{P}}_2)-\eta(\hat{\hat{P}}_1) \tag{14.40}$$

From inequalities 14.39 and 14.40 it follows that

$$-\mathop{\mathscr{C}}\limits_{\bar{P}^0}^{\hat{P}_1}(\hat{\hat{\mathscr{T}}}_1^l)+\eta(\hat{\hat{P}}_1)-\eta(\hat{\hat{P}}_2)\leqslant-\mathop{\mathscr{C}}\limits_{\bar{P}^0}^{\hat{P}_2}(\hat{\hat{\mathscr{T}}}_2^l)\leqslant-\mathop{\mathscr{C}}\limits_{\bar{P}^0}^{\hat{P}_1}(\hat{\hat{\mathscr{T}}}_1^l)+\eta(\hat{\hat{P}}_1)-\eta(\hat{\hat{P}}_2) \tag{14.41}$$

which immediately shows that the equality sign must hold. On the assumption that the infimum in equation 14.27 is uniquely attained†, one now concludes that

> If the optimal (in the sense of equation 14.27) transition from $\bar{\bar{P}}^0$ to $\hat{\hat{P}}_1\equiv\{C_1,e_1,\xi_1\}$ is $\hat{\hat{\mathscr{T}}}_1^l$, then the optimal transition from $\bar{\bar{P}}^0$ to $\hat{\hat{P}}_2\equiv\{C_2,e_2,\xi_1\}$ consists of $\hat{\hat{\mathscr{T}}}_1^l$ followed by any elastic transition from $\hat{\hat{P}}_1$ to $\hat{\hat{P}}_2$ in the hyperplane $\xi=\xi_1$. (14.42)

It is easy to follow a similar analysis, and show that for any two states $\hat{\hat{P}}_1$ and $\hat{\hat{P}}_2$ in the same hyperplane $\xi=\xi_1$, one has

$$\mathop{\mathscr{C}}\limits_{\hat{P}_1}^{\bar{P}^0}(\hat{\hat{\mathscr{T}}}_1^u)+\eta(\hat{\hat{P}}_1)-\eta(\hat{\hat{P}}_2)\leqslant\mathop{\mathscr{C}}\limits_{\hat{P}_2}^{\bar{P}^0}(\hat{\hat{\mathscr{T}}}_2^u)\leqslant\mathop{\mathscr{C}}\limits_{\hat{P}_1}^{\bar{P}^0}(\hat{\hat{\mathscr{T}}}_1^u)+\eta(\hat{\hat{P}}_1)-\eta(\hat{\hat{P}}_2) \tag{14.43}$$

where $\hat{\hat{\mathscr{T}}}_1^u$ and $\hat{\hat{\mathscr{T}}}_2^u$ are the optimal transitions from $\hat{\hat{P}}_1$ and $\hat{\hat{P}}_2$ to $\bar{\bar{P}}^0$, respectively, the optimal referring to the supremum in the sense of equation 14.34. Again, if it is assumed that the corresponding suprema are attained uniquely, it follows that

> If the optimal (in the sense of equation 14.34) transition from $\hat{\hat{P}}_1\equiv\{C_1,e_1,\xi_1\}$ to $\bar{\bar{P}}^0$ is $\hat{\hat{\mathscr{T}}}_1^u$, then the optimal transition from $\hat{\hat{P}}_2\equiv\{C_2,e_2,\xi_1\}$ to $\bar{\bar{P}}^0$ consists of any elastic transition from $\hat{\hat{P}}_2$ to $\hat{\hat{P}}_1$ in the hyperplane $\xi=\xi_1$ followed by $\hat{\hat{\mathscr{T}}}_1^u$. (14.44)

† This is clearly a mathematically and physically reasonable assumption.

The potential property of the bounds $\hat{\hat{\mathscr{H}}}_l$ and $\hat{\hat{\mathscr{H}}}_u$, defined respectively by equations 14.30 and 14.36, now follows from inequalities 14.41 and 14.43, and from the definition of partial differentiation. Briefly, one connects a given state $\hat{\hat{P}}_1 \equiv \{\boldsymbol{C}_1, e_1, \xi_1\}$ to a neighbouring state, say, $\hat{\hat{P}}_2 \equiv \{\boldsymbol{C}_1, e_1 + \Delta e, \xi_1\}$ by a line parallel to the e-axis, forms the limit

$$\lim_{\Delta e \to 0} \frac{\hat{\hat{\mathscr{H}}}_l(\hat{\hat{P}}_2) - \hat{\hat{\mathscr{H}}}_l(\hat{\hat{P}}_1)}{\Delta e} = \lim_{\Delta e \to 0} \frac{\displaystyle\int_{\hat{\hat{P}}_1}^{\hat{\hat{P}}_2} \frac{de}{\hat{\hat{\theta}}}}{\Delta e}$$

and immediately observes that $\partial \hat{\hat{\mathscr{H}}}_l / \partial e = 1/\hat{\hat{\theta}}$. In this manner it can easily be shown that at any typical state $\hat{\hat{P}}$, one has

$$\hat{\hat{\theta}} = \frac{1}{\partial \hat{\hat{\eta}}/\partial e} = \frac{1}{\partial \hat{\hat{\mathscr{H}}}_l/\partial e} = \frac{1}{\partial \hat{\hat{\mathscr{H}}}_u/\partial e}$$

$$\hat{\hat{\boldsymbol{S}}} = -2\frac{\partial \hat{\hat{\eta}}/\partial \boldsymbol{C}}{\partial \hat{\hat{\eta}}/\partial e} = -2\frac{\partial \hat{\hat{\mathscr{H}}}_l/\partial \boldsymbol{C}}{\partial \hat{\hat{\mathscr{H}}}_l/\partial e} = -2\frac{\partial \hat{\hat{\mathscr{H}}}_u/\partial \boldsymbol{C}}{\partial \hat{\hat{\mathscr{H}}}_u/\partial e} \tag{14.45}$$

Thus the functions $\hat{\hat{\eta}}$, $\hat{\hat{\mathscr{H}}}_l$, and $\hat{\hat{\mathscr{H}}}_u$ can differ from each other by additive functions of ξ's only.

Finally, it may be of interest to note that a calculation by Breuer and Onat[5] for a specific case in isothermal linear viscoelasticity has shown that optimal transition for their 'maximum recoverable work' which corresponds to equation 14.34, is attained by a step change in strain followed by a *relaxation*. This, of course, means an elastic transition followed by a second nonelastic transition, which is in accord with the general result 14.44.

14.6 Special Considerations

While the results of previous sections apply to wide classes of materials, they are not specific enough to yield sufficient information in actual specialised applications. For these, one must make additional constitutive assumptions.

A major difficulty is to establish, for a given class of materials, the dependency of the entropy function on the internal variables. From equation 14.16 it follows that, if the value of entropy is known at one point in a given hyperplane $\xi = \xi_0$, then its value can be calculated in a reasonably restricted neighbourhood on this plane. One interesting and practically useful possibility is to consider a sequence of equilibria (an equilibrium curve), each point corresponding to given values of internal variables. In fact, it may be possible to construct simple microscopic models which can be used to this end, or one may appeal totally to an experimental evaluation of such a curve; one may, of course, use both. The value of entropy is then calculated along this equilibrium curve.

The dependency of entropy on internal variables can be fixed completely, if a specific internal energy dissipation mechanism is prescribed. Such specification will also fix the manner by which internal variables can change. This is the approach of the classical thermodynamics of irreversible processes[6–11]. Here one sets

$$d = \hat{\hat{d}}(\boldsymbol{C}, e; \xi, \dot{\xi}$$
$$= \hat{\hat{\boldsymbol{Q}}}(\boldsymbol{C}, e; \xi, \dot{\xi}) \cdot \dot{\xi} = \hat{\hat{\theta}} \frac{\partial \hat{\hat{\eta}}}{\partial \xi} \cdot \dot{\xi} \geqslant 0 \tag{14.46}$$

where $\boldsymbol{Q} = \hat{\hat{\boldsymbol{Q}}}(\boldsymbol{C}, e;\ \xi, \dot{\xi})$ are the generalised forces associated with the internal variables, and d is the rate of dissipation per unit mass. From 14.46 differential equations which characterise the evolution of internal variables, may be written by

$$\hat{\hat{\theta}}(\boldsymbol{C}, e;\ \xi) \frac{\partial \hat{\hat{\eta}}}{\partial \xi}(\boldsymbol{C}, e;\ \xi) - \hat{\hat{\boldsymbol{Q}}}(\boldsymbol{C}, e;\ \xi, \dot{\xi}) = 0 \tag{14.47}$$

A further specialisation is to take the generalised forces in the following form

$$\hat{\hat{\boldsymbol{Q}}} = \dot{\xi}^{\mathrm{T}} \hat{\hat{\boldsymbol{A}}}(\boldsymbol{C}, e; \xi) \tag{14.48}$$

that is, linear in $\dot{\xi}$. Here, $\hat{\hat{\boldsymbol{A}}}$ is an m by m matrix whose elements are functions of state. Inequality 14.46 requires that $\dot{\xi}^{\mathrm{T}} \hat{\hat{\boldsymbol{A}}} \cdot \dot{\xi}$ be non-negative, vanishing only with $\dot{\xi}$. Hence, $\hat{\hat{\boldsymbol{A}}}$ must be a matrix with real positive eigenvalues everywhere in the considered region in the state space, that is, for all admissible values of $\boldsymbol{C}$, e and ξ. Such a restriction automatically implies a certain kind of *fading memory* measured in terms of the path parameter in the state space. As has been suggested by Ilyushin[12], and Pipkin and Rivlin[13], for rate-independent plasticity a kinematical quantity (that is, $\mathrm{d}t^2 = \mathrm{d}C_{AB}\mathrm{d}C_{AB}$) can be used as the time parameter; all the material time derivatives are then taken with respect to this time parameter. Valanis has[14] further generalised this and applied it to actual cases; see also reference 15.

In the classical approach, matrix $\hat{\hat{\boldsymbol{A}}}$ is taken to be constant and, according to the Onsager–Casimir reciprocity relation, symmetric. For problems which involve large deviation from equilibrium, $\hat{\hat{\boldsymbol{A}}}$ will, in general, be neither a constant nor a symmetric matrix, although it must remain positive-definite.

In certain cases it may be possible to prescribe differential or integro-differential equations whose solution gives the internal variables as functionals of the observable transitions. For example, one may write

$$\dot{\xi} = \hat{\hat{\boldsymbol{h}}}(\boldsymbol{C}, e; \xi) \tag{14.49}$$

For a given observable transition $\bar{\bar{\mathscr{T}}}(s) \equiv \{\boldsymbol{C}(s), e(s)\}$, $t_0 \leqslant s \leqslant t_1$, and subject to suitable assumptions, equation 14.49 may be solved to yield

$$\xi(t_1) = \mathop{\mathscr{F}}_{s=t_0}^{t_1} \big(\boldsymbol{C}(s), e(s)\big) \tag{14.50}$$

where $\mathscr{F}$ is a functional of the observable transition. The internal variables can now be eliminated, yielding

$$\theta(t) = \hat{\hat{\theta}}\big(\boldsymbol{C}(t), e(t); \mathop{\mathscr{F}}_{s=t_0}^{t} (\boldsymbol{C}(s), e(s))\big)$$

$$\boldsymbol{S}(t) = \hat{\hat{\boldsymbol{S}}}\big(\boldsymbol{C}(t), e(t); \mathop{\mathscr{F}}_{s=t_0}^{t} (\boldsymbol{C}(s), e(s))\big)$$

$$\eta(t) = \hat{\hat{\eta}}\big(\boldsymbol{C}(t), e(t); \mathop{\mathscr{F}}_{s=t_0}^{t} (\boldsymbol{C}(s), e(s))\big) \tag{14.51}$$

which are functionals of the observable transition, as well as functions of the instantaneous (at time t) observable state. These functionals are related by equations 14.13. Moreover, the Clausius–Planck inequality must be satisfied; subject to further smoothness assumptions, the Clausius–Duhem inequality

$$\dot{\hat{\hat{\eta}}} - \frac{1}{\hat{\hat{\theta}}}\{\dot{e} - \tfrac{1}{2}\hat{\hat{\boldsymbol{S}}}\cdot\dot{\boldsymbol{C}}\} \geqslant 0 \tag{14.52}$$

can be used instead. These restrictions are not sufficient to render entropy unique. It is seen therefore that the direct functional representation of constitutive relations implies *a-priori* knowledge of the manner by which internal variables can change, that is, the manner by which internal structural changes occur. Nevertheless, even such knowledge is not sufficient by itself to render the entropy unique.

Acknowledgement

This work has been supported by the National Science Foundation under Grant GK-31352.

References

1. S. Nemat-Nasser. On nonlinear thermoelasticity and nonequilibrium thermodynamics. *Symposium on Nonlinear Elasticity*, Dickey, R. W. (Ed.), Academic Press, N.Y. (1973) 289
2. K. C. Valanis. Irreversibility and Existence of Entropy. *Int. J. Non-Linear Mech.*, **6** (1971), 337
3. S. Nemat-Nasser. On Nonequilibrium Thermodynamics of Continua. *Mechanics Today*, **2**, Pergamon Press, N.Y., to appear

4. J. C. Willems. Dissipative dynamical systems. Part I: General theory. *Arch. Rat. Mech. Anal.*, **45** (1972), 321
5. S. Breuer and E. T. Onat. On recoverable work in linear viscoelasticity. *Z.A.M.P.*, **15** (1964), 12
6. M. A. Biot. Theory of stress–strain relations in anisotropic viscoelasticity and relaxation phenomena. *J. Appl. Phys.*, **25** (1954), 1385
7. J. Meixner. Thermodynamische theorie der elastischen relaxation. *Z. Naturf.*, **9a** (1954), 654
8. Y. C. Fung. *Foundations of Solid Mechanics*, Prentice Hall, Englewood Cliffs, N.J. (1965)
9. R. A. Schapery. On a thermodynamic constitutive theory and its application to various nonlinear materials. In *Proc. IUTAM Symposium on Thermoinelasticity*, ed. by B. A. Boley, Springer-Verlag, Berlin (1970), 259
10. K. C. Valanis. Thermodynamics of large viscoelastic deformations. *J. Math. Phys.*, **45** (1966), 197
11. J. Kestin and J. R. Rice. Paradoxes in the application of thermodynamics to strained solids. In *A Critical Review of Thermodynamics*, ed. by E. B. Stuart, B. Cal-Or and A. J. Brainard, Mono Book Corp., Baltimore (1970), 275
12. A. A. Ilyushin. On the relation between stresses and small deformations in the mechanics of continuous media. *P.M.M.*, **25** (1961), 746
13. A. C. Pipkin and R. S. Rivlin. Mechanics of rate-independent materials. *Z.A.M.P.*, **16** (1965), 313
14. K. C. Valanis. A Theory of viscoplasticity without a yield surface. Part I: General theory; Part II: Application to the mechanical behaviour of metals. *Archiwum Mechaniki Stosowanej*, **23** (1971), 517, 535
15. J. T. Oden and R. der Bhandari. Thermoplastic materials with memory. *A.S.C.E.*, EMI (1973), 131

15. Thermodynamics and Plasticity

J. Mandel†

Abstract

This study deals with the application of thermodynamics to materials which, besides viscoelastic deformations, exhibit plastic deformations (either purely plastic or viscoplastic). Attention is focussed on the definition of the thermodynamic state and on the expression of the second law. Three different formulations are presented

(1) With hidden variables and using an intermediate, *released*, configuration.
(2) With hidden variables and using a fixed reference configuration.
(3) In functional representation.

Finally an hypothesis about the dissipativity is investigated.

15.1 Some Definitions and Classical Results

Let X_i be the (orthogonal) coordinates of a material point in some configuration κ, x_i its present coordinates. The tensor γ of components $\gamma_{ij} = \partial x_i/\partial X_i$ is called the deformation gradient, $\boldsymbol{C} = \gamma^{\mathrm{T}}\gamma = \mathbf{1}+2\boldsymbol{\Delta}$ (T denoting the transpose) is the right Cauchy–Green tensor, while $\boldsymbol{\Delta}$ is the Green strain tensor. With respect to the configuration κ, the Kirchhoff stress tensor $\boldsymbol{\Pi}$ is defined from the (Eulerian) Cauchy stress tensor $\boldsymbol{\sigma}$ by

$$\boldsymbol{\Pi} = (\det\gamma)\gamma^{-1}\boldsymbol{\sigma}\gamma^{\mathrm{T}-1} \qquad (15.1)$$

The absolute temperature is denoted by θ and the time by t.

A material is said to be simple if $\boldsymbol{\Pi}(t)$ depends only on $\gamma(\tau)$, $\theta(\tau)$ for $\tau \leqslant t$ (excluding the space derivatives of γ and θ). Using the principle of objectivity it is then shown that $\boldsymbol{\Pi}(t)$ depends only on $\boldsymbol{C}(\tau)$, $\theta(\tau)$ for $\tau \leqslant t$. The present values $\boldsymbol{C}(t)$, $\theta(t)$ may have a special significance, as well as the present values of their time derivative (viscous fluids, Kelvin solids for example). On the other hand, if $\boldsymbol{\Pi}$ and θ are used as commanded variables, the present values of the time derivative of these variables do not appear in the functional giving $\boldsymbol{C}(t)$ (principle of nonduality[1]).

Let u, s, $\varphi = u-\theta s$ be the internal energy, entropy and free energy per unit mass, $\boldsymbol{q}$ the heat flux vector, r the heat supply per unit volume inside the

† Laboratoire de Mécanique des Solides, Ecole Polytechnique, Paris.

material, ρ the present mass density, ρ_κ the mass density in the reference configuration κ. The first law of thermodynamics is expressed (in local form) by the relation

$$\rho\dot{u} = [\boldsymbol{\sigma}\mathscr{D}] + r - \operatorname{div} \boldsymbol{q} \tag{15.2}$$

$\mathscr{D}$ is the rate of deformation tensor and the *bracket denotes the trace of the product of two tensors.*

For the second law, we shall assume that it can be formulated by the Clausius–Duhem inequality which, using equation 15.2 and the definition of φ, reads

$$D = \frac{[\boldsymbol{\sigma}\mathscr{D}]}{\rho} - (\dot{\varphi} + s\dot{\theta}) - \frac{\boldsymbol{q}}{\rho\theta} \operatorname{grad} \theta \geqslant 0 \tag{15.3}$$

The term $[\boldsymbol{\sigma}\mathscr{D}]/\rho$ in equations 15.2 and 15.3 can be replaced by $[\boldsymbol{\Pi}\dot{\boldsymbol{\Delta}}]/\rho_\kappa$.

15.2 Definition of the Thermodynamic State

The thermodynamic state of a material element at time t, and its orientation can be described by its functional response $\boldsymbol{\Pi}(\tau)$ to strains $\boldsymbol{\Delta}(\tau)$ and temperature $\theta(\tau)$ imposed for $\tau > t$, or by its response $\boldsymbol{\Delta}(\tau)$ to imposed stress $\boldsymbol{\Pi}(\tau)$ and temperature $\theta(\tau)$. In other words, for two elements we shall say that the thermodynamic state and the orientation are the same, if its functional response is the same. We shall say that the state (independently of the orientation) is the same, if the functional responses can be identified through a proper orthogonal transformation (both on the excitation and the response).

The state and orientation variables are the variables, the values of which at time t must be given for the further evolution to be determined (up to a rotation) under imposed stress $\boldsymbol{\Pi}(\tau)$ (or strains $\boldsymbol{\Delta}(\tau)$) and temperature $\theta(\tau)$ for $\tau > t$†.

For an elastic material element, $\boldsymbol{\Delta}$ (or $\boldsymbol{\Pi}$) and θ can be taken as state variables. But these variables are not sufficient for a material element exhibiting viscosity or plasticity. The definition of the state can then be completed in two different ways

(1) either by giving the history of the preceding variables from $-\infty$ up to t, or

(2) by giving a certain number of supplementary variables which are called *hidden* (while the preceding variables are called *observable*) and in which the past history is condensed.

The first method leads to some difficulties when applied to bodies which are able to exhibit instantaneous plastic deformations (classical plasticity)

† It follows that the rate of change of the state variables are functions of the values of these variables and eventually of the time derivative of $\boldsymbol{\Pi}$ (or $\boldsymbol{\Delta}$) and θ.

because of the different behaviour during loading and unloading.

This is why it is preferable to present first the application of thermodynamics according to the second method. Before starting that, we shall make some remarks on the hidden variables and on the kind of description which is used. On the second point let us say now that we can choose a Lagrangian description or a Eulerian description, but in fact the most suitable description for plastic materials introduces an intermediate configuration, which is called the *present relaxed configuration.* Its superiority is quite obvious in the case of perfectly plastic bodies, for which the thermodynamic state does not depend on the permanent deformations undergone. It can be said that the interest of the intermediate configuration lies in the fact that it exhibits the real state variables.

15.3 Some Remarks on the Hidden Variables

15.3.1 What are these variables?

They are chemical or physical variables such as the proceeding degree of a chemical reaction inside the element: the extent of water saturation (concrete, soils); the variables which describe the distribution of dislocations in a crystal, for example[2] the density of dislocation loops $(1/V)\sum \boldsymbol{n} \otimes \boldsymbol{b}$ where $\boldsymbol{n}$ is the normal to the loop, $\boldsymbol{b}$ the Burgers vector of this loop, $\sum$ the sum extended to the volume V; the residual stresses between the microelements† contained in the macroscopic element of a polycrystal, a rock or a sand.

Where tensor variables are concerned, they can be referred either to a fixed reference configuration (Lagrangian description), to the present stressed configuration (Eulerian description), or to a present released configuration. In the two last cases, it is necessary to determine in some way the orientation of the present (stressed or released) configuration, so that an orientation variable must be added to the state variables. We shall use the following mode of orientation. We consider a material plane of unit normal $\boldsymbol{n}$, and in this plane a material direction $\boldsymbol{m}$ (a unit vector)‡. The element is oriented by the couple $(\boldsymbol{m}, \boldsymbol{n})$, or by the tensor $\boldsymbol{m} \otimes \boldsymbol{n}$, or by the orthonormal triad formed from $\boldsymbol{m}$ and $\boldsymbol{n}$, and which will be called a director triad. There is obviously a great freedom in the choice of the director triad. In a polycrystal, it can be attached to any monocrystal, or be defined by a weighted average of their orientations[3,4].

15.3.2 Are all the hidden variables internal variables?

This is not always the case for variables which depend on the orientation;

† microelements: part of the macroelement in which the deformation can be considered as homogeneous.

‡ $\boldsymbol{m}$ and $\boldsymbol{n}$ are attached to a microelement (any one of them). The relative orientations of the different microelements are state variables.

for example, the three Euler angles determining the orientation of the chosen director triad, or the matrix of the components of the unit vectors along its axes with respect to the fixed axes, are not internal variables. A variable is considered as internal if it follows the tensorial rule when the orientation of the element is modified, or in a change of orthonormal frame. In other words, the internal variables are tensors (scalars or vectors as special cases).

15.3.3 Can any internal variable be chosen to define the state?

In principle yes, but for a convenient use of the inequality 15.3 it is better to choose these variables in such a way that it will be physically possible to impose a fast change (at least in some sense) to the observable variables without any change of the internal variables.

Let us consider for example the Maxwell model, figure 15.1.

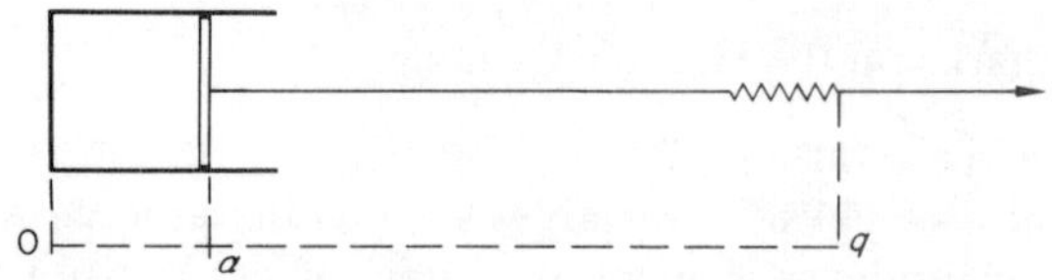

Figure 15.1

The observable variable q, relative displacement of the two ends of the model, is not enough for the determination of its state, *A priori* we can take as hidden variables either the abscissa α of the piston in the dashpot or the elongation $x = q - \alpha$ of the spring. But if a fast change of q is imposed, x changes while α remains the same. Thus we will take α and not x as a hidden variable. Let us notice that α is the variable exhibited in the released configuration.

15.5 Application of Thermodynamics using Isoclinic Released Configurations

Let (0) be the initial configuration, with zero stress and temperature θ_0, (a) the present configuration with stress $\boldsymbol{\sigma}$ and temperature θ. We assume that at time t the material element is very rapidly unloaded and brought back to temperature θ_0. This unloading process is elastic†. We thus obtain a present released configuration (κ) which is only defined up to an arbitrary rotation. Denoting by $\boldsymbol{F}$ the gradient of the total transformation $(0) \rightarrow (a)$, by $\boldsymbol{E}$ the gradient of the present elastic transformation $(\kappa) \rightarrow (a)$, and by $\boldsymbol{P}$ the gradient of the inelastic (plastic + differed elastic) transformation $(0) \rightarrow (\kappa)$, we then have

$$\boldsymbol{F} = \boldsymbol{E}\boldsymbol{P} \tag{15.4}$$

† In some case the actual transformation by a very rapid unloading may induce plastic deformations opposite to the deformations which have occurred in the loading process. Then a *virtual* unloading must be considered according to the thermoelastic behaviour, that is, assuming the hidden variables remain constant. This behaviour is defined without ambiguity.

$$\text{grad}\,\boldsymbol{v} = \dot{\boldsymbol{F}}\boldsymbol{F}^{-1} = \dot{\boldsymbol{E}}\boldsymbol{E}^{-1} + \boldsymbol{E}\boldsymbol{V}_P\boldsymbol{E}^{-1} \qquad (\text{where } \boldsymbol{V}_P = \dot{\boldsymbol{P}}\boldsymbol{P}^{-1}) \tag{15.5}$$

$$\mathscr{D} = \{\text{grad}\,\boldsymbol{v}\} = \{\dot{\boldsymbol{E}}\boldsymbol{E}^{-1}\} + \{\boldsymbol{E}\boldsymbol{V}_P\boldsymbol{E}^{-1}\} \tag{15.6}$$

$\boldsymbol{v}$ is the velocity, grad $\boldsymbol{v}$ its gradient with respect to the present coordinates x_i, $\mathscr{D}$ the rate of deformation (with respect to the present configurations (a)), $\{\ \}$ the symmetric part of a tensor, and $\boldsymbol{V}_P$ the plastic transformation rate with respect to the configuration (κ), this velocity being independent on the choice of the initial configuration (0).

Each term in the right-hand side of equations 15.5 and 15.6 depends on the choice of the released configuration, or more precisely on how its orientation changes with time. Indeed if $\boldsymbol{E}' = \boldsymbol{E}\boldsymbol{R}$ ($\boldsymbol{R}$ being an orthogonal tensor), we have

$$\dot{\boldsymbol{E}}'\boldsymbol{E}'^{(-1)} = \dot{\boldsymbol{E}}\boldsymbol{E}^{-1} + \boldsymbol{E}\dot{\boldsymbol{R}}\boldsymbol{R}^{-1}\boldsymbol{E}^{-1} \tag{15.7}$$

In the following, we shall use configurations (κ) such that the chosen director triad always keeps the same orientation with respect to the fixed axes (isoclinic configurations). Thus we introduce only hidden variables which are internal. The derived expressions can easily be carried over to any released configuration simply by replacing the time derivatives of the tensors with respect to fixed axes by time derivatives taken in the motion with respect to the director triad[3,4,5].

15.5 Application of Thermodynamics using Isoclinic Released Configurations

The thermodynamic state of the material element will be defined by

- $\boldsymbol{\Delta}_e$: Green strain tensor in the transformation (κ) → (a) or equivalently $\boldsymbol{C}_e = \mathbf{1} + 2\boldsymbol{\Delta}_e$.
- θ: absolute temperature.
- $\boldsymbol{\alpha}_j$: scalar or tensor internal hidden variables†.

We can also take as variables θ, $\boldsymbol{\alpha}_j$ and

- $\boldsymbol{\Pi}$: Kirchhoff stress tensor with respect to the configuration (κ) related to the Cauchy stress tensor $\boldsymbol{\sigma}$ by

$$\boldsymbol{\Pi} = (\det \boldsymbol{E})\boldsymbol{E}^{-1}\boldsymbol{\sigma}\boldsymbol{E}^{(-1)\mathrm{T}}$$

The first term in inequality 15.3, the power of the stresses per unit mass, can then be written (bracket denoting the trace)

$$\mathscr{P} = \left[\frac{\boldsymbol{\Pi}}{\rho_\kappa}\boldsymbol{E}^{\mathrm{T}}\mathscr{D}\boldsymbol{E}\right] = \left[\frac{\boldsymbol{\Pi}}{\rho_\kappa}\boldsymbol{E}^{\mathrm{T}}\dot{\boldsymbol{E}}\right] + \left[\frac{\boldsymbol{\Pi}}{\rho_\kappa}\boldsymbol{E}^{\mathrm{T}}\boldsymbol{E}\boldsymbol{V}_P\right]$$

† For arbitrary released configurations deduced from the isoclinic configurations by the orthogonal transformation $\xi' = \boldsymbol{\beta}(t)\xi$ then the orientation variable $\boldsymbol{\beta}$ must be added to the state variables $\boldsymbol{\alpha}_j$. The passage from one director triad to another director triad corresponds to the case when $\boldsymbol{\beta} = g(\boldsymbol{\alpha}_j)$.

or
$$\mathscr{P} = \left[\frac{\boldsymbol{\Pi}}{\rho_\kappa}\dot{\boldsymbol{\Delta}}_e\right] + \left[\frac{\boldsymbol{\Pi}}{\rho_\kappa}\boldsymbol{C}_e\boldsymbol{V}_P\right] \tag{15.8}$$

Expressing φ with the variables $\boldsymbol{\Delta}_e$, θ, $\boldsymbol{\alpha}_j$ the inequality can be written as

$$D = \left[\left(\frac{\boldsymbol{\Pi}}{\rho_\kappa} - \frac{\partial\varphi}{\partial\boldsymbol{\Delta}_e}\right)\dot{\boldsymbol{\Delta}}_e\right] - \left(\frac{\partial\varphi}{\partial\theta} + s\right)\dot{\theta} + \left[\frac{\boldsymbol{\Pi}}{\rho_\kappa}\boldsymbol{C}_e\boldsymbol{V}_P - \frac{\partial\varphi}{\partial\boldsymbol{\alpha}_k}\dot{\boldsymbol{\alpha}}_k^{\mathrm{T}}\right] - \frac{\boldsymbol{q}}{\rho\theta}\,\mathrm{grad}\,\theta \geqslant 0 \tag{15.9}$$

In agreement with our definition of the state we shall admit that φ, $\boldsymbol{\Pi}$, s as well as the rates of variation $\boldsymbol{V}_P$, $\dot{\boldsymbol{\alpha}}_k$ do not depend on grad θ†. We can then assume grad $\theta = 0$ from which follows the inequality, called the intrinsic dissipated power inequality

$$\psi = \left[\left(\frac{\boldsymbol{\Pi}}{\rho_\kappa} - \frac{\partial\varphi}{\partial\boldsymbol{\Delta}_e}\right)\dot{\boldsymbol{\Delta}}_e\right] - \left(\frac{\partial\varphi}{\partial\theta} + j\right)\dot{\theta} + \left[\frac{\boldsymbol{\Pi}}{\rho_\kappa}\boldsymbol{C}_e\boldsymbol{V}_P\right] - \left[\frac{\partial\varphi}{\partial\boldsymbol{\alpha}_k}\dot{\boldsymbol{\alpha}}_k^{\mathrm{T}}\right] \geqslant 0 \tag{15.10}$$

To make use of this inequality, let us consider instantaneous deformation and temperature change ($\dot{\boldsymbol{\Delta}}_e$, $\dot{\theta}$ infinite). As a result of the choice of the internal variables (see section 15.3.3) there is no instantaneous change of $\boldsymbol{\alpha}_k$ ($\dot{\boldsymbol{\alpha}}_k$ remains finite), at least if the loading point does not reach the hereafter defined boundary of instantaneous plasticity, and in this case $\boldsymbol{V}_P$ also remains finite since there are no instantaneous permanent deformations. The first two terms only of ψ must then be considered.

First case: There are no instantaneous permanent deformations and the six components of the instantaneous elastic deformations are arbitrary in sign and magnitude. The inequality then requires

$$\frac{\boldsymbol{\Pi}}{\rho_\kappa} = \frac{\partial\varphi}{\partial\boldsymbol{\Delta}_e} \tag{15.11}$$

$$s = -\frac{\partial\varphi}{\partial\theta} \tag{15.12}$$

and it remains

$$\psi = \left[\frac{\boldsymbol{\Pi}}{\rho_\kappa}\boldsymbol{C}_e\boldsymbol{V}_P - \frac{\partial\varphi}{\partial\boldsymbol{\alpha}_k}\dot{\boldsymbol{\alpha}}_k^{\mathrm{T}}\right] \geqslant 0 \tag{15.13}$$

Second case: There are no instantaneous permanent deformations but the

† We could have added $\boldsymbol{g} = \mathrm{grad}\,\theta$ to the state variables. The term $-[(\partial\varphi/\partial\boldsymbol{g})\dot{\boldsymbol{g}}]$ must then be added to $\boldsymbol{D}$, giving to $\dot{\boldsymbol{g}}$ arbitrary values, it can be proved that this term vanishes if $\boldsymbol{\Pi}$, s, $\boldsymbol{V}_P$ and $\dot{\boldsymbol{\alpha}}_k$ are independent of $\dot{\boldsymbol{g}}$. Later in the first case of the discussion the relations 15.11 and 15.12 are derived, showing that $\boldsymbol{\Pi}$ and s do not depend on $\boldsymbol{g}$. In the second case similar results hold by duality. But inequality 15.13 can be derived only if we assume that $\boldsymbol{V}_P$ and $\dot{\boldsymbol{\alpha}}_k$ are independent of $\boldsymbol{g}$.

instantaneous elastic deformations are restricted by internal constraints (incompressibility, for example) or by the viscosity. If there exist between the instantaneous deformations $n \leqslant 6$ constraints of the form

$$r_{ij}^{(k)} \Delta_{ij}^{e} = 0$$

then instead of equation 15.11, we obtain with Lagrange multipliers $\lambda^{(k)}$

$$\frac{\mathbf{\Pi}}{\rho_\kappa} = \frac{\partial \varphi}{\partial \mathbf{\Delta}_e} + \lambda^{(k)} r^{(k)} \tag{15.14}$$

equations 15.12 and 15.13 remaining unchanged.

Instead of the free energy we can also introduce the partial Legendre transform

$$\overset{*}{\varphi} = \left[\frac{\mathbf{\Pi}\mathbf{\Delta}_e}{\rho_\kappa}\right] - \varphi$$

(which is minus the free enthalpy) expressed as a function of the variables $\mathbf{\Pi}$, θ, α_j. We obtain

$$\psi = \left[\left(\frac{\partial \overset{*}{\varphi}}{\partial(\mathbf{\Pi}/\rho_\kappa)} - \mathbf{\Delta}_e\right)\frac{\mathrm{d}}{\mathrm{d}t}\left(\frac{\mathbf{\Pi}}{\rho_\kappa}\right)\right] + \left(\frac{\partial \overset{*}{\varphi}}{\partial \theta} - j\right)\dot{\theta} + \left[\frac{\partial \overset{*}{\varphi}}{\partial \boldsymbol{\alpha}_k} \dot{\boldsymbol{\alpha}}_k^{\mathrm{T}}\right] + \left[\frac{\mathbf{\Pi}}{\rho_\kappa} \boldsymbol{C}_e V_P\right]$$

But arbitrary instantaneous variations can be imposed on $\mathbf{\Pi}$ and θ (principle of nonduality). It follows that we always have[6]

$$\mathbf{\Delta}_e = \frac{\partial \overset{*}{\varphi}}{\partial(\mathbf{\Pi}/\rho_\kappa)} = \rho_\kappa \frac{\partial \overset{*}{\varphi}}{\partial \mathbf{\Pi}} \tag{15.15}$$

and two other relations which are the same as equations 15.12 and 15.13 according to

$$\frac{\partial \overset{*}{\varphi}}{\partial \theta} = -\frac{\partial \varphi}{\partial \theta} \qquad \frac{\partial \overset{*}{\varphi}}{\partial \boldsymbol{\alpha}_k} = -\frac{\partial \varphi}{\partial \boldsymbol{\alpha}_k}$$

Third case: There are instantaneous permanent deformations. They occur when the loading point $\mathbf{\Pi}, \theta$ (or $\mathbf{\Delta}_e, \theta$) reaches a hypersurface F

$$f(\mathbf{\Pi}, \theta, \alpha_j) = 0$$

which will be called the boundary of instantaneous plasticity. But, since these instantaneous permanent deformations vanish as long as the loading point does not lie on this surface, it is sufficient to remain beside this boundary to be taken back to the preceding cases. $\mathbf{\Pi}$ and s being continous functions of the state variables, the relations 15.11 (or 15.14, 15.15) and 15.12 remain valid and so does 15.13. The only point to be noted is that in inequality 15.13, V_P and $\dot{\boldsymbol{\alpha}}_k$ do not have the same expression on and beside the boundary.

Indeed we have[3,4,5]

$$\begin{aligned} \boldsymbol{V_P} &= \boldsymbol{A}(\boldsymbol{\Pi}, \theta, \boldsymbol{\alpha}_j) + \lambda \boldsymbol{B}(\boldsymbol{\Pi}, \theta, \boldsymbol{\alpha}_j) \\ \dot{\boldsymbol{\alpha}}_k &= \boldsymbol{h}_k(\boldsymbol{\Pi}, \theta, \boldsymbol{\alpha}_j) + \lambda \boldsymbol{l}_k(\boldsymbol{\Pi}, \theta, \boldsymbol{\alpha}_j) \end{aligned} \tag{15.16}$$

with
$$\lambda = \left[\frac{\partial f}{\partial \boldsymbol{\Pi}} \dot{\boldsymbol{\Pi}}\right] + \frac{\partial f}{\partial \theta}\dot{\theta} + \left[\frac{\partial f}{\partial \boldsymbol{\alpha}_k} \boldsymbol{h}_k^{\mathrm{T}}\right]$$

if $f(\boldsymbol{\Pi}, \theta, \boldsymbol{\alpha}_j) = 0$ and $\lambda \geqslant 0$, while the terms in λ vanish if $f < 0$ or $\lambda < 0$.

Let us now go back to expression 15.8 of the power of the stresses. The first term on the right-hand side

$$\mathscr{P}_1 = \left[\frac{\boldsymbol{\Pi}\dot{\boldsymbol{\Delta}}_e}{\rho_\kappa}\right] = \left[\frac{\boldsymbol{\sigma}\dot{\boldsymbol{E}}\boldsymbol{E}^{-1}}{\rho}\right] \tag{15.17}$$

is in all cases, according to equation 15.14, equal to $[\partial\varphi/\partial\boldsymbol{\Delta}_e)\dot{\boldsymbol{\Delta}}_e]$, that is, to the rate of change of the free energy due to the change in $\boldsymbol{\Delta}_e$.

The second term

$$\mathscr{P}_2 = \left[\frac{\boldsymbol{\Pi}}{\rho_\kappa}\boldsymbol{C}_e\boldsymbol{V}_P\right]$$

is, from equation 15.13, equal to

$$\mathscr{P}_2 = \psi + \left[\frac{\partial\varphi}{\partial\boldsymbol{\alpha}_k}\dot{\boldsymbol{\alpha}}_k^{\mathrm{T}}\right] \tag{15.18}$$

It must be noted that $\mathscr{P}_1$ and $\mathscr{P}_2$ do depend on the director triad chosen (except in the case where there is isotropy in the released configurations)†. Indeed the elastic transformation rate $\dot{\boldsymbol{E}}\boldsymbol{E}^{-1}$ in $\mathscr{P}_1$ and the inelastic transformation rate $\boldsymbol{V_P}$ in $\mathscr{P}_2$ are different for two frames rotating with respect to one another‡.

If $\boldsymbol{\omega}_{21}$ denotes the rate of rotation of the second triad with respect to the first one, we have

$$\boldsymbol{V}_P^{(1)} = \boldsymbol{V}_P^{(2)} + \boldsymbol{\omega}_{21}$$

hence
$$\mathscr{P}_2^{(1)} = \mathscr{P}_2^{(2)} + 2\,\mathrm{tr}\left(\frac{\boldsymbol{\Pi}}{\rho_\kappa}\boldsymbol{\Delta}_e\boldsymbol{\omega}_{21}\right)$$

So, the values of $\mathscr{P}_2$ are different in the two frames. However the relative

† In this case $\boldsymbol{\sigma}$ is an isotropic function of $\boldsymbol{E}\boldsymbol{E}^{\mathrm{T}}$, and $\boldsymbol{E}^{-1}\boldsymbol{\sigma}\boldsymbol{E}$ is symmetric, so $\mathrm{tr}(\boldsymbol{\sigma}\boldsymbol{E}\dot{\boldsymbol{R}}\boldsymbol{R}^{-1}\boldsymbol{E}^{-1}) = 0$ which shows that from equation 15.7, $\mathscr{P}_1$ is independent of the director triad chosen.

‡ It can also be noted that the rate of change $\dot{\boldsymbol{\alpha}}$ and the expression for φ are modified. When going from one frame to another through the orthogonal transformation $\boldsymbol{\xi}' = \boldsymbol{\beta}\boldsymbol{\xi}$, the matrix of the tensors become $\boldsymbol{\Delta}' = \boldsymbol{\beta}\boldsymbol{\Delta}\boldsymbol{\beta}^{\mathrm{T}}$, $\boldsymbol{\alpha}' = \boldsymbol{\beta}\boldsymbol{\alpha}\boldsymbol{\beta}^{\mathrm{T}}$ (if the $\boldsymbol{\alpha}_k$ are second-order tensors) from which follows

$$\varphi'(\boldsymbol{\Delta}', \theta, \boldsymbol{\alpha}_j') = \varphi(\boldsymbol{\beta}^{\mathrm{T}}\boldsymbol{\Delta}'\boldsymbol{\beta}, \theta, \boldsymbol{\beta}^{\mathrm{T}}\boldsymbol{\alpha}'\boldsymbol{\beta})$$

difference of these two values is only of the order of $\boldsymbol{\Delta}_e$ when ω_{21} is of the order of V_P.

Let us assume that, with respect to a certain director triad φ can be written in the form

$$\varphi(\boldsymbol{\Delta}_e, \theta, \boldsymbol{\alpha}_j) = \varphi_1(\boldsymbol{\Delta}_e, \theta) + \varphi_2(\theta, \boldsymbol{\alpha}_j) \tag{15.19}$$

$\varphi_1(\boldsymbol{\Delta}_e, \theta)$ is the free energy which can be instantaneously recovered by unloading, φ_2 is the frozen (for a while, or for ever) energy, corresponding to the dislocations, the residual stresses, etc. This assumption means that, with respect to this particular director triad, the instantaneous elastic moduli are independent of the hardening and more generally of the internal state in the released configuration. A triad which is attached to the atomic lattice is, for a monocrystal, such a special director triad. It can be admitted, at least as an approximation, that there also exists such a triad for a polycrystal. With this preferred director triad, $\mathscr{P}_1$ and $\mathscr{P}_2$ both have a definite physical meaning: $\mathscr{P}_1$ is the rate of increase of the free energy which can be instantaneously recovered; $\mathscr{P}_2$, the power developed in the inelastic (plastic and viscoelastic) transformation, is the sum of the intrinsic dissipated power and of the rate of variation (at constant θ) of the frozen energy.

In the general case, there is in the function φ a coupling between $\boldsymbol{\Delta}_e$ and $\boldsymbol{\alpha}_j$, whatever director triad is used. The rate of variation of the *frozen* energy (which subsists in the released configuration) is, at constant θ

$$\left[\frac{\partial \varphi}{\partial \boldsymbol{\alpha}_k}(0, \theta, \boldsymbol{\alpha}_k)\dot{\boldsymbol{\alpha}}_k^{\mathrm{T}}\right]$$

and no $[\partial\varphi/\partial\boldsymbol{\alpha}_k(\boldsymbol{\Delta}_e, \theta, \boldsymbol{\alpha}_k)\dot{\boldsymbol{\alpha}}_k^{\mathrm{T}}]$ term which appears in $\mathscr{P}_2$. The rate of variation of the recoverable free energy is, at constant θ

$$\left[\frac{\partial \varphi}{\partial \boldsymbol{\Delta}_e}(\boldsymbol{\Delta}_e, \theta, \boldsymbol{\alpha}_k)\dot{\boldsymbol{\Delta}}_e\right] + \left[\left(\frac{\partial \varphi}{\partial \boldsymbol{\alpha}_k}(\boldsymbol{\Delta}_e, \theta, \boldsymbol{\alpha}_k) - \frac{\partial \varphi}{\partial \boldsymbol{\alpha}_k}(0, \theta, \boldsymbol{\alpha}_k)\right)\dot{\boldsymbol{\alpha}}_k^{\mathrm{T}}\right]$$

which is different from $\mathscr{P}_1$ (which is only its first term).

15.6 Formulation in Lagrangian Variables

We assume φ to be a function of $\boldsymbol{C}_0 = \boldsymbol{F}^{\mathrm{T}}\boldsymbol{F} = \mathbf{1} + 2\boldsymbol{\Delta}_0$ and of certain hidden variables. The problem lies in the choice of these variables. It has been proposed to take as hidden variables the right Cauchy–Green tensor of the plastic deformation $\boldsymbol{C}_P = \boldsymbol{P}^{\mathrm{T}}\boldsymbol{P} = \mathbf{1} + 2\boldsymbol{\Delta}_P$ and one or several scalar variables. In fact the only tensorial parameter $\boldsymbol{C}_P$ is not sufficient, at least for anisotropic plastic materials. From section 15.5 when using arbitrary released configurations, φ is a function of the variables $\boldsymbol{C}_e$, θ, $\boldsymbol{\alpha}_j$ and of the orientation variable $\boldsymbol{\beta}$ which characterises the orientation of the director triad with respect to the fixed axes. Because

$$\boldsymbol{C}_e = \boldsymbol{E}^{\mathrm{T}}\boldsymbol{E} = \boldsymbol{P}^{\mathrm{T}-1}\boldsymbol{C}_0\boldsymbol{P}^{-1} \tag{15.20}$$

φ is in general a function of $\boldsymbol{C}_0, \boldsymbol{P}, \theta, \boldsymbol{a}_j$ (which are the tensors $\boldsymbol{\alpha}_j$ transported in the fixed configuration (0)) and $\boldsymbol{\beta}$. If $\boldsymbol{\beta}$ does not appear (as happens in the case of isotropy in the released configurations), or if $\boldsymbol{\beta}$ is related to $\boldsymbol{P}$ (as happens when the deformation of the macroelement is homogeneous, for viscoelastic simple materials) the application of the principle of objectivity enables us to replace $\boldsymbol{P}$ by its symmetric part $\boldsymbol{L}$ in the polar decomposition $\boldsymbol{P} = \boldsymbol{RL}$ ($\boldsymbol{R}$ being a proper orthogonal tensor), or by $\boldsymbol{C}_P = \boldsymbol{L}^2$.

But, and this is the point we stressed in references 4 and 5, in the case of plastic deformations, $\boldsymbol{\beta}$ is not related to $\boldsymbol{P}$, because these deformations result from discontinuities of the displacements and rotations between micro-elements, the reunion of which constitutes the macroelement. The example of the monocrystal which deforms by slipping along some atomic planes shows that clearly. The rotation of the crystals differs from that of the lattice (director triad). In this case the application of the principle of objectivity (we replace the position vector ξ in the released configuration by $\xi' = \boldsymbol{Q}\xi$, $\boldsymbol{Q}$ being a proper orthogonal tensor, and then we choose $\boldsymbol{Q} = \boldsymbol{\beta}^{\mathrm{T}}$) only reduces the function $\varphi(\boldsymbol{\Delta}_0, \boldsymbol{P}, \theta, \boldsymbol{a}_j, \boldsymbol{\beta})$ to the form

$$\varphi_0(\boldsymbol{\Delta}_0, \hat{\boldsymbol{P}}, \theta, \boldsymbol{a}_j) \qquad \text{where} \qquad \hat{\boldsymbol{P}} = \boldsymbol{\beta}^{\mathrm{T}}\boldsymbol{P} \tag{15.21}$$

the tensors $\boldsymbol{\Delta}_0$ and $\boldsymbol{a}_j$, referring to the fixed configuration, are not changed. $\hat{\boldsymbol{P}} = \boldsymbol{\beta}^{\mathrm{T}}\boldsymbol{P}$ is the gradient of the plastic transformation defined by keeping fixed the orientation of the director triad.

In the following, we shall use this reduced form, that is, we shall assume that the orientation of the director triad is kept fixed ($\boldsymbol{\beta} = \mathbf{1}$) in the plastic transformation, or more generally the inelastic transformation.

$\boldsymbol{\Pi}_0$ denoting the Kirchhoff stress tensor with respect to the fixed configuration (0), the dissipated power is now

$$\begin{aligned}\psi &= \left[\frac{\boldsymbol{\Pi}_0\boldsymbol{\Delta}_0}{\rho_0}\right] - (\dot{\varphi}_0 + s\dot{\theta}) \\ &= \left[\left(\frac{\boldsymbol{\Pi}_0}{\rho_0} - \frac{\partial\varphi_0}{\partial\boldsymbol{\Delta}_0}\right)\dot{\boldsymbol{\Delta}}_0\right] - \left(\frac{\partial\varphi_0}{\partial\theta} + s\right)\dot{\theta} - \left[\frac{\partial\varphi_0}{\partial\hat{\boldsymbol{P}}}\dot{\hat{\boldsymbol{P}}}^{\mathrm{T}} + \frac{\partial\varphi_0}{\partial\boldsymbol{a}_k}\dot{\boldsymbol{a}}_k^{\mathrm{T}}\right] \geqslant 0\end{aligned} \tag{15.22}$$

We also have

$$\psi = \dot{\overset{*}{\varphi}}_0 - s\dot{\theta} - \left[\frac{\dot{\boldsymbol{\Pi}}_0\boldsymbol{\Delta}_0}{\rho_0}\right]$$

where $$\overset{*}{\varphi}_0 = \left[\frac{\mathbf{\Pi}_0 \mathbf{\Delta}_0}{\rho_0}\right] - \varphi_0 \tag{15.23}$$

The argument of section 15.5 leads to the following results

$$\frac{\mathbf{\Pi}_0}{\rho_0} = \frac{\partial \varphi_0}{\partial \mathbf{\Delta}_0} \tag{15.24}$$

or more generally

$$\frac{\mathbf{\Pi}_0}{\rho_0} = \frac{\partial \varphi_0}{\partial \mathbf{\Delta}_0} + \lambda^{(k)} \boldsymbol{r}_0^{(k)}$$

or $$\mathbf{\Delta}_0 = \rho_0 \frac{\partial \overset{*}{\varphi}_0}{\partial \mathbf{\Pi}_0} \tag{15.25}$$

$$s = -\frac{\partial \varphi_0}{\partial \theta} \tag{15.26}$$

$$\psi = -\left[\frac{\partial \varphi_0}{\partial \hat{\boldsymbol{P}}} \dot{\hat{\boldsymbol{P}}}^{\mathrm{T}}\right] - \left[\frac{\partial \varphi_0}{\partial \boldsymbol{a}_k} \dot{\boldsymbol{a}}_k^{\mathrm{T}}\right] \geqslant 0 \tag{15.27}$$

Equation 15.22 shows that in a relaxation process ($\dot{\mathbf{\Delta}}_0 = \theta = 0$) the free energy cannot increase.

If φ is expressed by means of the tensors $\boldsymbol{\alpha}_k$ taken in the released configuration, that is

$$\varphi_0'(\mathbf{\Delta}_0, \hat{\boldsymbol{P}}, \theta, \boldsymbol{\alpha}_k)$$

the relations 15.24 to 15.27 remain valid if φ_0 and $\dot{\boldsymbol{a}}_k$ are replaced by φ_0' and $\dot{\boldsymbol{\alpha}}_k$ (but if the $\boldsymbol{a}_k$ and $\boldsymbol{\alpha}_k$ are tensors, each of the terms in 15.27 are changed)†.

When φ is expressed with the tensors $\boldsymbol{\alpha}_k$, the term

$$-\left[\frac{\partial \varphi_0'}{\partial \hat{\boldsymbol{P}}} \dot{\hat{\boldsymbol{P}}}^{\mathrm{T}}\right]$$

represents, as will be shown later, the power developed in the inelastic transformation.

15.6.1 Isotropy in the released configurations

Isotropy implies the following conditions[3,4]. The orientation $\boldsymbol{\beta}$ of the director triad does not appear in φ. The variables $\boldsymbol{\alpha}_k$ are isotropic tensors (of even order). The function $\varphi(\boldsymbol{C}_e, \theta, \boldsymbol{\alpha}_j)$ is an isotropic function of $\boldsymbol{C}_e$ and $\boldsymbol{\alpha}_j$ (this expresses the objectivity) and then of $\boldsymbol{C}_e$ only.

But $$\boldsymbol{C}_e = \boldsymbol{P}^{\mathrm{T}-1} \boldsymbol{C}_0 \boldsymbol{P}^{-1} = \boldsymbol{R} \boldsymbol{L}^{-1} \boldsymbol{C}_0 \boldsymbol{L}^{-1} \boldsymbol{R}^{\mathrm{T}}$$

† The time derivatives $\dot{\boldsymbol{\alpha}}_k$ in the motion with respect to the director triad do not correspond to the derivatives $\dot{\boldsymbol{a}}_k$ by the covariance rule.

($\boldsymbol{P} = \boldsymbol{RL}$, $\boldsymbol{R}$ being an orthogonal tensor). φ being an isotropic function of $\boldsymbol{C}_e$, $\boldsymbol{R}$ disappears. We thus obtain a function φ'_0 which is an isotropic function of $\boldsymbol{C}_0$, $\boldsymbol{L}$ (or $\boldsymbol{C}_P$), θ and $\boldsymbol{\alpha}_j$ (isotropic tensors). The latter may be replaced by the corresponding tensors $\boldsymbol{a}_k$ in the fixed configuration (replacing $\boldsymbol{P}$ by $\boldsymbol{QP}$, $\boldsymbol{Q}$ being orthogonal, $\boldsymbol{\alpha}_k$ being an isotropic tensor is not changed, and so $\boldsymbol{a}_k$ depends on $\boldsymbol{P}$ only through $\boldsymbol{L}$).

The form proposed for φ_0 (or φ'_0) in the framework of plasticity, by P. Perzyna and W. Wojno[7], P. Perzyna[8], is valid in this case of isotropy and only in this case†.

15.6.2 Verification of the agreement with the results of section 15.5

To make the notation simpler, we shall omit the ^ above $\boldsymbol{P}$.

Relations 15.11 and 15.24. We have

$$\frac{\boldsymbol{\Pi}_0}{\rho_0} = \boldsymbol{P}^{-1}\frac{\boldsymbol{\Pi}}{\rho_\kappa}\boldsymbol{P}^{\mathrm{T}-1} = 2\boldsymbol{P}^{-1}\frac{\partial\varphi}{\partial\boldsymbol{C}_e}\boldsymbol{P}^{\mathrm{T}-1}$$

According to equation 15.20, we get equation 15.24.

Relations 15.13 and 15.27 (the latter being expressed with the tensors $\boldsymbol{\alpha}_k$ in the intermediate configuration). We have

$$\varphi'_0(\boldsymbol{C}_0, \boldsymbol{P}, \theta, \boldsymbol{\alpha}_k) = \varphi(\boldsymbol{C}_e, \theta, \boldsymbol{\alpha}_k)$$

$$\frac{\partial\varphi'_0}{\partial P_{hk}} = \frac{\partial\varphi}{\partial C^e_{ij}}\frac{\partial C^e_{ij}}{\partial P_{hk}}$$

From equation 15.20 follows

$$\frac{\partial C^e_{ij}}{\partial P_{hk}} = -(C^e_{hi}P^{-1}_{kj} + C^e_{hj}P^{-1}_{ki})$$

hence
$$\frac{\partial\varphi'_0}{\partial\boldsymbol{P}} = -2\boldsymbol{C}_e\frac{\partial\varphi}{\partial\boldsymbol{C}_e}\boldsymbol{P}^{\mathrm{T}-1} \tag{15.28}$$

and as a consequence

$$-\left[\frac{\partial\varphi'_0}{\partial\boldsymbol{P}}\dot{\boldsymbol{P}}^{\mathrm{T}}\right] = \left[\boldsymbol{C}_e\frac{\boldsymbol{\Pi}}{\rho_\kappa}\boldsymbol{P}^{\mathrm{T}-1}\dot{\boldsymbol{P}}^{\mathrm{T}}\right] = \left[\frac{\boldsymbol{\Pi}}{\rho_\kappa}\boldsymbol{C}_e\boldsymbol{V}_P\right]$$

15.7 Another Presentation in Lagrangian Variables

We can put $\hat{\boldsymbol{P}}$ in the hidden variables $\boldsymbol{a}_k$. Relation 15.27 reduces then to

$$\psi = -\left[\frac{\partial\varphi_0}{\partial\boldsymbol{a}_k}\dot{\boldsymbol{a}}^{\mathrm{T}}_k\right] \quad \text{or} \quad -\left[\frac{\partial\varphi'_0}{\partial\boldsymbol{\alpha}_k}\dot{\boldsymbol{\alpha}}^{\mathrm{T}}_k\right] \tag{15.29}$$

† It is difficult to draw a conclusion from the form proposed by A. E. Green and P. M. Naghdi[9,10]. These authors introduce, under the name *plastic strain*, a tensorial parameter $\boldsymbol{E}''$ the clear definition of which we did not grasp. If $\boldsymbol{E}''$ (which is a symmetric tensor) is interpreted as being identical to $\boldsymbol{L} = (\boldsymbol{C}_P)^{1/2}$ the proposed theory is only valid in the case of isotropy.

forms which have been proposed by K. C. Valanis[11], P. Perzyna and W. Wojno[7], J. R. Rice[12].

Another way of interpreting this relation is the following. We assume that the internal variables are chosen in such a way that $\boldsymbol{P}$, or more precisely $\dot{\hat{\boldsymbol{P}}}$, is no longer an independent variable. It is not even necessary that we are able to define such variables. It is sufficient[12] that the infinitesimal change between time t and time $t+\mathrm{d}t$, that is, the rate of change, can be defined as a function of a finite number of parameters. For the sake of convenience, however, we shall represent, in the following, these parameters by the derivatives $\dot{\boldsymbol{a}}_k$ of the variables $\boldsymbol{a}_k$. With this point of view, we can write

$$\dot{\hat{\boldsymbol{P}}} = \boldsymbol{w}_0^{(k)} \dot{\boldsymbol{a}}_k{}^{\mathrm{T}} \tag{15.30}$$

$\hat{\boldsymbol{P}}$ is a functional of the history, the present value of which is an ordinary function of the $\boldsymbol{a}_k$. Deriving φ_0 and taking this fact into account

$$\frac{\mathrm{D}\varphi_0}{\mathrm{D}\boldsymbol{a}_k} = \frac{\partial \varphi_0}{\partial \boldsymbol{a}_k} + \frac{\partial \varphi_0}{\partial \boldsymbol{P}} \boldsymbol{w}_0^{\mathrm{T}(k)} \tag{15.31}$$

(T denotes the transpose on the indexes which are not satured by $\dot{\boldsymbol{a}}_k$).

$$\psi = -\frac{\mathrm{D}\varphi_0}{\mathrm{D}\boldsymbol{a}_k} \dot{\boldsymbol{a}}_k^{\mathrm{T}} = \frac{\mathrm{D}\overset{*}{\varphi}_0}{\mathrm{D}\boldsymbol{a}_k} \dot{\boldsymbol{a}}_k^{\mathrm{T}} \tag{15.32}$$

On the other hand the relation 15.25 when derived with respect to t gives

$$\dot{\boldsymbol{\Delta}}_0 = \rho_0 \left(\frac{\partial^2 \overset{*}{\varphi}_0}{\partial \boldsymbol{\Pi}_0 \partial \boldsymbol{\Pi}_0} \dot{\boldsymbol{\Pi}}_0 + \frac{\partial^2 \overset{*}{\varphi}_0}{\partial \boldsymbol{\Pi}_0 \partial \theta} \dot{\theta} \right) + \rho_0 \frac{\mathrm{D}^2 \overset{*}{\varphi}_0}{\mathrm{D}\boldsymbol{a}_k \partial \boldsymbol{\Pi}_0} \dot{\boldsymbol{a}}_k^{\mathrm{T}} \tag{15.33}$$

The first term in equation 15.33 defines a thermoelastic rate of deformation, the second one a plastic rate of deformation. This decomposition[12] based on an infinitesimal unloading instead of a global unloading does not coincide with the one we have used until now, when the free energy cannot be separated as in equation 15.19, that is, when the elastic properties depend on the hardening. Figure 15.2 shows the reason for that.

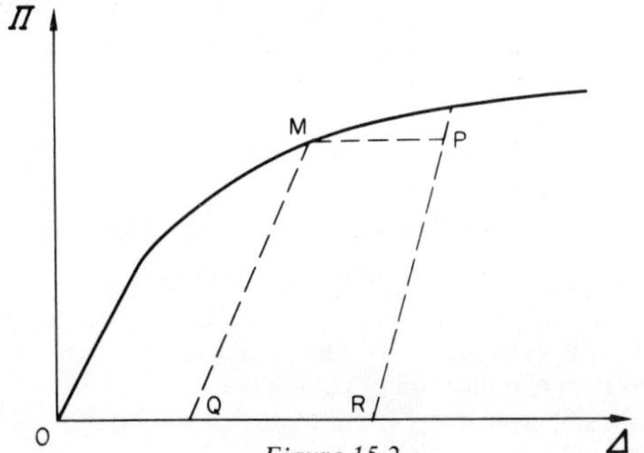

Figure 15.2

(The plastic variation of the deformation is measured by MP in infinitesimal unloading and by QR in global unloading). Rice's decomposition has the advantage that it is free of the notion of director triad. Furthermore it leads to an interesting relation for the plastic rate of deformation $\boldsymbol{D}_0^{\mathrm{pl}}$. Indeed defining

$$\boldsymbol{B}_k = \frac{\mathrm{D}\overset{*}{\varphi}_0}{\mathrm{D}\boldsymbol{a}_k} = -\frac{\mathrm{D}\varphi_0}{\mathrm{D}\boldsymbol{a}_k} \tag{15.34}$$

we obtain†

$$\boldsymbol{D}_0^{\mathrm{pl}} = \rho_0 \frac{\partial \boldsymbol{B}_k}{\partial \boldsymbol{\Pi}_0} \dot{\boldsymbol{a}}_k^{\mathrm{T}} \tag{15.35}$$

Denoting by $\boldsymbol{\Delta}_e$ the elastic strain tensor with respect to a director triad, the thermoelastic and plastic rate of deformation are now defined by (these rates being taken in the director frame)

$$\boldsymbol{D}_e = \dot{\boldsymbol{\Delta}}_e - \frac{\partial \boldsymbol{\Delta}_e}{\partial \boldsymbol{\alpha}_k} \dot{\boldsymbol{\alpha}}_k^{\mathrm{T}} \qquad \boldsymbol{D}^{\mathrm{pl}} = \{\boldsymbol{E}\boldsymbol{V}_P\boldsymbol{E}^{-1}\} + \frac{\partial \boldsymbol{\Delta}_e}{\partial \boldsymbol{\alpha}_k} \dot{\boldsymbol{\alpha}}_k^{\mathrm{T}}$$

where $\boldsymbol{\Delta}_e$, given by equation 15.15 is expressed as a function of $\boldsymbol{\Pi}$, θ, $\boldsymbol{\alpha}_k$. It can be seen that these rates are independent of the chosen director frame. The power developed by the stresses is decomposed in

$$
\begin{aligned}
{}'_1 &= \left[\frac{\boldsymbol{\Pi}}{\rho_\kappa} \boldsymbol{D}_e\right] = \left[\frac{\partial \varphi}{\partial \boldsymbol{\Delta}_e}\left(\dot{\boldsymbol{\Delta}}_e - \frac{\partial \boldsymbol{\Delta}_e}{\partial \boldsymbol{\alpha}_k} \dot{\boldsymbol{\alpha}}_k^{\mathrm{T}}\right)\right] \\
{}'_2 &= \left[\frac{\boldsymbol{\Pi}}{\rho_\kappa} \boldsymbol{D}_{\mathrm{pl}}\right] = \left[\left(\frac{\partial \varphi}{\partial \boldsymbol{\Delta}_e}\frac{\partial \boldsymbol{\Delta}_e}{\partial \boldsymbol{\alpha}_e} + \frac{\partial \varphi}{\partial \boldsymbol{\alpha}_k}\right)\dot{\boldsymbol{\alpha}}_k^{\mathrm{T}}\right] + \psi
\end{aligned}
$$

$\boldsymbol{B}_k$ and $\dot{\boldsymbol{a}}_k$ are functions of $\boldsymbol{\Pi}_0$, θ, and $\boldsymbol{a}_j$. Let us consider, as does Rice[12], the case where these variables are scalars.

J. R. Rice's hypothesis: $\dot{\boldsymbol{a}}_k$ depends on $\boldsymbol{\Pi}_0$ only through $\boldsymbol{B}_k$, the thermodynamic force associated with the variable $\boldsymbol{a}_k$.

If this condition is satisfied‡, then the expression $\dot{\boldsymbol{a}}_k \partial \boldsymbol{B}_k / \partial \boldsymbol{\Pi}_0 \, \mathrm{d}\boldsymbol{\Pi}_0$ is the differential at constant θ, $\boldsymbol{a}_j$ of a function $\Omega(\boldsymbol{\Pi}_0, \theta, \boldsymbol{a}_j)$. We can then write

$$\boldsymbol{D}_0^{\mathrm{pl}} = \rho_0 \frac{\partial \Omega}{\partial \boldsymbol{\Pi}_0} \tag{15.36}$$

Ω is the *viscoplastic potential* (which gives the classical plastic potential in the case of pure plasticity, that is, without viscosity).

† The symbols $\partial/\partial \boldsymbol{\Pi}$ and $\mathrm{D}/\mathrm{D}\boldsymbol{a}_k$ can be permuted. On the contrary $\mathrm{D}/\mathrm{D}\boldsymbol{a}_j$ and $\mathrm{D}/\mathrm{D}\boldsymbol{a}_k$ cannot be permuted. It follows in particular that $\boldsymbol{B}_k \, \mathrm{d}\boldsymbol{a}_k^{\mathrm{T}}$ is not a total differential and that $\boldsymbol{D}_0^{\mathrm{pl}}$ is not the time derivative of a function of $\boldsymbol{\Pi}_0, \theta, \boldsymbol{a}_j$.

‡ This condition is not sufficient if the $\boldsymbol{a}_k$ are tensors: for a given k, $\dot{\boldsymbol{a}}_k \, \mathrm{d}\boldsymbol{B}_k^{\mathrm{T}}$ must be a total differential at constant θ and $\boldsymbol{a}_j$.

Relation 15.33 also has interesting consequences for the propagation of *ordinary* waves. Let us consider an acceleration wave.

(1) If the material cannot present instantaneous irreversible deformations $[\dot{\boldsymbol{a}}_k] = 0$ (the bracket denoting here the jump of a quantity across the surface of discontinuity), then equation 15.33 shows that the instantaneous behaviour is the behaviour of a hyperelastic material. The number of waves and their velocity depend on the instantaneous elasticity, which can be complete or restricted (see section 15.5, second case). If n is the rank of the 6×6 matrix of the instantaneous compliances, it can be shown[13] that provided the corresponding eigenvalues of the acoustic tensor are positive the number of possible waves is equal to $(n-3)$ (zero if $n \leqslant 3$), except from some particular directions of the normal to the wave surface. The corresponding eigenvectors are orthogonal to one another.

(a) The material is a definite conductor ($\boldsymbol{q} \cdot \operatorname{grad} \theta < 0$ if $\operatorname{grad} \dot{\theta} \neq 0$) instantaneous irreversible deformations under the following (sufficient) conditions.

(a) The material is a definite conductor ($\boldsymbol{a} \cdot \operatorname{grad} \theta < 0$ if $\operatorname{grad} \theta \neq 0$) from which it follows that the wave is homothermal $[\dot{\theta}] = 0$.

(b) There exists a plastic potential

$$\boldsymbol{D}_0^{\mathrm{pl}} = g\lambda \frac{\partial f}{\partial \boldsymbol{\Pi}_0}$$

$f(\boldsymbol{\Pi}_0, \theta, \hat{\boldsymbol{P}}, \boldsymbol{\alpha}_j)$ denotes the function f of section 15.5, h is a scalar and λ, the loading rate, is a scalar defined by

$$\lambda = \operatorname{tr}\left(\frac{\partial f}{\partial \boldsymbol{\Pi}_0} \dot{\boldsymbol{\Pi}}_0 + \frac{\partial f}{\partial \theta} \dot{\theta} + \frac{\partial f}{\partial \hat{\boldsymbol{P}}} \dot{\hat{\boldsymbol{P}}}^{\mathrm{T}} A^{\mathrm{T}} + \frac{\partial f}{\partial \boldsymbol{\alpha}_k} \boldsymbol{h}_k^{\mathrm{T}}\right)$$

which gives

$$[\lambda] = \frac{\partial f}{\partial \boldsymbol{\Pi}_0} [\dot{\boldsymbol{\Pi}}_0]$$

$$[\boldsymbol{D}_0^{\mathrm{pl}}] = g \frac{\partial f}{\partial \boldsymbol{\Pi}_0} \operatorname{tr}\left(\frac{\partial f}{\partial \boldsymbol{\Pi}_0} [\dot{\boldsymbol{\Pi}}_0]\right)$$

The matrix

$$g \frac{\partial f}{\partial \boldsymbol{\Pi}_0} \otimes \frac{\partial f}{\partial \boldsymbol{\Pi}_0}$$

is symmetric like the elastic matrix

$$\rho_0 \frac{\partial^2 \overset{*}{\varphi}_0}{\partial \boldsymbol{\Pi}_0} \partial \boldsymbol{\Pi}_0$$

from which follows the announced result (which has been proved in reference 6 by using the functional representation). Furthermore if $g > 0$ and more generally if

$$g^{-1} + \mathrm{tr}\left(\frac{\partial f}{\partial \mathbf{\Pi}_0} \mathbf{\Lambda} \frac{\partial f}{\partial \mathbf{\Pi}_0}\right) > 0$$

$\mathbf{\Lambda}$ denoting the matrix of the elastic moduli (stiffness), the velocity of the plastic waves is smaller than or equal to the velocity of the elastic wave of the same order[6]. These results do not assume infinitesimal deformations.

15.8 Formulation in Functional Representation

From the principle of objectivity, the state is defined by the history of the variables $\boldsymbol{C}_0(\tau)$ (the right Cauchy–Green tensor with respect to a fixed reference configuration) or $\mathbf{\Pi}_0(\tau)$ (the Kirchhoff stress tensor) and $\theta(\tau)$ for $-\infty < \tau \leqslant t$. We do not need here to introduce the decomposition of the transformation and the rotation of the director triad (the hidden variable of orientation $\boldsymbol{\beta}$), just as we do not introduce the internal hidden variables, all these variables being determined by the history.

$\mathbf{\Pi}_0$ and the free energy φ are functionals of $\boldsymbol{C}_0(\tau)$, $\theta(\tau)$ which may depend on the present values $\boldsymbol{C}_0(t)$, $\theta(t)$ and eventually on their time derivative $\dot{\boldsymbol{C}}_0(t)$, $\ddot{\boldsymbol{C}}_0(t)\ldots$ (as far as $\mathbf{\Pi}_0$ is concerned). $\boldsymbol{C}_0$ and the opposite of the enthalpy

$$\overset{*}{\varphi} = \left[\frac{\mathbf{\Pi}_0 \mathbf{\Delta}_0}{\rho_0}\right] - \varphi$$

are functionals of $\mathbf{\Pi}_0(\tau)$, $\theta(\tau)$ which can depend on the present values $\mathbf{\Pi}_0(t)$, $\theta(t)$ but not on their time derivatives (principle of nonduality). The following differentiability assumption is made on these functionals which are ordinary functions of the present values.

The functional

$$y(t) = \mathscr{F}(x(\tau), x(t)), \; -\infty < \tau < t$$

in which we have separated the past history and the present values $x(t)$, can be derived with respect to the present values of which they are function and with respect to time, in the following way

$$\dot{y} = \frac{\partial \mathscr{F}}{\partial x(t)} \dot{x}(t) + \dot{\mathscr{F}}_x \tag{15.37}$$

$\dot{\mathscr{F}}_x$ is the rate of change of y when x is kept constant after time t (that is, $\dot{x}(t+) = 0$, figure 15.3).

However, in the case of instantaneous plastic deformations, the partial derivatives at a regular point of the boundary of instantaneous plasticity $\boldsymbol{F}$

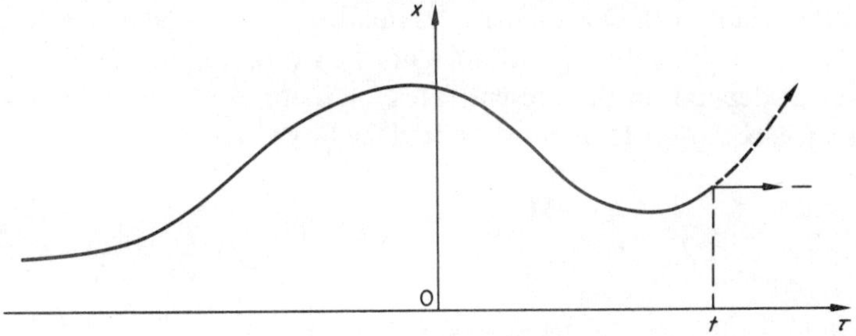

Figure 15.3

can take two different values (and even more at a conical point) according to whether the point moves inward from the boundary or remains on it. The index — will denote the derivatives taken inwards. They are the derivatives obtained by assuming the mechanisms which are responsible for the instantaneous deformations to be frozen, that is, by taking $\lambda = 0$ in the relations 15.16.

Now, the inequality of the intrinsic dissipated power

$$\psi = \left[\frac{\mathbf{\Pi}_0 \dot{\mathbf{\Delta}}_0}{\rho_0}\right] - (\dot{\varphi} + s\dot{\theta}) \geqslant 0 \tag{15.38}$$

is written, assuming that φ depends on the present values $\mathbf{\Pi}_0$, θ and on their first derivatives

$$\psi = \left[\left(\frac{\mathbf{\Pi}_0}{2\rho_0} - \frac{\partial \varphi}{\partial \boldsymbol{C}_0(t)}\right)\dot{\boldsymbol{C}}_0(t)\right] - \left(\frac{\partial \varphi}{\partial \theta(t)} + s\right)\dot{\theta}(t)$$
$$- \left[\frac{\partial \varphi}{\partial \dot{\boldsymbol{C}}_0} \ddot{\boldsymbol{C}}_0(t)\right] - \frac{\partial \varphi}{\partial \dot{\theta}} \ddot{\theta}(t) - \dot{\varphi}_{\boldsymbol{C}_0, \theta} \geqslant 0$$

It can be discussed in the same way as before.

First case: The loading point does not lie on the boundary $\boldsymbol{F}$, the stresses do not depend on the present rates $\dot{\boldsymbol{C}}_0^{(t)}$, $\dot{\theta}(t)$ and there are no constraints.

Giving $\ddot{\boldsymbol{C}}_0(t_+)$, $\ddot{\theta}_0(t_+)$ arbitrary values (of large magnitude and arbitrary sign), it can be seen that φ cannot depend on $\dot{\boldsymbol{C}}_0(t)$ and $\dot{\theta}_0(t)$ (the argument can be carried over to higher order derivatives). Giving then $\dot{\boldsymbol{C}}_0(t_+)$ and $\dot{\theta}(t_+)$ arbitrary values, we get

$$\frac{\mathbf{\Pi}_0}{\rho_0} = 2\frac{\partial \varphi}{\partial \boldsymbol{C}_0(t)} = \frac{\partial \varphi}{\partial \mathbf{\Delta}_0(t)} \tag{15.39}$$

$$s = -\frac{\partial \varphi}{\partial \theta(t)} \tag{15.40}$$

$$\psi = -\dot{\varphi}_{\boldsymbol{C}_0, \theta} \tag{15.41}$$

This is the result of B. D. Coleman[14] extended to viscoplastic bodies.

Second case: The loading point does not lie on the boundary $\boldsymbol{F}$ but either the stresses depend on the present rates, or there exist internal constraints. In this case, equation 15.39 must be replaced by

$$\frac{\boldsymbol{\Pi}}{\rho_0} = \frac{\partial \varphi}{\partial \boldsymbol{\Delta}_0(t)} + \lambda^{(k)} r_0^{(k)} \tag{15.42}$$

φ depending still only on the present values of $\boldsymbol{\Delta}_0(t)$, $\theta(t)$.

The functional $\overset{*}{\varphi}$ of $\boldsymbol{\Pi}_0(\tau)$, $\theta(\tau)$ can be introduced, which allows us to derive general relations. The inequality

$$\psi = \dot{\varphi}^* - s\dot{\theta} - \left[\frac{\dot{\boldsymbol{\Pi}}_0 \boldsymbol{\Delta}_0}{\rho_0}\right] \geqslant 0$$

then shows that $\overset{*}{\varphi}$ does not depend on the present values of the time derivatives of $\boldsymbol{\Pi}_0(t)$, $\theta(t)$ and that we always have[1,13]

$$\boldsymbol{\Delta}_0 = \rho_0 \frac{\partial \overset{*}{\varphi}}{\partial \boldsymbol{\Pi}_0(t)} \qquad s = \frac{\partial \overset{*}{\varphi}}{\partial \theta(t)} \qquad \psi = \dot{\overset{*}{\varphi}}_{\boldsymbol{\Pi}_0, \theta} \tag{15.43}$$

Third case: The loading point lies on the boundary. We only need to stay a little beside this boundary to be brought back to the preceding cases. But the derivatives to be used are the derivatives *taken inwards*[6], so that for example

$$\frac{\boldsymbol{\Pi}_0}{\rho_0} = \left(\frac{\partial \varphi}{\partial \boldsymbol{\Delta}_0(t)}\right)_- + \lambda^{(k)} r_0^{(k)}$$

or

$$\boldsymbol{\Delta}_0 = \rho_0 \left(\frac{\partial \overset{*}{\varphi}}{\partial \boldsymbol{\Pi}_0(t)}\right)_-$$

The parallelism with the results of sections 15.6 and 15.7 is obvious.

15.9 The Hypothesis of Normal Dissipativity

From equations 15.32 and 15.34 the intrinsic dissipated power is

$$\psi = [\boldsymbol{B}_k \dot{\boldsymbol{a}}_k^{\mathrm{T}}] \tag{15.44}$$

$\boldsymbol{B}_k = \mathrm{D}\overset{*}{\varphi}_0 / \mathrm{D}\boldsymbol{a}_k$ denotes the thermodynamic force associated with the variable $\boldsymbol{a}_k$. The hypothesis of normal dissipativity consists in assuming that the expression

$$[\dot{\boldsymbol{a}}_k \, \mathrm{d}\boldsymbol{B}_k^{\mathrm{T}}] = \mathrm{d}_\theta \Omega \tag{15.45}$$

is the differential at constant θ of a certain function Ω of $\boldsymbol{B}_i$ and θ.

When this hypothesis is satisfied, the laws of evolution for the internal variables are obtained as

$$\dot{\boldsymbol{a}}_k = \frac{\partial \Omega}{\partial \boldsymbol{B}_k} \tag{15.46}$$

As a consequence the two functions $\overset{*}{\varphi}_0(\boldsymbol{\Pi}_0, \theta, \boldsymbol{a}_k)$ and $\Omega(\boldsymbol{B}_i, \theta)$ completely determine (by equations 15.25 and 15.46) the evolution of the state of an element under imposed stresses and temperature θ as a function of time.

Instead of equation 15.46 we can also write

$$\boldsymbol{B}_i = \frac{\partial \overset{*}{\Omega}}{\partial \dot{\boldsymbol{a}}_i} \tag{15.47}$$

by introducing the function $\overset{*}{\Omega} = \dot{\boldsymbol{a}}_i \boldsymbol{B}_i - \Omega$ of $\dot{\boldsymbol{a}}_i$ and θ.

The inelastic rate of deformation defined by equation 15.35 is

$$\boldsymbol{D}_0^{\mathrm{pl}} = \rho_0 \dot{\boldsymbol{a}}_k \frac{\partial \boldsymbol{B}_k^{\mathrm{T}}}{\partial \boldsymbol{\Pi}_0} = \rho_0 \frac{\partial \Omega}{\partial \boldsymbol{\Pi}_0}$$

Thus we obtain the plastic potential of J. R. Rice (Ω is a function of $\boldsymbol{\Pi}_0$ and $\boldsymbol{a}_k$ through the $\boldsymbol{B}_i$).

Using as reference configurations, the isoclinic released configurations, the expression for ψ becomes

$$\psi = \left[\frac{\boldsymbol{\Pi}}{\rho_\kappa} \boldsymbol{C}_e \boldsymbol{V}_P\right] + \left[\boldsymbol{A}_k \dot{\boldsymbol{\alpha}}_k^{\mathrm{T}}\right] \tag{15.48}$$

where

$$\boldsymbol{A}_k = \frac{\partial \overset{*}{\varphi}}{\partial \boldsymbol{\alpha}_k} = -\frac{\partial \varphi}{\partial \boldsymbol{\alpha}_k}$$

The hypothesis of normal dissipativity then becomes, if we assume that the elastic deformations can be neglected ($\boldsymbol{C}_e = \mathbf{1}$)†,

$$\left[\boldsymbol{V}_P \, \mathrm{d}\left(\frac{\boldsymbol{\Pi}}{\rho_\kappa}\right)\right] + \left[\dot{\boldsymbol{\alpha}}_k \, \mathrm{d}\boldsymbol{A}_k^{\mathrm{T}}\right] = \mathrm{d}_\theta \Omega \tag{15.49}$$

Ω being now a function of $\boldsymbol{\Pi}/\rho_\kappa$, θ and the thermodynamic actions $\boldsymbol{A}_k$. From

† The choice of the director triad does not matter if $\boldsymbol{C}_e = \mathbf{1}$, because ψ contains only the symmetric part of $\boldsymbol{V}_P$, which is independent of this choice.

it we get

$$\{V_P\} = \left\{\frac{\partial\Omega}{\partial(\Pi/\rho_\kappa)}\right\}^\dagger \tag{15.50}$$

$$\dot{\alpha}_k = \frac{\partial\Omega}{\partial A_k} \tag{15.51}$$

Equation 15.51 is the evolution law for the internal variables which has been proposed by Q. S. Nguyen and B. Halphen[15]. It characterises the materials which they called 'generalised standard materials'. It enables us, if we admit that the potential Ω is convex with respect to Π, A_k, to carry over to these hardening materials, the classical general theorems, which have been established for perfectly plastic materials.

The agreement between equations 15.49 and 15.45 is easily proved, under a condition which will be given below, in the case where the variables are scalar (so that $a_k = \alpha_k$). From equation 15.30, we have

$$V_P = \hat{\dot{P}}\hat{P}^{-1} = w^{(k)}\dot{\alpha}_k \tag{15.52}$$

with

$$w^{(k)} = w_0^{(k)}\hat{P}^{-1}$$

From equations 15.31 and 15.28 (and using the fact that $\partial\varphi_0/\partial\alpha_k = \partial\varphi/\partial\alpha_k$, see section 15.6), we have

$$B_k = A_k + C_e\frac{\Pi}{\rho_\kappa}w^{(k)\mathrm{T}} \tag{15.53}$$

If $w^{(k)}$ is constant, then equation 15.45 gives equation 15.49. Let us notice that Ω being a function of B_i only, we have from equations 15.52, 15.51 and 15.53 and taking $C_e = 1$

$$V_P = w^{(k)}\frac{\partial\Omega}{\partial A_k} = w^{(k)}\frac{\partial\Omega}{\partial B_k} = \frac{\partial\Omega}{\partial(\Pi/\rho_\kappa)} \tag{15.54}$$

† In this relation, the derivative is taken at constant A_k and not at constant α_k. This result however is in agreement with J. R. Rice's result. Indeed let us substitute in Ω the variables α_k to the variables A_k. We have

$$\mathrm{d}A_k = \frac{\partial^2\overset{*}{\varphi}}{\partial\alpha_k\partial(\Pi/\rho_\kappa)}\mathrm{d}\left(\frac{\Pi}{\rho_\kappa}\right) + \frac{\partial^2\overset{*}{\varphi}}{\partial\alpha_k\partial\alpha_l}\mathrm{d}\alpha_l^{\mathrm{T}} = \frac{\partial\Delta_e}{\partial\alpha_k}\mathrm{d}\left(\frac{\Pi}{\rho_\kappa}\right) + \frac{\partial^2\overset{*}{\varphi}}{\partial\alpha_k\partial\alpha_l}\mathrm{d}\alpha_l^{\mathrm{T}}$$

Using the relation between V_P and D^{pl} (see section 15.7) equation 15.49 can then be written as

$$D^{\mathrm{pl}}\mathrm{d}\left(\frac{\Pi}{\rho_\kappa}\right) + \dot{\alpha}_k\frac{\partial^2\overset{*}{\varphi}}{\partial\alpha_k\partial\alpha_l}\mathrm{d}\alpha_l^{\mathrm{T}} = \mathrm{d}_\theta\Omega'\left(\frac{\Pi}{\rho_\kappa}, \theta, \alpha_k\right)$$

and

$$D^{\mathrm{pl}} = \frac{\partial\Omega'}{\partial(\Pi/\rho_\kappa)}$$

which is Rice's result.

and equation 15.49 is valid without restriction to the symmetric part (Ω must be considered as being not symmetric in Π_{ij} and Π_{ji}, which follows the fact that $\boldsymbol{\Pi}$ appears through the products $\boldsymbol{\Pi}\boldsymbol{w}^{(k)\mathrm{T}}$).

15.9.1 Discussion of this hypothesis

Let us consider the plastic deformations of a crystal, deformations which occur by slipping in planes of unit normal $\boldsymbol{n}^{(k)}$ along directions of unit vector $\boldsymbol{m}^{(k)}$. $\dot{\boldsymbol{\alpha}}^{(k)}$ is the corresponding velocity of slipping. $\boldsymbol{\alpha}^{(k)}$ is the area swept per unit volume by the dislocations the slip plane of which is the plane $\boldsymbol{n}^{(k)}$ and the Burgers vectors of which are parallel to $\boldsymbol{m}^{(k)}$. In this case $\boldsymbol{w}^{(k)} = \boldsymbol{m}^{(k)} \oplus \boldsymbol{n}^{(k)}$, and the second term in equation 15.53 is the *resolved cission* τ_k corresponding to the tensor $\boldsymbol{C}_e\boldsymbol{\Pi}$ (that is, the shear stress on the plane $\boldsymbol{n}^{(k)}$ in the direction $\boldsymbol{m}^{(k)}$).

For the active slipping mechanisms, we would have from equation 15.47 (where $\boldsymbol{a}_k = \boldsymbol{\alpha}_k$)

$$\tau_k = \rho \frac{\partial \varphi}{\partial \boldsymbol{\alpha}_k} + \frac{\partial \overset{*}{\Omega}}{\partial \dot{\boldsymbol{\alpha}}_k}$$

$\overset{*}{\Omega}$ being a function of θ and $\dot{\boldsymbol{\alpha}}_k$. If $\dot{\boldsymbol{\alpha}}_i = 0$, that is, on the elastic boundary

$$\tau_k = \rho \frac{\partial \varphi}{\partial \boldsymbol{\alpha}_k} + c_k = \mathscr{F}_k \qquad c_k = \mathrm{Cte}$$

hence

$$\frac{\partial \mathscr{F}_k}{\partial \alpha_j} = \frac{\partial \mathscr{F}_j}{\partial \alpha_k} \tag{15.55}$$

If $\dot{\alpha}_i \neq 0$

$$\tau_k - \mathscr{F}_k = \frac{\partial \overset{*}{\Omega}}{\partial \dot{\alpha}_k} - c_k \tag{15.56}$$

J. Zarka[16] has computed from the dislocation theory the yield limit $\mathscr{F}_k$ and the rate $\dot{\alpha}_k$. For the yield limit, relation 15.55 is not satisfied. For the rate $\dot{\alpha}_k$, it depends, not only on the difference $\tau_k - \mathscr{F}_k$, but also, and this is quite natural, on the density per unit volume of the dislocations of the k family and on the average density per unit area of a plane k of the dislocations of the other families crossing this plane (and so constitute obstacles to the slipping). Rice's hypothesis is satisfied, but relations of the type 15.56 are not.

It is then necessary (at least) to modify the hypothesis of normal dissipativity, as we have formulated it. The discussion of this question has at least shown that thermodynamics can open interesting prospects for the study of the laws of plasticity.

References

1. J. Mandel. *Comptes-Rendus Acad. Sc. Paris*, **264A** (1967), 133
2. E. Kröner. *J. Math. Phys.*, **12,** no. 1 (1963), 27
3. J. Mandel. *Cours au CISM*, Editions du CISM, Udine (1971)
4. J. Mandel. *Int. J. Solids Structures*, **9** (1973), 725
5. J. Mandel. *Symposium on the Foundations of Plasticity*, Varsovic (1972)
6. J. Mandel. *J. Mech. Phys. Solids*, **17** (1969), 125
7. P. Perzyna and W. Wojno. *Arch. Mech. Stosowanej*, **20** (1968), 499
8. P. Perzyna. *Bull. Acad. Polonaise Sc.*, **19,** 4, (1971), 178
9. A. E. Green and P. M. Naghdi. *Arch. Rat. Mech. Anal.*, **18,** no. 4 (1965), 251
10. A. E. Green and P. M. Naghdi. *Proc. IUTAM Symposia Vienna*, Springer (1966), 117
11. K. C. Valanis. *Symp. on Mech. Behaviour of Materials under Dynamic Loads*, Springer (1967), 343
12. J. R. Rice. *J. Mech. Phys. Solids*, **19** (1971), 433
13. J. Mandel and L. Brun. *J. Mech. Phys. Solids*, **16** (1968), 33
14. B. D. Coleman. *Arch. Rat. Mech. Anal.*, **17** (1964), 230
15. Q. S. Nguyen and B. Halphen. To be published
16. J. Zarka. *J. Mech. Phys. Solids*, **20** (1971), 179

16. Thermodynamics and Plasticity; Discussion Paper

H. Pina†

A discussor is supposed to bring to the audience any material he believes might instigate a lively discussion. In science as in any other human activity, objectives, method and doctrine are more controversial and prone to polemic than detail or *know-how*. Assuming this to be the wishes and expectations of both organisers and participants I will try to arrange my remarks accordingly.

16.1 The Scope of Plasticity

Thus it might be useful to recollect briefly some facts about plasticity and there is no better way to start than by its definition, because even at this point agreement has not yet been reached.

The term plasticity has been used with two connotations. The first and older means the study of material behaviour associated with permanent deformations, that is, deformations remaining for ever in the material after the load is decreased to zero. So time effects like creep, stress relaxation, etc., are kept outside the scope of plasticity and resulting theories are rate independent. The second and more recent involves all deformations of inelastic type, including therefore viscoelastic behaviour as well as plastic behaviour.

Because a sufficient general proof that the first case can be obtained from the second as a limit has not been produced up to this date (at least as far as I know) it seems that we have to face two groups of theories until a connecting link, if it exists, is discovered.

At this point one surely is tempted to raise a methodological question: if rate effects can be dealt with satisfactorily by viscoelasticity would it not be sounder to isolate them from plasticity by requiring it to be rate independent? Or is it that this latter condition proves to be more an obstacle to the construction of the theory than otherwise?

Another preliminary but nonetheless important question concerns the very title, that of Professor Mandel's lecture (chapter 15): Thermodynamics and Plasticity. In what sense is thermodynamics brought into play: as an intrinsic, essential component of plasticity theory or as an auxiliary one? In other words, should we abandon the idea of purely mechanical theory of

† Instituto Superior Técnico, Lisbon.

plasticity, in exchange for an obviously more elaborate one of, say, thermoplasticity?

Before proceeding with the analysis of possible answers to those questions, let us sketch the main features that a plasticity theory should exhibit.

Naming

$\boldsymbol{T}$—the stress tensor
F—the deformation gradient
ϑ—A string of thermodynamic variables we find relevant to the problem, for instance:
θ—the temperature
$g = \text{grad}\,\theta$, etc.
ψ^t—the history of variable ψ up to time t

and assuming for the sake of simplicity a simple, homogeneous material, plasticity should provide us with a constitutive equation of the form

$$\boldsymbol{T}(t) = \mathscr{F}(F^t, \vartheta^t) \tag{16.1}$$

or with means to arrive at equations like the one above. Should we merely want a purely mechanical constitutive relation the thermodynamic variables should drop from equation 16.1. The functional $\mathscr{F}$ should have the invariance properties as required by the material frame indifference principle and material symmetries.

If rate invariance is to be an intrinsic feature of the theory then one must have

$$\mathscr{F}\left(F^t(\delta), \vartheta^t(\delta)\right) = \mathscr{F}\left(F^t(\varphi(\tau)), \vartheta^t(\varphi(\tau))\right) \tag{16.2}$$

for all monotonically increasing function φ. Should we prefer the second approach referred to a moment ago then rate invariance as represented by equations 16.2 is to be obtained by some limit operation.

This is the general setting in which the several plasticity theories will be judged.

16.2 The Classical Theory

We will outline now the most common approach to plasticity and also the oldest. Its main features are the subject of many textbooks; Hill's (reference 1) is probably the best known.

This theory assumes the following principles

(1) There is a natural (stress-free) configuration.

(2) In a certain domain around this configuration the deformations are elastic, that is,

$$\boldsymbol{T}(t) = f(F(t)) \quad \text{or} \quad \boldsymbol{T} = f(F) \tag{16.3}$$

where f is a function.

(3) This domain is bounded by a surface in stress space outside which plastic deformations are present. The equation of this surface is generally

$$g(\boldsymbol{T}) = 0 \tag{16.4}$$

and is known as the yield criterion.

(4) The deformation rate in the plastic domain is thought of as the result of the sum on an elastic part verifying equation 16.3, and a plastic one obeying a so-called flow rule. If D^e and D^p are the elastic and plastic deformation rates respectively, then we have

$$D = D^e + D^p \tag{16.5a}$$

$$\dot{\boldsymbol{T}} = \frac{\partial f}{\partial F} \cdot \dot{F}^e \tag{16.5b}$$

and the flow rule is assumed to be of the form

$$D^p = \lambda \frac{\partial g}{\partial \boldsymbol{T}} \cdot \dot{\boldsymbol{T}} \tag{16.5c}$$

where $\lambda \geqslant 0$ for loading and $\lambda = 0$ for unloading. The value of λ when loading must be such that the yield criterion is verified at every moment.

As we can see from the above equations rate invariance is not only guaranteed but mandatory. So, the material response depends on the path in stress-space regardless of the time taken to accomplish it. Moreover, this dependence is rather limited, because only the stress at time t can influence the deformation rate at this instant. Besides, equation 16.5a shows that the plastic deformation rate D^p is normal to the yield surface (λ is taken here as a scalar).

The shape of the yield surface has not been restricted so far but in classical plasticity either it is assumed to be convex or a work principle is invoked in order to achieve this convexity.

To take account of strain-hardening some modification has to be made in the yield surface equation, in order that it could be changed by the deformation process itself. This modification usually takes the form of an additional parameter K, function of the strain history in an appropriate way. Thus we have instead of equation 16.4

$$g(\boldsymbol{T}, K) = 0 \tag{16.6}$$

showing that the yield surface moves in stress-space according to the amount K of strain-hardening.

The phenomena of hysteresis, so characteristic of certain metals, cannot be explained in the context at this theory, as unloading and subsequent loading follow the same path and Bauschinger effects are also difficult to introduce.

As one goes through classical plasticity one cannot avoid feeling the absence of a unified principle which binds together all this special phenomena, and thus avoids the kind of patchwork classical plasticity produced. For this reason the theory can be very much criticised, but we must also compliment it as being the one most used in applications.

16.3 The Rational Theory

Here by *rational* we mean only that school of continuum mechanics which devoted itself to the study of the mathematically admissible classes of material behaviour, and is well portrayed in the two volumes of the *Encyclopedia of Physics*, by Truesdell and Toupin[2], and Truesdell and Noll[3]. Unfortunately, no constitutive relations have been offered, within this line of thought, which compare with what has been achieved with other aspects of solids like elasticity and viscoelasticity, for instance.

As it is clearly avowed by Truesdell and Toupin 'Thus, as far as the exact theory is concerned, very little is known regarding it' (reference 2, p. 723). Nevertheless, some partial achievements did take place that open a promising road to plasticity. I am talking about hypoelasticity which exhibits two interesting features: it's rate independence and a yield phenomenon. Its constitutive equation is defined by

$$\mathring{\boldsymbol{T}} = \mathrm{H}(\boldsymbol{T})[D] \tag{16.7}$$

where $\mathring{\boldsymbol{T}}$ is the corotational stress rate given by

$$\mathring{\boldsymbol{T}} = \dot{\boldsymbol{T}} - \boldsymbol{W}\boldsymbol{T} + \boldsymbol{T}\boldsymbol{W} \tag{16.8}$$

where $\boldsymbol{W}$ is the spin tensor. The operator $\mathrm{H}(\boldsymbol{T})$ is linear, so equation 16.7 is rate independent. As it was shown by Truesdell and Toupin (reference 2, p. 415) when the dependence of H on $\boldsymbol{T}$ is adequate, a hypoelastic yield is possible.

Recently, Tokuoka[4] showed that by defining yield criterion as the locus of points in stress-space for which $\mathrm{H}(\boldsymbol{T})$ is singular and by defining plastic deformation rate D^p as the null-space of $\mathrm{H}(\boldsymbol{T})$ it is possible to derive in fact two types of yield: a normal and a shear one. With plausible assumptions he derived von Mise's yield criterion from the normal type and the Tresca criterion from the shear type.

This is remarkable and points to the fact that a purely mechanical theory of plasticity is indeed feasible and probably on the way.

Here one might suggest that instead of equation 16.7 other constitutive relations may give memory effects a more pronounced position. For instance the equations

$$\dot{T} = \mathscr{H}(F^t)[D] \tag{16.9}$$

or

$$\dot{T} = \mathscr{G}(T^t)[D] \tag{16.10}$$

where $\mathscr{H}$ and $\mathscr{G}$ are functionals of the deformation and stress history, respectively, and operate linearly on D, could prove to contain the necessary ingredients to represent the more interesting features of plastic behaviour. What is important is that yield is predicted by the theory and not imposed on it as an extra hypothesis.

16.4 Plasticity with Internal Variables

Because classical plasticity seems to have exhausted its possibilities and rational plasticity is not yet fully developed, interest has turned to new approaches. As often happens, thermodynamics has been used, and indeed has provided the inspiration that permitted the internal variables theories we shall discuss now.

Plastic deformation presents the interesting characteristic that no retardation of its rate can make it reversible.

Here we have a quasistatic phenomenon which is truly irreversible. A drastic change has to be made if classical thermodynamics is not to declare itself powerless. The impasse is solved by the introduction of the so-called internal variables, which has the additional advantage of using the function of state structure with mild modifications. This brings us to Professor Mandel's lecture (chapter 15), where use of such variables is made to explain plasticity from a thermodynamic standpoint.

The first difficulty one senses immediately is the characterisation of internal variables, as opposed to, say, external ones. What is really meant by internal variables? Should we be satisfied with the usual explanation that internal variables are the macroscopic representatives of microscopic phenomena? But as far as we believe matter to be made of atoms and molecules every gross, macroscopic variable should have, at least in principle, some interpretation in terms of microscopic ones. Whether or not we know it and express it mathematically is irrelevant. Thus, the above explanation does not help very much and besides is no definition at all.

The problem we face can be summarised in the following way. If a physical distinction between internal and external variables is not laid down from the beginning there is no corresponding differentiation in the subsequent mathematical treatment both types of variables receive within the framework of thermodynamics. Only the hope remains that at the end some interpretation might be provided by the theory itself. If this is the case then the use of internal variables is justified, otherwise we cannot avoid to see them as a mere stratagem to obtain results known beforehand. Should the situation prove to be that fortunate, then we are forced to conclude that thermodynamics is able to extract concrete results from loose hypothesis, or, putting it in another way, that it does not belong to the class of theories where conclusions can be no better than the data used to derive them.

There is another objection to the use of internal variables which results from the fact that the ultimate objective of constitutive equations is to permit the solution of field problems. That is, the stress–strain or heat flux–temperature gradient relationships, for instance, are introduced in the balance of mass, momentum, moment of momentum, and energy equations. In general the internal variables will not be eliminated before being introduced in those balance equations (or at least no one has proved that this can always be done). So appropriate initial and boundary values for these variables are also to be prescribed in order to have a well-set problem. And here lies the main difficulty of the use of internal variables, for we do not know, because of lack of any physical interpretation, how to specify initial and/or boundary values. This simply precludes the solution of any initial/boundary value problem with internal variables, which means that something is definitely wrong with them, or at least, with the manner in which they are introduced and justified.

All this criticism is not intended to prevent or demean the use of internal variables for much can be learned from them, but to point to their weak foundations. Probably, they are the forerunners of a higher theoretical structure yet to be revealed. Taken from that point of view it would be unwise not to give them a fighting chance. At least, they provide a simple means to introduce history dependence without the heavy use of functionals.

As a result of what has just been said the attribution of a tensorial character to internal variables is somewhat arbitrary. The principle of frame indifference and material symmetries can be used to restrict the range of possible choices (see Coleman and Gurtin[5], for an example), but this is all it can do.

Professor Mandel seems to establish a difference between internal and hidden variables which I did not quite understand. A little more elaboration on this point would be welcome.

The yield surface is also *postulated* as in classical plasticity, and does not result in a natural intrinsic way from the constitutive equation as in hypoelasticity. An exception is Professor Valanis' recent work[6] on plasticity, where no yield surface is required. His equations express the stress as a functional on the strain history, through the use of an intrinsic time. This latter concept renders his theory rate independent and keeps, in some sense, long range memory effects.

An interesting feature is that there is no purely elastic deformation, plastic strains are present everywhere from the natural state on. However, their magnitude becomes significant only after a certain value of the intrinsic time is reached. This formulation is able to predict strain-hardening, Bauschinger effects, cross-hardening and hysteresis loops, which is sufficiently remarkable to make it worth our attention. Besides, Professor Valanis took the trouble to show that his theory can do more than give qualitative explanation, by presenting examples of very good agreement with experimental results.

The same criticism regarding internal variables applies here, and the concept of intrinsic time looks as much *ad hoc* as the yield surface of classical plasticity.

16.5 Closure

It was our intention to provide material for a lively discussion about plasticity, by pointing to some critical points and facts we believe to be relevant. What was said was intended to leave the impression that plasticity is far from being a solved problem, and that the pursuit of a better understanding of it can not only lead to new plasticity theories, but also help thermodynamics to deal with irreversible processes.

Acknowledgements

The author thanks Professor D. Domingos and Professor J. Kestin for stimulating discussions about the relations of thermodynamics and plasticity. This work was supported by I.A.C. under Research Project TLE–2.

References

1. R. Hill. *The Mathematical Theory of Plasticity*, Oxford (1950)
2. G. Truesdell and R. Toupin. The classical field theories. *Encyclopedia of Physics*, ed. by S. Flugge, vol. III/1, Springer (1960)
3. C. Truesdell and W. Noll. The non-linear field theories of mechanics. *Encyclopedia of Physics*, ed. by S. Flugge, vol. III/3, Springer (1965)
4. T. Tokuoka. Fundamental relations of plasticity derived from hypoelasticity. *Foundations of Plasticity*, ed. by A. Sawczuk, Noordhoff (1973)
5. B. D. Coleman and M. E. Gurtin. Thermodynamics with internal state variables *J. Chem. Phys.*, **47** (1967), 2
6. K. C. Valanis. *A Theory of Viscoplasticity without a Yield Surface*, Parts I and II, Dept. of Mechanics and Hydraulics, College of Engineering, University of Iowa

Discussion

KESTIN

I should like to congratulate Professor Mandel on his lucid presentation of a difficult subject. It is pleasant to note that the vexing problem of creating a thermodynamic framework for thermoplasticity is now coming to a successful conclusion and that several lines of research have merged. In particular, I am pleased to note that Professor Mandel has accepted the ideas conceived by my colleague, J. R. Rice, as expressed in our joint paper†. Finally, may I be permitted once again to call attention to the current semantic problems of this subject. Even though some of us would use different words and different lines of reasoning, our understanding of the essentials of the physics of the situation has become the same. Professor Mandel's summary is *equivalent* to the adoption of the hypothesis of local state together with the Gibbs equation (equation (a) in chapter 8, or the equation *in fra*).

In order to discuss Dr. Pina's remarks, I would like to make a distinction between the facts of thermoplasticity, as they are presented to us by experiments, and the problem of the best tactics to use when we set out to make a theory around them. In the latter case (as we know from quantum mechanics), there is no need to insist (as some physicists did half a century ago) that every quantity which occurs in our equations must necessarily be directly measurable. Often it is useful to work with purely conceptual quantities which we eliminate when we derive results which are to be directly compared with experiments. So, from this point of view, there would be no objection to the introduction of internal variables even if we had no direct physical interpretation for them. In this particular case, however, such an interpretation exists and this amounts to endowing internal variables with an operational definition. Broadly speaking, the internal variables represent the deformations which are introduced into an element in two ways: when dislocations move at constant density, and when dislocations are multiplied. A theory which disregards this is not likely to succeed because such phenomena do occur and account for the plastic behaviour of metals.

The epistemological question as to whether we should strive for a purely mechanical or a thermodynamic theory of plasticity is easily answered. In the second case we include a vastly increased set of experimental situations (creep, rate effects, varying temperature) at comparatively little cost. For example, a mechanical theory would be adequate for the calculation of civil

† J. Kestin and J. R. Rice. Paradoxes in the application of thermodynamics to strained solids. *A Critical Review of Thermodynamics*, Mono Press (1970), 275.

engineering structures, but the design of fuel elements in nuclear reactors is possible only in terms of a thermodynamic theory.

The further epistemological question as to whether the yield surface and its migrations in stress-space should be imposed on the theory as an additional datum, or whether this should be derived as a result of the basic theory, depends on the complexity of the rate equations which we use in a particular case. In the general case, the theory based on the hypothesis of local state and the Gibbs equation

$$\mathrm{d}U = T\,\mathrm{d}S - A_\alpha \mathrm{d}\xi_\alpha + \sigma_{ij}\mathrm{d}(\varepsilon_{ij} - e_{ij})$$

will lead to the existence of a set of potential surfaces in stress-space. The yield surface is merely a region of very close accumulations of such potential surfaces.

SIDOROFF

Let me stress once more what we mean when using internal variables: we have a set Λ of independent variables (γ, θ for example) and a set π of dependent variables (φ, $\boldsymbol{\sigma}$, s for example) and we want to obtain $\pi(t)$, given the history of Λ up to time t. This is the natural functional representation

$$\pi(t) = \mathop{\mathscr{L}}_{\zeta < t}\{\Lambda(\zeta), \Lambda(t)\}$$

where we have distinguised the past history of Λ from its actual value. Now this is hardly of any help in solving practical problems. That is why we summarise the influence of the past history into a finite number of internal variables ω ($\hat{P}, a_j$ in the framework of Professor Mandel's lecture, chapter 15) and we replace the functional $\mathscr{L}$ by a function L

$$\pi(t) = L\big(\Lambda(t), \omega(t)\big)$$

to which we must add some equation giving the rate of change of the internal variables. In plasticity it introduces some complicated function of $\Lambda(t)$, $\omega(t)$ and $\dot{\Lambda}(t)$.

$$\dot{\omega}(t) = \Omega\big(\Lambda(t), \omega(t), \dot{\Lambda}(t)\big)$$

Given a history $\Lambda(\zeta)$, this gives an ordinary differential equation which gives $\omega(t)$ as a functional of $\Lambda(\zeta)$

$$\omega(t) = \mathop{\mathscr{R}}_{t < \zeta}\{\Lambda(\zeta)\}$$

Thus an internal variable theory is nothing but a *finite dimensional approximation* of the general functional.

It is quite obvious, then, that *we do not need any boundary condition for the internal variables.* We need only initial values for them in order to integrate the differential equations describing their evolution. Now there may be two interpretations for internal variables. In some cases they have more or less precise physical meaning, the relevant initial values then result from this. In other cases they are purely abstract quantities but then only their variations in time are important. Indeed, I think there will be no problem in assigning the relevant initial values in any specific problem.

PINA

Professor Sidoroff seems to consider only homogeneous problems, that is, his variables Λ and ω are not functions of the space coordinates. In that case it is obvious that boundary conditions are not required. However initial ones are. If internal variables do have a precise physical meaning there is no problem in assigning boundary and/or initial conditions, but in that case I see no reason to draw any distinction between internal and *external* variables. If they are purely abstract quantities I do not know how to specify the respective boundary and/or initial conditions, which means that I cannot conduct a single experiment to check the theory.

Also Professor Sidoroff's claim that only the rates $\dot{\omega}$ are relevant does not seem to hold true. In fact it is ω which enters the equation giving π and not $\dot{\pi}$. As

$$\omega = \omega_0 + \int_{t_0}^{t} \dot{\omega}\, \mathrm{d}t$$

$$\pi(t) = L(\Lambda(t), \omega_0 + \int_{t_0}^{t} \dot{\omega}\, \mathrm{d}t)$$

and $\pi(t)$ depends indeed on ω_0.

If 'the internal variable theory is nothing but a finite dimensional approximation of the general functional', then the problem shifts immediately from the grounds of the mechanics of materials to mathematics. Therefore approximation theorems are to be stated and proved, and the class of functionals being approximated as well as the class of approximating functions are to be explicitly declared. The subject becomes highly technical, but I do not see how we can avoid it, if we wish to remain rigorous. It is clear that that is not the course pursued usually when dealing with internal variables.

MANDEL

I would like to comment on the theory which has been called rational by Dr. H. Pina, and on hypoelasticity.

The very interesting idea of Truesdell was that, when starting from non-holonomic differential relations, then the strain tensor does not depend on the stress path which has been followed; this is an important aspect of plasticity. When the stress moves along a nondegenerated cycle, then the strain path is not closed. Unfortunately, if the stress cycle is degenerate (going and returning back along the same path), then the hypoelastic relations (which do not depend on the direction in which the path is described) lead to a strain path which is degenerate in the same way, that is, to a total closed path. This is obviously not the case for plastics materials.

To avoid this conclusion it must be admitted that there are two different relations according to the direction of the stress-rate vector, the transition from one relation to the other occurring when this vector lies in the tangent plane to some surface in the stress-space. But when we reinject the concept of a yield or loading surface, which we wanted to eliminate.

It seems to me difficult, in conclusion, to admit that a theory based solely on hypoelastic relations is a rational theory.

PINA

I referred to hypoelasticity because it has two features which I believe to be of interest to plasticity: rate independence and the prediction of yield phenomena. The analogy between hypoelasticity and plasticity stops right here, and I fully agree with Professor Mandel with respect to the differences in the loading–unloading cycles of the two types of material. However, I do not see as necessary the reinjection of the yield surface as separating two domains of different behaviour each one of them with a constitutive relation of its own. That this is the case was proved by Professor Valanis' work where only one stress–strain relation applies to both loading and unloading. Equations 16.9 and 16.10 of my discussion were advanced as plausible generalisations of hypoelasticity in order that loading and unloading paths could be different.

17. The Role of Thermodynamics in Continuum Mechanics

P. Germain†

Abstract

In this paper, devoted to the review of achievements of the *International Symposium on the Foundations of Continuum Thermodynamics*, I have tried to describe the role of thermodynamics in the mechanics of continua in the light of all the information which has been revealed and recent progress which has been made. Some of the main points considered in this review paper are the crucial necessity of thermodynamic results, the lack of fully satisfactory and accepted basic concepts for a thermodynamic description of a system very far from equilibrium, and the recent attempts to overcome this difficulty.

17.1 Introduction

One of the main purposes of this symposium, which cannot be over emphasised, was to bring together for a full week scientists belonging to different, although very close, fields and to make them work in a very friendly environment. Of course, that is a very frequent comment, nearly always presented at the end of any symposium. But today it seems to me that it is especially necessary to underline this point and to give full credit to our Portuguese hosts, who planned this symposium with precisely this fundamental objective in mind, and who, consequently, have made a very useful and substantial contribution to the development of our common scientific field.

It is the main objective of this final paper to attempt, at the end of the meeting, to review the main achievements of this working week; to state the progress and conclusions which have been reached; to formulate the problems which need further clarification; to describe the different methods of approach which have been proposed and to try to analyse their convergence or their divergence. But before going into the detailed sections of this report, it may be convenient, as an introduction, to begin with a general review of this symposium.

First of all, the central topic has its deepest roots in the problems which have arisen in continuum mechanics, where it was realised that the develop-

† Institut de Mecanique Theoretique et Appliquée, Université de Paris.

ment of the field and its ability to represent a large body of applications rest upon the possibility of a thermodynamics which may be applied with confidence to continuum mechanics in general and, therefore, to situations far from equilibrium. Classical thermodynamics, which is in fact thermostatics, and even the more recent thermodynamics of irreversible processes (TIP) were discovered to be unsatisfactory and inadequate. This is the reason why, in the recent past, with the pressure of necessity and the possibility of important discoveries, a great number of experts in continuum mechanics have devoted their efforts to the search for a more satisfactory thermodynamical theory. In the last ten years, a great number of papers, several symposia and several books have been devoted to this problem. Some of the aims of this symposium were to evaluate the results of this tremendous activity, to look critically at the foundations of the theories which have been proposed and to evaluate their applicability. This is why the author of the present review has been chosen from the workers on continuum mechanics and not from the very distinguished physicists who have taken part in this symposium, despite the fact that the latter are obviously the thermodynamics experts.

If one tries to make a preliminary survey of the various topics which have been treated during the working sessions of this symposium, it may be said that, after the introductory lecture of Professor Delgado Domingos, who defined precisely the problem of the passage *from thermostatics to thermodynamics*, the invited papers may be divided according to three main lines of thought and purpose. Firstly, one must mention the contributions of the physicists who came from various branches of this science. We have learnt a lot during this symposium with such a wonderful team of teachers. Professor Callen gave a very suggestive and dynamic talk, full of very personal and profound insights. Professor Prigogine was at least as enthusiastic and opened new directions of thought and work. The relation of the fundamental inequality of thermodynamics with the *privileged direction of time* towards the future is important and stimulating, as well as the concept of the stability of systems which lie, *beyond bifurcation*, outside *the thermodynamic branch.* Professor de Groot was very precise in his presentation of the theoretical foundations of the Onsager reciprocity relations. Professors Schlögl and Tisza have given very stimulating views from the statistical theory. All this first set of contributions was very useful for those working on continuum mechanics. But, as the central theme of the symposium was *continuum thermodynamics*—and that is why it was not possible to deal with some more specific problems of interest to the physicists, for example, phase transition—the two other parts of this symposium were more specifically oriented in this direction. One can distinguish the group of contributions of Professors Miller, Mason, Meixner and Kestin which were concerned mostly with the classical *thermodynamics of irreversible processes* and its ability to provide a method to deal with the problems arising from continuum mechanics. The third set of contributions—those of Professors Müller, Rivlin, Lee, Nemat-Nasser, Mandel and Pina—were concerned with the general *nonequilibrium situation.* They deal either with the foundation of a *general thermodynamics,* that is, far from equilibrium, or with more specific situations such as those met in nonlinear elasticity, viscoelasticity and viscoplasticity. The purpose of this paper, as was said before, is to try to derive some conclusions from these two last parts of the working sessions.

17.2 Preliminary Remarks on the Methodological Status of Continuum Thermodynamics

Perhaps it is in order to recall briefly some elementary characteristics of the methodology of continuum mechanics because, obviously, *continuum thermodynamics* means thermodynamics viewed from the continuum point of view, that is, formulations of thermodynamics homogeneous with those of the classical physics and adapted to the necessities of this discipline. More specifically, continuum physics deals at the *macroscopic level* with complex physical phenomena which have to be *schematised,* rather drastically, by an *ideal mathematical model* which is able to lead to *predictions* which can be experimentally *checked.* In other words, pushed forward by applications of an *engineering type,* continuum mechanics is based essentially on a *phenomenological description* and a related *mathematical treatment.* Let us emphasise some of these points.

17.2.1 The necessity of macroscopic formulations and the role of experience in this formulation

This was said perfectly in section 11.2 that: 'we need macroscopic formulations to handle those problems and those systems that are too complex and too intractable to treat by a molecular-scale theory—dense gases, liquid solutions, complicated solids and so on'. That is one of our requirements with respect to physicists. We do not feel tied up by the progress or the difficulties of the molecular theories. In fact, our discipline is in some sense independent of these theories. The tests we need in order to justify the macroscopic or phenomenological laws rest on experience and, in particular, on experiments to investigate the value of the laws that we have been led to postulate, may be with 'some spirit of adventure', by a confrontation of the predictions based upon it. As a consequence, I think we have to be very modest about our statements. For instance, I think that the word *principle* is dangerous, ambiguous or misleading. I think it is preferable to talk of a *working assumption* or, in a more mathematical context of an *axiom,* in order to emphasise that we attach no ontological significance to our statement, no metaphysical truth. Consider all the misconceptions which arose with the *principle of determinism*, which was subsequently replaced by a *principle of undeterminism*, or those arising from the *second principle of thermodynamics*. It is not surprising that today the expression of *principle of equipresence* gives rise to some controversy. It is nothing more than a *working assumption* seems reasonable as a starting assumption, but, in fact, leads to the conclusion that all the variables are not equally present in the assumed constitutive laws. It is why also, I will not follow Professor Mason's suggestion to elevate the Casimir–Onsager reciprocity relations (CORR) to the status of a paradigm.

17.2.2 The necessity of a mathematical study of the problems and in particular of a mathematical understanding of the physical world we are dealing with

If everybody agrees that a mathematical analysis must lead to a solution of our problems, it must be emphasised also that the search for a beautiful mathematical theory having the character of generality, simplicity, elegance and rigour is a real and very valuable motivation for working in continuum mechanics. All these factors represent an aesthetic requirement, maybe a *utopia*, but a look at the history of Mechanics or Physics reveals that this requirement is the source, quite often, of the best and complete understanding of the physical phenomenon. Some of the themes of Professor Callen's or Professor Prigogine's lectures provide adequate confirmation of this statement. The research of an elegant and general theory is a good guideline for progress. That is a very sane attitude, provided the third point is not overlooked.

17.2.3 The necessity to arrive at a formulation of problems which can be solved and whose solutions may be compared with experiments

This is a very important requirement which must not be forgotten. A *theory* which gives rise to a system of equations and associated boundary and initial conditions is *mathematically consistant* if the boundary value problem so defined has a unique solution depending continuously on the data (in a convenient topology). Also the quantities which arise in the formulation of the problem and in its solution must be *observable quantities* and, hopefully, accessible to some kind of *measurements*. Even if these two conditions are not and cannot be satisfied by a theory which has not yet found its final shape and which is still in its development period, they must always be present as goals which have to be achieved as soon as possible. A theory may be very elegant, it may describe the physical reality in great detail, but if there is no hope of attaining the third requirement—at least partially—in a reasonable time, such a theory may be said (at least) to be *premature*.

Let us conclude this section by two remarks related to the context in which the building of continuum thermodynamics has to be started. First, everybody agrees on the three conservation laws (mass, linear, and angular momentum and energy) which may be considered as the foundation stone of the topic†. It is in this manner that I understand the statement of Professor Callen in section 4.4 where he says 'the extended first law of thermodynamics is the symmetry of the laws of physics under space and time translations and under spatial rotation'.

The supplementary information needed to build a theory applicable to a given material is provided by the *constitutive equations.* But a continuum theory at this stage can say nothing, or at least very little: only a few statements of consistency such as invariance or symmetry. It must ask for help. As thermomechanical effects usually have to be considered, this help is provided by thermodynamics, the body of knowledge which studies heat, temperature and related phenomena. Generally these constitutive equations will rest on a purely phenomelogical basis; in special cases they may rest directly on an analysis starting at a microscopic level (for example kinetic theory of gases). But finally, in my opinion, it is in its ability to check the three criteria previously mentioned that a theory has to be appreciated.

Continuum thermodynamics, if this term may receive a precise meaning, appears as a frame constituted by a set of rules or recipes which can help safely in the formulation of constitutive equations.

The last remark relating to the context in which the question of continuum mechanics arises, concerns *fluid mechanics.* Compressible flow theory has been developed with great success in the past and has been confirmed by experience. One has used the information coming from the classical results of thermodynamics—that is, in fact, from thermostatics—concerning a fluid, i.e. its ability to be described thermodynamically by a potential—for instance the specific free energy ψ as a function of absolute temperature T and τ (the specific volume $\tau = \rho^{-1}$)—from which the *thermodynamic properties* like pressure p, specific entropy s, specific internal energy e, sound velocity a, may be derived. p appears for instance, as a known function of T and s; say $p = g(T, s)$, the equation of state. The knowledge of the inequalities that may be added to these equations is very important for the development of further applications. They are relative to the question of thermodynamic stability, classically and generally; for instance convexity of $e(T, s)$ is a condition which is imposed. But can we say that this convexity condition, (or others which are equivalent) apply in a completely general situation (the lecture of Professor Rivlin, despite the fact that it is concerned with an incompressible material, raises this very interesting question) or must it be supplemented by other inequalities? This question is usually answered in fluid dynamics

† There are different ways to state the conservation of energy, according to the assumptions made on the existence of a specific energy. See for instance a recent paper of Green and Naghdi[1] and a more recent one[2] which indicates the consequences for continuum thermodynamics.

on a phenomenological basis with H. Weyl's inequalities which are $g_\tau < 0$, $g_s > 0$, $g_{\tau\tau} > 0$. This last one seems to go beyond the convexity requirement of $g(T, s)$. It is remarkable that these useful inequalities have been proposed by a mathematician[3,4], to satisfy elegance and generality requirements as well as some global experimental phenomena (for instance, that pressure always increases through a shock wave).

But these classical relations of thermodynamics are not sufficient for viscous compressible flows. The equations of state have to be supplemented by writing a complementary constitutive equation. Considering the stress tensor $\boldsymbol{\sigma}_{ij}$ as the sum of the spherical tensor defined by the thermodynamic pressure, $p\delta_{ij}$, and the viscous stress, τ_{ij}, the Navier–Stokes equations are obtained by saying that τ_{ij} is a linear and isotopic function of the strain rate tensor (the symmetric part of the velocity gradient tensor).

Then, everything was simple and without question. Of course it is known that situations may arise in which this frame will not be satisfactory. But one cannot emphasise too much the tremendous success of the Navier–Stokes equations in a large variety of applications, going from slow to hypersonic flows. Even the most complex flows are described by the Navier–Stokes equations provided they are completed by their natural extensions to chemically active and diffusing gas mixtures.

Now, it is clear that, when we turn to solids, the situation cannot be as simple. Even if one tries to follow the same scheme, we know that the number of thermodynamic variables will be greater than two—at least four in the most simple three-dimensional cases. We will not have the explicit expression of the free energy (in gas dynamics very often it is enough to postulate that the gas is *perfect* with constant specific heats). We will have no information about *material stability inequalities.* Moreover, one may wonder whether the basic concepts of classical thermodynamics which deals with equilibrium, are still valid in all the nonequilibrium situations we expect to have to face in continuum mechanics.

Sections 17.3 and 17.4 will analyse the various answers which have been given to these questions, especially by the participants of this symposium. The sections are headed 'The Cautious Attitude' and 'The Ambitious Attitude'. By choosing these words, it is hoped to avoid reducing the debate too early to a semantic level. I want to underline that a choice of one or other of these two main attitudes is motivated more by a question of personal taste and psychological reason than, for the time being at least, by decisive scientific arguments.

17.3 The Cautious Attitude

In this section I consider those theories which start with the *assumption of a local state*, or with the *quasithermostatic assumption*, or as suggested by Dr. Schlögl with the assumption of *accompanying state*. It was generally agreed during this symposium to avoid talk of a *local thermodynamic equilibrium* despite the fact that this terminology is widely used. It is not necessary here to repeat, in detail, what was excellently said by many people during this symposium and especially by Dr. Meixner and Dr. Kestin. The reader is referred to their lectures, chapters 7 and 8. The general point of view adopted with this attitude is to start as in fluid mechanics; it is a cautious and conservative one.

17.3.1 The thermodynamical potential

One has to be ready to admit some generalisations in order to be able to describe the complicated situations which appears in continuum mechanics, and especially in solids. The first one is to assume that the determination of the *state* at one point (any particule) requires not only the introduction of its specific internal energy e, of the n parameters a_i $(i = 1, 2, \ldots, n)$ introduced in the thermostatic description of the material (external information variables), but also of r so-called internal variables† (internal deformation variables) ξ_α $(\alpha = 1, 2, \ldots, r)$. On the whole, there are $r+n+1$ independent variables. It is assumed that, in equilibrium, the ξ_α have given expressions in terms of e and a_i and vary accordingly in a reversible transformation. When the continuum is in motion, it is assumed that we can still define a frozen temperature T, a frozen specific entropy s, and that a thermodynamic potential, say a specific free energy

$$\psi(T, a_i, \xi_\alpha)$$

may be introduced from which it is possible to derive s, and also the thermodynamical properties P_i and A_α such that

$$\mathrm{d}\psi = -s\,\mathrm{d}T + P_i\,\mathrm{d}a_i + A_\alpha\,\mathrm{d}\xi_\alpha \tag{17.1}$$

The $r+n$ equations giving the P_i and A_α in terms of the a_i, T and ξ_α are the *equations of state* and constitute *partial information of the constitutive equations.*

Let us note at this stage that despite the simplicity of this starting point some questions arise. *May one safely write that $e(s, a_i, \xi_\alpha)$ is a convex function of its arguments.* Let us recall that such a requirement is practically necessary in order to assure the possibility of defining the various Legendre transforms which are very often used if one wants to avoid multivalued potentials. But, on the other hand, do not forget Professor Rivlin's lecture, chapter 12! What is the exact *physical significance of frozen temperature and entropy*; can we

† By definition, internal variables do not appear when one writes the balance of momentum, or when one computes the rate of work of internal forces.

attach to these concepts the same physical meaning as the one attached to them in equilibrium? Lastly, and probably most important, *what exactly are the internal variables*? Are they quantities which can be precisely defined or which will receive precise definitions later—related to dislocations in a plastic material or to the configurations of macromolecules in a viscoelastic material—or are they unknown quantities, *hidden variables*, introduced for the purpose of gaining some flexibility and which have to be specified *phenomenologically* by the results of experimental stress–strain analysis. The two points of view are not contradictory; the first is the one which emphasises the value of the method not only by its global ability to predict phenomena but also to use concepts which have all one direct physical significance. The reader is advised to look back to the papers of Kestin, Mandel and Nemat-Nasser, chapters 8, 15 and 14, to see that these internal variables may be viewed in different ways. We will have to return to these important questions below.

17.3.2 Entropy production and fundamental inequality

After this first body of information, arising from the assumption of a thermodynamic potential which is just an extension of the potential used in thermostatics (and exactly this one if no internal variables are necessary), one has to specify the entropy production.

The classical way, and the most widely used, assumes that the frozen T and s behave like temperature and entropy in thermostatics or in situations close to equilibrium and, consequently, that the entropy production is given by

$$\sigma = \rho \frac{\mathrm{d}s}{\mathrm{d}t} + \nabla \cdot \left(\frac{\boldsymbol{q}}{T} \right) \tag{17.2}$$

if $\boldsymbol{q}$ is a heat flow vector (volumic heat supplied is neglected). Using the values of s and the equations of states arising from equation 17.1, and the conservation of energy and momentum to eliminate the body force and heat supplied, leads to an expression on the form

$$\sigma = \sum_{\alpha=1}^{m} X_\alpha Y_\alpha \tag{17.3}$$

where the right-hand side is written as the sum of products of two factors (we will return to this crucial point in section 17.3.3). The fundamental inequality, which is the way to write the inequality arising from the second law (or Clausius–Duhem inequality) says that σ is never negative.

Another suggestion has been made by Meixner. According to an analysis based on electrical networks, Meixner does not want to admit that the concept of entropy is meaningful in nonequilibrium and, if he assumes that a temperature T may be defined in nonequilibrium, he assumes also that this T is different from the frozen one introduced above. In Meixner's theory, one will denote by s_f and T_f the frozen specific entropy and absolute temperature. Then equation 17.2 is replaced, in Meixner's theory, by

$$\sigma = \rho \frac{\mathrm{d}s_f}{\mathrm{d}t} + \nabla \cdot \frac{\boldsymbol{q}}{T} \tag{17.4}$$

and, as a result the sum on the right-hand side of equation 17.3, has $m+1$ terms ($0 \leqslant \alpha \leqslant m$), the extra term corresponding to $\alpha = 0$ being given by

$$\left(\frac{1}{T_f} - \frac{1}{T}\right)\rho \dot{e} \tag{17.5}$$

where $\dot{e}$ is the material derivative of the specific internal energy†.

17.3.3 Complementary constitutive relations

All the methods we intend to describe presently in the frame of the working assumption of local state adopt a formulation of the complementary constitutive relations in which each X_α is expressed as a function of the Y_β. But that can be done in various ways.

TIP *thermodynamics of irreversible processes* can be considered to be a well-founded theory whose statements can be derived from the statistical theory. As far as our present interest is concerned, the complementary constitutive relations appear, roughly speaking, through linear relations

$$X_\alpha = L_{\alpha\beta} Y_\beta \qquad L_{\alpha\beta} = L_{\beta\alpha} \tag{17.6}$$

These relations $L_{\alpha\beta} = L_{\beta\alpha}$ are the Casimir–Onsager reciprocity relations (CORR). We refer to previous lectures for more details and more precision. From the phenomenological point of view, which is presently ours, the CORR appear to have been tested experimentally with great success. The well-documented lecture of Dr. Miller, and the comments of Dr. Mason, chapter 11, confirm that we are in the presence of a physical law of great value. Moreover, as was recalled above, the Navier–Stokes equations are obtained as a special case of equation 17.6.

One cannot forget the very severe criticisms that these phenomenological constitutive relations have received. The first thing is to be able to make the distinction between the Y_α (the fluxes) and the X_α (the forces). I must confess that among all the propositions presented none appear to be completely

† Professor Kestin in chapter 8, discussing Professor Meixner's paper, chapter 7, has formulated some questions concerning this suggestion. Time did not allow a full confrontation on both points of view. The reviewer has no personal well-founded opinion about this controversy. He will, here again, follow his natural tendancy which is to use the most simple scheme until a comparison with experience shows that the scheme is too simple and that new effects have to be taken into account.

general, satisfactory, without ambiguity and at the same time simple. I am fully convinced of the importance of these laws, but think that a clear and rigorous recipe, formulated in the spirit of continuum mechanics, has to be produced in order to give a definitive answer to the very rough objections formulated against these laws.

Assumption of the quasipotential of dissipations. One way to express the relations 17.6 is to say that there exists a non-negative quadratic function $\mathscr{D}(\boldsymbol{Y})$ ($\boldsymbol{Y}$ is a vector with components $Y_\alpha; \alpha = 1, \ldots, m$) such that the complementary constitutive relations are simply written as

$$\boldsymbol{X} = \tfrac{1}{2}\,\mathbf{grad}_Y\,\mathscr{D}(\boldsymbol{Y}) \tag{17.7}$$

with

$$\mathscr{D}(\boldsymbol{Y}) = L_{\alpha\beta} Y_\alpha Y_\beta\,;$$

of course $\mathscr{D}(\boldsymbol{Y})$ may also depend on the $r+n+1$ thermodynamical parameters.

With such a formulation, it is easy to find a quite natural generalisation when following Ziegler[5]. A non-negative quadratic function is a non-negative convex function. So, one is tempted to say that, if one assumes that the dissipation $\mathscr{D}$ may be expressed as a non-negative convex function of $\boldsymbol{Y}$, one may be able to find a generalisation of equation 17.7, expressing $\boldsymbol{X}$ in terms of $\mathbf{grad}_Y\mathscr{D}$ and eventually $\mathscr{D}$. That can be done without difficulty for $\mathscr{D}$ which are *quasihomogeneous* (Germain[6]). The decisive generalisation is due to Moreau[7]. One may assume that there exists a *lower semicontinuous convex function* $\phi(\boldsymbol{Y})$ such that

$$\boldsymbol{X} = \mathbf{grad}\,\phi(\boldsymbol{Y}) \qquad \boldsymbol{Y}\cdot\mathbf{grad}\,\phi(\boldsymbol{Y}) \geqslant 0 \tag{17.8}$$

If $\phi(\boldsymbol{Y})$ is not differentiable the constitutive equality 17.8, will be replaced by

$$\boldsymbol{X} \in \partial\phi(\boldsymbol{Y}) \tag{17.9}$$

which says that $\boldsymbol{X}$ is one of the elements of the subgradients set of ϕ at $\boldsymbol{Y}$. As ϕ is convex, one may write these constitutive relations as

$$\boldsymbol{Y} \in \partial\phi^*(\boldsymbol{X})$$

if $\phi^*(\boldsymbol{X})$ is the semicontinuous convex function of $\boldsymbol{X}$ defined as the Legendre–Fenchel transformation

$$\phi^*(\boldsymbol{X}) = \sup_Y(\boldsymbol{X}\cdot\boldsymbol{Y} - \phi(\boldsymbol{Y}))$$

All these notions are very useful in the theory of plasticity where they receive a direct and elegant application. *It must be emphasised that, as in the laws of* TIP, *this formulation rests strongly on the possibility of making a non-ambiguous distinction between the* **Y** *and the* **X**. This is a new reason why such a question is important. Note also the characterisation of a law such as 17.8,

given by Edelen, as we were informed by Professor Rivlin during a discussion.
General case. The previous proposition has great advantages. First, all the constitutive relations are defined by two convex scalar valued functions (a thermodynamical potential, a quasipotential of dissipations). They automatically satisfy the conditions of orthogonality and convexity which have been mentioned so often in connection with plasticity or viscoelasticity. Finally, from a mathematical point of view, these formulations provide the possibility to apply, to problems related to materials of this type, the very efficient results obtained in convex analysis and more generally in functional analysis[8,9]. This fact was explicitly mentioned by Mandel at the end of his lecture, chapter 15, when he reported the recent theory of Nguyen and Halphen[10] and Nguyen[11]. But Mandel told us that we cannot hope such a simple frame to apply in any situation. When it appears that such a theoretical description is not applicable, we are obliged, either to apply it only partly (it seems that this is precisely what is done in the recent theories of Rice and Mandel in viscoplasticity) or to postulate more general relations, without restrictions on, for example, scalar independent implicit relations connecting the Y_α and the X_α, depending parametrically on the thermodynamical variables of course.

We may introduce, if we wish, a functional dependence between the X_α and the Y_α (see, for instance, Meixner[12]).

In those phenomenological complicated constitutive relations which are reported here, it must be emphasised that very little remains of the results of TIP, in contrast to the case examined above, and that the corresponding mathematical problems may be quite difficult.

17.4 The Ambitious Attitude

17.4.1 The motivations

The previous attitude was to use, as far as possible, the concepts and the results of thermostatics and of the thermodynamics of irreversible processes (which considers systems close to thermodynamic equilibrium) which have been justified largely by other theories and by experience, and to leave them only when it becomes mandatory. The ambitious attitude is, in contrast, to face directly the general problem of thermodynamics, that is, to consider thermostatics as a special case of thermodynamics (for *past history* which remain constant during a long time) and not to try to build thermodynamics from thermostatics (namely dynamics is not built from statics by considering slow motions). This new formulation of thermodynamics must also be rigorous from the mathematical point of view. Another general claim of the tenants of this attitude is to avoid talk of *internal or hidden variables*, and to deal only with observable and (theoretically at least) measurable quantities.

Roughly speaking, they deal with the basic concept of *process* instead of starting with the concept of *state*.

Let me say that these objectives, among those followed by the scientists who have worked in this direction during the last decade, seem to me very good and very attractive. And if one considers the number of papers improving the first presentation given by Coleman[13], the books devoted to this *new* and *true* thermodynamics—let us quote only those of Truesdell[14] and Day[15]—one must recognise that these ideas have value†. Even the strongest critics of this attitude must confess that this line of thought and research have obliged them to make their statements and views more precise and to think more deeply of the topic‡.

This is why, personally and as a member of the Scientific Committee, I deeply regret that professors Coleman and Gurtin, who were invited by the Committee to take part to this symposium and who initially accepted, decided quite recently not to come to Bussaco. Our work would have been more conclusive, I am convinced, if they had been present. Let us try nevertheless in spite of their absence to mention some of the main steps and the main achievements of these numerous and important works devoted to such theories.

17.4.2 Main steps and achievements

Validity of the concepts of temperature and entropy in general thermodynamics as primitive and fundamental quantities. That is, maybe, the biggest claim! The one which looks the more suspicious to physicists traditionally devoted to the study of thermodynamics. To be more exact, one must mention some propositions made in order to prove the existence of this concept, (entropy), starting with some different axioms. See for instance Day[15] or the lecture of Nemat-Nasser, chapter 14. In the cautious attitude, only *frozen* entropy and temperature were introduced and, even more, Meixner who admits the existence of temperature in the nonequilibrium case (but not an entropy) assumes that these two temperatures must be considered in general as different.

Clausius–Duhem Inequality. With these two concepts in hand, the fundamental inequality of thermodynamics is written as in the preceding section (equation 17.2) and again the heat flux vector $\boldsymbol{q}$ when it appears (as in $\nabla \cdot \boldsymbol{q}$) is

† We refer the reader to the books of Truesdell[14] and Day[15] for bibliographies of this topic.

‡ There still remain a few people who continue to think that *continuum thermodynamics* is a *false problem* and who indicate that related work is useless. I cannot provide a better reply than the two following quotations from a recent paper of Kestin[16] '... I have discovered that this marriage between thermodynamics and continuum mechanics is neither simple nor straight forward' and a little later speaking of the works we are talking about '... developments on those lines have compelled the more traditional practitioners of thermodynamics to sharpen up their thoughts, concepts and words'.

eliminated using the energy equation. But *the final form obtained is different from equation 17.3* because, in these methods, no relation is assumed *a priori* between the specific internal energy (or the specific free energy) the specific entropy and the absolute temperature. In other words, identity 17.1, often called Gibb's equation, is not assumed.

This is the place to mention the different and interesting attitude of Dr. Müller, who did not assume *a priori* the classical Clausius–Duhem inequality nor the existence of an absolute temperature, but only a kind of *Liapounoff* function ϕ as the flux associated with the entropy. Equation 17.2 is then written

$$\rho \frac{\mathrm{d}s}{\mathrm{d}t} + \mathrm{div}\,(\phi) \geqslant 0$$

This assumption, which fits very well the general spirit of this attitude, leads to the concept of *coldness* which replaces the classical T^{-1}, to which it reduces in the case of equilibrium. Müller's theory may be, perhaps, interpreted as a warning that the starting assumptions of this general thermodynamics may be found to be too narrow in the future.

A priori formulation of the constitutive equations as processes. This is, as mentioned previously, one of the important differences with the preceding development. The constitutive equations are supposed to define the fundamental quantities used to describe the physical phenomenon in terms of chosen quantities (describing generally the deformations and temperature distributions during the past history). Then thermodynamic statements are derived only *for the class of material defined by this kind of initial assumption.* Let us note that it is at this stage that one appeals to the so-called *principle of equipresence* which, according to our opinion and as was said above, is no more than a reasonable working assumption.

A point which must be emphasised again is the mathematical rigour and precision, largely beyond the usual practice of thermodynamics, which is used by the tenants of this formulation. Definitions are very precise. When the constitutive equations are written in functional form, the independent arguments are defined in specified Banach space and, for further applications, differentiability of the functionals must be precisely formulated.

A systematic method of writing that a process is a thermodynamically admissible process. According to the full flexibility with which the body force and eventually the exterior heat supplied may be taken, the only condition to be satisfied is the fundamental inequality. The systematic method which is used is quite interesting, very attractive and has become very popular. In my opinion, it is one of the credits which must be given fully and without any restriction to the people who have invented this method. It presents many similarities with the method of virtual power†. The working assumption which is used says that, at a given time t, the Clausius–Duhem inequality, when the expressions of the constitutive equations have been injected, must be satisfied for a class of *continuations* (which may present some discontinuities with the past history); roughly speaking, one may say that each instant t can be considered as an initial time at which some initial conditions may be specified independently.

So many papers have been written on this method, many of them bringing some improvement to previous ones, that it is not necessary here to give examples in detail. I prefer to spend some time on a tentative comparison.

17.5 Tentative Comparison of the two Attitudes

As far as I know, no systematic comparison between these two kinds of formulation has been published. Thus the following comments must be taken as very provisional. They are more precisely *open questions* than statements.

If the difference in the starting points of view are quite far from each other, if the claims of the most systematic tenants of each team cannot be reconciled, it is nevertheless interesting to note that, provided one uses complementary constitutive relations which are sufficiently general, one may recover, at least for some particular materials, the same working formulae for the constitutive equations by both methods. This is quite clear, for instance, for materials of differential type when the quantities describing the properties (stress, heat flow vector, specific entropy s, specific free energy ψ) at time t are supposed to be functions of $F(t)$, the actual matrix gradient $\dot{F}(t)$, $T(t)$, and $\boldsymbol{g}(t)$, $\boldsymbol{g}$ being the temperature gradient. Application of the method described in section 17.4 shows that ψ must be independent of $\dot{F}$ and $\boldsymbol{g}$, and that s must be $-\partial\psi/\partial T$. Here, the result so obtained, agrees completely with the result which can be derived from the method starting with the assumption of local state. *The application of the method of section 17.4 to the Clausius–Duhem inequality avoids the particular assumptions of the thermodynamic potential and the Gibb's equation used in a method based on a local state, but gives rise finally to the same result.*

It would be interesting to discuss to what extent such a result is true, that is, for what classes of materials, the final result obtained with the application of the *ambitious method* may be interpreted completely—eventually artificially—in terms of a method of local state. Of course, in order to do that, one would be obliged to introduce convenient internal variables and convenient laws for their evolution: this emphasises one of the difficulties of the method of local state and may, in some cases, render its application very

† The idea of using simultaneously virtual solutions for the dynamical and thermodynamical properties of a system may be found in reference 17.

artificial. On the other hand, when one tries to identify the dependence of, say, the specific free energy with respect to the independent variables, by some experiments for a given material, one will be obliged to leave free among the independent variables only a few parameters (instead of keeping the full functional indeterminacy) and one will be led to a situation very similar to the one which results from starting with the assumption of a local state with hidden variables. A conjecture, I would be tempted to introduce, is that in such a case working formulae in both kinds of theory are isomorphs of each other. Thus, when such a statement is acceptable, despite the fact that the language and the interpretation of the concepts would be different, each of these two theories would lead to the same working theory in a specific application of an engineering type. In support of this opinion, I note that when Professor Mandel presented his paper on Thermodynamics and Plasticity, chapter 15, he used both hidden variables and the method of section 17.4 without any special mention of the kind of school he has decided to follow†.

Then, without diminishing the importance of the basic questions which fed the recent controversies in continuum thermodynamics, (Is the concept of state relevant in a general thermodynamics? Is the concept of entropy meaningful in nonequilibrium thermodynamics? Is it possible to write the Clausius–Duhem inequality in its classical form?...), without underestimating other important questions to be answered (for instance in mixtures), one can reasonably think that, in dealing with a specific material at the present time, one must not be submerged by a great perplexity. The method of local state gives a simple starting point and suggests simple descriptions of the constitutive equations. The methods introduced by Coleman and his followers have provided a good mathematical frame and rigour, a good systematic method to write that a process is admissible. In each case, one may try to use all these advantages. This conclusion does not mean that we think that the line of research which works on foundations and investigates new paths (like the line followed by Meixner, Müller, or others...) is not important, not at all. But despite the controversies, sometimes a little too rough, one wants to conclude on a peaceful note for the users of thermodynamics in continuum theory.

17.6 Beyond Thermodynamics and the Second Law

As a conclusion, I would like to emphasise that the role of thermodynamics in continuum mechanics is a crucial one but, nevertheless, it does not appear

† This is why we do not think that the dispute: 'finite number of internal variables versus functional description' has a vital importance. A physicist may prefer the first term because he believes in the concept of state, a mathematician may prefer the second term for love of generality.

as the final goal of the discipline. It is merely an indispensable building stone. It may help to write physically sound constitutive equations. As was said in section 17.2, it is in its ability to solve problems that a theory will be judged. In this respect the theory may be a satisfactory theory if the solutions, obtained with it, satisfy the three Hadamard's requirements: existence, uniqueness and continuity with respect to the data of the problem.

This last requirement may be looked upon as a stability requirement. In continuum mechanics, one has to distinguish between material stability and structural stability. Only the first one is a thermodynamic property, the second depends on the geometry of the system and on the conditions imposed on it. In particular, the inequality of the second law leads to necessary conditions for material stability; its value rests mainly on its very general character. But these conditions so obtained will not always be sufficient.

It was clear for many of us during this symposium, that the stability of systems and especially of those systems in a steady state but 'beyond the thermodynamic branch' is one of the most important stimulating problems for the near future and its importance goes significantly beyond its application to continuum mechanics†. Even if the kind of thermodynamic description, presently at our disposal, is not completely satisfactory and even if we are not sure of the exact content of the concepts introduced and of the validity of the laws which are assumed, it is remarkable that it nevertheless provides a frame which appears to be sufficient at the present time for a first attack on decisive problems including those very far from the classical equilibrium situation. Obviously, stability theory and bifurcation theory are no longer in the field of thermodynamics. But thermodynamics is the gate one has to go through in order to reach this exciting domain.

References

1. A. E. Green and P. M. Naghdi. On thermodynamics, rate of work and energy. *A.R.M.A.*, **40** (1971), 37–49
2. A. E. Green and P. M. Naghdi. On continuum thermodynamics. *A.R.M.A.*, **48** (1972), 352–78
3. H. Weyl. Shock waves in arbitrary fluids. *Com. Pure and App. Math.* (1948)
4. W. D. Hayes. *The Basic Theory of Gasdynamic Discontinuities in High Speed Aerodynamics*, III, Princeton Univ. Press, Princeton (1958), 416–81
5. H. Ziegler. Some extremum principles in irreversible thermodynamics with applications to continuum mechanics. *Progress in Solid Mechanics*, **IV** (1963), 93–193
6. P. Germain. *Cours de Mécanique des Milieux Continus*, Masson et Cie, Paris (1973)
7. J. J. Moreau. Sur les lois de frottement de viscosité et de plasticité. *C. R. Ac. Sc., Paris*, **270** (1970), 608–11.

† We are referring here to some very interesting comments and views formulated by Professor Prigogine during this symposium and relating to the possibility of applying such concepts in order to understand and investigate some biological systems which present a well-ordered structure.

8. G. Duvaut and J. L. Lions. *Les Inéquations en Physique et en Mécanique*, Dunod, Paris (1972)
9. J. J. Moreau. Rafle par un convexe variable. *Seminaire d'Analyse Convexe*, Montpellier (1971)
10. Q. S. Nguyen and B. Halphen. Sur les lois de comportement élasto-viscoplastique à potentiel généralisé. *C.R. Ac. Sc. Paris*, **276,** A (1973)
11. Q. S. Nguyen. Matériaux élasto-viscoplastiques à potentiel généralisé. *C.R. Ac. Sc., Paris*, **276,** A (1973)
12. J. Meixner. Processes in simple thermodynamic materials. *A.R.M.A.*, **33** (1969), 33–53
13. B. D. Coleman. Thermodynamics of materials with memory. *A.R.M.A.*, **17** (1964), 1–46
14. C. Truesdell. *Rational Thermodynamics*, McGraw-Hill, New York (1969)
15. W. A. Day. *The Thermodynamics of Simple Materials with Fading Memory*, Springer-Verlag, Berlin; Heidelbry, New York (1972)
16. J. Kestin. *Thermodynamics in Thermoplasticity*. Summer School, Jablonna, Poland (1973)
17. M. Roy. *Mécanique des Milieux Continus et Déformables*, Gauthier-Villars, Paris (1950)

Index